Contents

1 The National Numeracy Strategy

The National Context

At the heart of the National Numeracy Strategy is the Framework for Teaching Mathematics. This document provides a structured sequence of teaching objectives for each year. Since September 1999, all schools in England have been expected to draw upon the Framework for Teaching Mathematics in planning their lessons. In March 2000 the Framework documents were extended to include Year 7. The Year 7 Framework can be referred to by teachers in Year 6 who are planning work for their most able pupils.

The Abacus programme

Abacus follows the detailed plan of teaching objectives outlined in the Framework for Teaching Mathematics. Furthermore, Abacus, from its inception, has been designed and written with precisely the same approach to the teaching of mathematics as that of the National Numeracy Strategy. Abacus is based on three principles:

Direct and interactive teaching is at the heart of the process of helping children learn mathematics. Children often do not 'discover' strategies; they have to be taught them.

Many mathematical skills and facts, particularly those which help children become fluent in mental calculations, need to be taught clearly, and then rehearsed regularly on a 'little-and-often' basis.

Materials need to support teachers in their teaching, and to help keep classroom management simple and effective. It is not necessary, nor is it desirable, for every classroom teacher to 'reinvent the wheel'. A clear structure of key objectives (with sufficient flexibility for important professional decisions to be left to each teacher in their own specific context) will minimise the hours spent planning and preparing, and maximise the teacher's effectiveness in the classroom.

As well as being based on the same philosophy, Abacus shares several assumptions with the National Numeracy Strategy.
- There will be a daily mathematics lesson.
- The lesson will have a three-part structure (oral/mental starter, main teaching activity, plenary). This is flexible, and timing will vary from lesson to lesson, class to class and school to school, but the key elements will be common to all years and classroom contexts. It is designed to accommodate individual teaching styles as well as differences in situation, organisation and content. For Abacus 7, it is likely that the main teaching activity will include direct teaching to a small group of the most able pupils, but that this group will rejoin the whole class for the starter and plenary activities.
- Planning will be carried out on a weekly basis, with reference to the medium term planning grids in the Framework for Teaching Mathematics.
- In their direct teaching, with the whole class, in groups or with individuals and pairs, teachers will require simple practical resources. These will include number lines, number grids, digit cards and place-value cards.

② The Abacus materials

Abacus 7

The Abacus 7 materials are written to follow the content of the Year 7 Framework, and are intended for use by teachers in Year 6 with their more able pupils. The materials are flexible enough to be used in different ways, though there are likely to be two main modes of use:
- as a resource that can be referred to during the year for a particular group of pupils who need further extension in Year 6
- as a comprehensive programme of work for the whole class to be used if the core Year 6 objectives are completed ahead of schedule.

In both cases, it is assumed that pupils have completed the necessary work from the Year 6 Framework, before attempting any work in Abacus 7.

Teacher Cards

For each Unit of work the Teacher Card identifies for you:
- the direct teaching (introductory and follow-up) to the group
- group differentiated activities
- appropriate Textbook pages and Photocopy Masters.

The Abacus 6 and Abacus 7 Teacher Cards will enable you to plan effectively for the whole class, covering a wide range of ability.

The front of each Teacher Card provides:
- support for group (or whole class) teaching to introduce a new topic
- a list of the key teaching points addressed by the Unit
- a list of any materials necessary for the teaching
- key vocabulary either introduced or used during the course of the Unit.

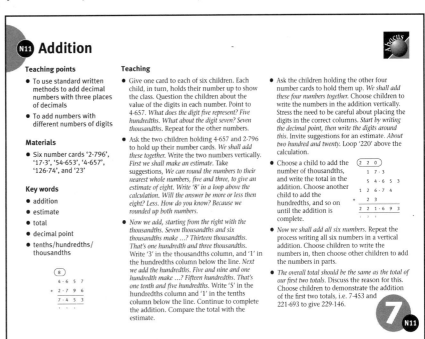

Teacher Card provides:
- support for further teaching for a subsequent day
- references to practical activities
- guidance on key points for use during round-up sessions
- references to additional Abacus resources: Photocopy Masters, Textbook, and the appropriate Unit from Abacus 6.

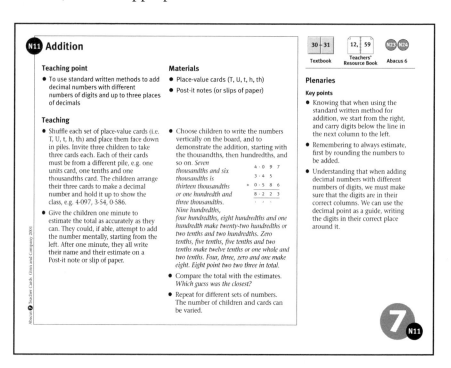

Teacher Cards are divided into five sets: *Number* (coded N), *Algebra* (coded A), *Shape and Space* (coded S), Measures (coded M) and *Data Handling* (coded D).

Textbook

The Textbook in Abacus 7 is divided into the five strands: *Number, Algebra, Shape and Space, Measures* and *Data Handling*.

The instructions on the page are in speech bubbles. This has the dual function of keeping text to a minimum, as well as aiding readability. Key mathematical vocabulary is reinforced throughout. A key feature of the pages is the inclusion of 'Extras' (coded ⊘) and 'Explores', which provide additional activities usually with an investigational or practical focus away from the Textbook page. Word problems are also included throughout the Textbook in 'Problems' sections.

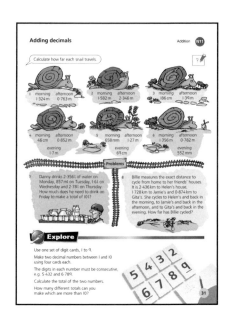

Relevant Textbook pages are referenced on each Teacher Card.

Teachers' Resource Book

The Teachers' Resource Book provides all the extra support you need to get the most from Abacus 7. It includes:

Photocopy Masters
The Photocopy Masters (pages 1 to 47) contain activities to enhance the pupils' learning and are identified on the relevant Teacher Cards. They include:
- more work for reinforcement
- extension and enrichment material
- games, and other shared, practical activities.

Group Activities
The Group Activities are photocopiable activities that can be presented directly to the pupils (pages 48 to 94). These encourage language development by allowing pupils to interpret instructions themselves. Each activity includes the following information:
- appropriate number of children
- a list of relevant materials and 'specialist resources' (included as photocopiables on pages 121 to 127)
- clear instructions can be easily interpreted by children, allowing the teacher to focus on other groups.

Assessment
The Assessment section (pages 95 to 120) provides photocopiable sheets and teacher guidance for each of the Abacus 7 Units. The teachers' notes include a summary of skills assessed, oral questions and practical activities for children who require further consolidation. A record-keeping grid is also provided.

Resource Masters
Occasionally the practical activities require some 'specialist' resources, e.g. fraction cards. These are included as photocopiables on pages 121 to 127.

Matching charts
Several matching charts are included (pages 128 to 142) to assist planning and assessment:
- Numeracy Framework – a chart matching the Year 7 Framework to units in Abacus 7
- Exemplar Planning Grids – showing how the Abacus 7 Units can be planned in alongside Abacus 6
- Scotland and Northern Ireland – a chart matching the Abacus 7 Units to the Scottish 5–14 guidelines and the Northern Ireland Curriculum.

Answers
Answers to the exercises in the Textbook, Photocopy Masters and Assessment Sheets are included from page 144 onwards.

❸ Classroom management

The planning grids at the back of this book (pages 132 to 137) show how the Abacus 7 Units can be easily planned to fit in with the Abacus 6 Units during the course of the year. Where the Abacus 7 materials are used in this way alongside Abacus 6, one possible way of working is as follows.

1. Use the appropriate Abacus 6 Mental Warm-up Activity and Teacher Card to introduce the topic to the whole class.

2. Set up group activities, using the more stretching activities for the top group.

3. Give all pupils the opportunity to work on the relevant pages from the Abacus 6 Textbook.

4. Whilst the core of the class are working on activities or practice materials from Abacus 6, you can work directly with the top group using the appropriate Abacus 7 Unit to extend the topic or introduce new concepts.

5. Reinforce the work of the top group with materials from the Abacus 7 Textbook and/or Teachers' Resource Book.

Some points worth noting are:

- You will decide on the best organisation of groups to suit your needs at any time.
- The composition of the groups will vary depending on the Unit of work being studied.
- You can plan within your group structure, how, during the Unit, you can work in a focused way with your more able group.
- You will need to judge how much time to allow for different children to complete any task.
- Other adults can be used to assist with the activities.
- Often more able children can be used in a peer-tutoring role within the activity carousel.

4 Mathematical content

Abacus 7 may be used as extension material with a group of Year 6 pupils alongside Abacus 6, or with pupils who have not previously been working with the Abacus approach. It is assumed that before introducing Abacus 7 to children, they will have completed the necessary work from the Year 6 Framework and achieved the associated skills. To get the best out of the Abacus materials, you are advised to note the following:

Numbers and the number system

Abacus 7 extends much of the number work of Y6. Work on positive and negative numbers extends to their addition and subtraction. Square numbers are extended to include cube numbers, square roots and cube roots. Children are introduced to index notation, then use this to write numbers as the product of prime numbers. Relationships between fractions, decimals and percentages are consolidated and extended, and the use of the calculator to support this is included. Place-value of decimals is also extended, e.g. to include multiplying and dividing by 0·1 and 0·01, as well as rounding to 1 and 2 decimal places.

Calculations

Written methods developed in Y6, are consolidated in Abacus 7. Addition and subtraction are extended to include numbers with 3 places of decimals. Multiplication and division are refined and extended to include numbers with 2 places of decimals. Similarly, mental calculation skills and strategies are developed, often to involve decimal numbers.

Algebra

Abacus 7 includes ten units which introduce algebra using concepts and skills met previously. Children have already met 'unknowns', e.g. boxes in equations. Here letters as unknowns, and notation and rules for operating on them, are introduced. These units develop the skills and understanding of collecting algebraic terms, solving equations, using algebraic formulae, using brackets, and substituting numbers in algebraic expressions. Work on sequences and functions is also extended to include expressing terms in a sequence algebraically, as well as defining a function algebraically. The use of coordinates in four quadrants is extended to drawing straight-line graphs of algebraic functions. Children are also introduced to distance-time graphs.

Shape, space and measures

More advanced consideration of the transformations of reflection, rotation and translation is included, linking these to the transformation of polygons on a four-quadrant coordinate grid. The relationship between angles made by a line intersecting parallel lines, and the concept of an exterior angle of a triangle, are introduced. Other new ideas include rotational symmetry, the construction of different triangles using rulers and protractors, the concept of congruency, and the 2-d drawing and interpretation of 3-d shapes (using plans and elevations). Abacus 7 also develops work on area to include the use of formulae for calculating, e.g. the area of a right-angled triangle and the surface area of a cuboid.

Handling data

Abacus 7 extends work on averages by comparing two sets of data using range as a measure of spread. Methods of finding the mean of a frequency distribution are introduced. Work on probability further consolidates the concept of assigning probabilities to events.

5 Photocopy Masters

Purpose

The Photocopy Masters contain a variety of activities to enhance the children's learning. They provide additional practice to reinforce the key mathematical skills introduced in the Teacher Cards and Textbook pages.

Structure

One Photocopy Master sheet is provided for each Unit of teaching and these are clearly referenced on the matching Teacher Card. They include:

- more work to allow children to practise independently
- material for further extension and enrichment
- games, and other shared, practical activities.

It is assumed that children will have completed the relevant work from the appropriate Teacher Card and Textbook pages, before attempting the material contained within the Photocopy Masters.

Using the Photocopy Masters

All instructions given are directed towards the children, so that the work can be undertaken without the need for further teacher support.

For many of the Photocopy Masters, children can record their work on the sheet. However, in some of the more investigational-type activities, extra paper may be required.

Children should be encouraged to record their work clearly and systematically.

Big deal

Deal out six number cards, and write a 5-place decimal. Round the number correct to 3 decimal places, 2 decimal places and 1 decimal place.

Deal out six new cards for each line.

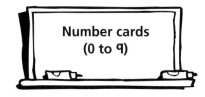

**Number cards
(0 to 9)**

		3 decimal places	2 decimal places	1 decimal place
1.	4·7 8 5 3 6	4·785	4·79	4·8
2.	_ · _ _ _ _ _	_____	_____	_____
3.	_ · _ _ _ _ _	_____	_____	_____
4.	_ · _ _ _ _ _	_____	_____	_____
5.	_ · _ _ _ _ _	_____	_____	_____
6.	_ · _ _ _ _ _	_____	_____	_____
7.	_ · _ _ _ _ _	_____	_____	_____
8.	_ · _ _ _ _ _	_____	_____	_____
9.	_ · _ _ _ _ _	_____	_____	_____
10.	_ · _ _ _ _ _	_____	_____	_____

Doubling decimals

Arrange six number cards from a 0 to 9 set to make two 3-digit decimal numbers. The second number must be double the first.

Record ten of your pairs here.

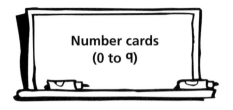

Number cards
(0 to 9)

doubled

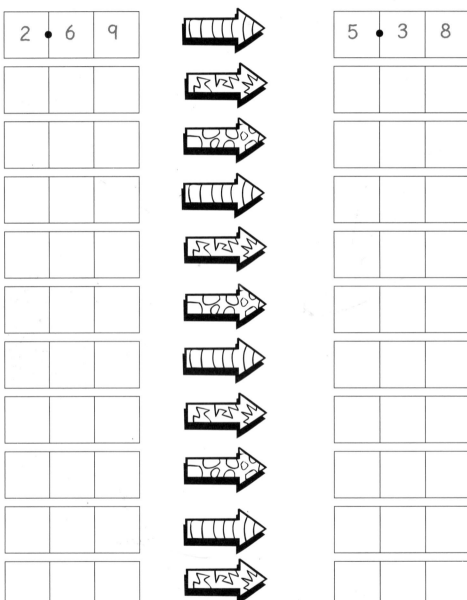

Investigate how many different pairs you can find.

Try making a number and its double like this:

Russian multiplication

This method of multiplying is an old method from Russia.

Write down the two numbers to be multiplied. Make two columns by halving the number on the left and doubling the number on the right. Ignore any halves.

PHOTOCOPY MASTERS

34 × 29

34	29
17	58
8	116
4	232
2	464
1	928

Cross out any numbers in the right-hand column that are opposite an even number.

Add the remaining numbers on the right for the answer.

~~34~~	~~29~~
17	58
~~8~~	~~116~~
~~4~~	~~232~~
~~2~~	~~464~~
1	928

34 × 29 = 986

Is the result the same if you swap the two numbers? Can you see why it works?

Use the Russian method on these multiplications.

1. 57 × 34   2. 27 × 76   3. 34 × 26

    4. 19 × 31   5. 43 × 47   6. 92 × 33

Name _____

Fraction number lines

Draw a pointer to show the position of each fraction and decimal on the number line.

Write the numbers in order, smallest to largest

I.

$$\frac{3}{4} \quad \frac{5}{8} \quad \frac{3}{8} \quad 0.25$$
$$\frac{7}{8} \quad \frac{1}{8} \quad 0.5$$

0 ├──┬──┬──┬──┬──┬──┬──┤ 1

2.

$$0.5 \quad \frac{1}{3} \quad \frac{1}{6} \quad \frac{5}{6} \quad \frac{7}{12}$$
$$\frac{2}{3} \quad 0.75 \quad \frac{5}{12} \quad 0.25$$

0 ├──┬──┬──┬──┬──┬──┬──┤ 1

3.

$$0.3 \quad \frac{2}{5} \quad \frac{1}{4} \quad \frac{9}{10} \quad \frac{4}{5}$$
$$0.45 \quad \frac{1}{2} \quad 0.85$$

0 ├──┬──┬──┬──┬──┬──┬──┤ 1

4.

$$\frac{4}{5} \quad \frac{3}{4} \quad \frac{2}{5} \quad \frac{6}{10} \quad 0.7$$
$$\frac{11}{20} \quad 0.35 \quad 0.95$$

0 ├──┬──┬──┬──┬──┬──┬──┤ 1

5.

$$\frac{1}{3} \quad 0.64 \quad 0.4 \quad \frac{3}{4}$$
$$\frac{11}{20} \quad 0.12 \quad 0.9$$

0 ├┈┈┈┈┈┈┈┈┈┈┈┈┈┈┈┈┈┤ 1

6.

$$\frac{18}{100} \quad \frac{4}{5} \quad \frac{9}{25} \quad 0.36$$
$$\frac{37}{50} \quad 0.82 \quad \frac{1}{4} \quad 0.6$$

0 ├┈┈┈┈┈┈┈┈┈┈┈┈┈┈┈┈┈┤ 1

Pick your pair

1.

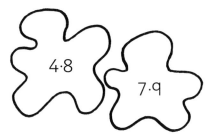

4·8

7·9

2.

6·3

5·8

3.

12·2

9·3

4.

14·72

8·5

5.

15·3

6·94

6.

7·61

2·34

7.

5·48

1·96

8.

6·75

6·75

9.

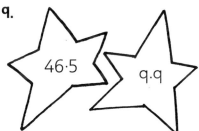

46·5

9·9

10.

7·9

12·6

11.

0·35

0·84

12.

1·95

0·8

13.

3·7

4·62

14.

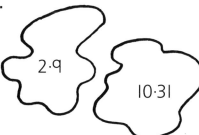

2·9

10·31

15.

15·8

23·7

Instructions

A game for two players. Take turns to look at each pair of numbers. Roll a dice. If the dice score is odd, add the pair of numbers. If it is even, subtract the smaller number from the larger. Calculate mentally and say the answer to your partner. The other person says whether they agree or disagree and checks with the calculator. If you are correct, score 1 point. If you are wrong and the other person thought you were, they score 1 point. The winner is the first to score 7 points.

Materials
A dice
Calculator

Prime cards

Make sets of prime numbers.
They can be 1-digit, 2-digit or 3-digit prime numbers.

Each card may be used once only in a set.

Here is one set:

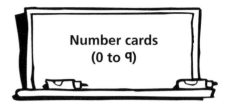
Number cards
(0 to 9)

| 2 | 3 | 4 | 7 | 5 | 1 | 9 |

The cards 0 6 and 8 have not been used.

Here is another set:

| 7 | 3 | 5 | 9 | 6 | 1 |

The cards 0 2 4 and 8 have not been used.

Investigate other possibilities.

Ten calculations

Look at the cloud numbers. Write ten calculations for each with the cloud number as the answer.

5·72

x 10 _____

÷ 100 _____

x 1000 _____

÷ 0·1 _____

_____ x 0·1

÷ 10 _____

x 0·01 _____

_____ ÷ 0·01

x 100 _____

÷ 1000 _____

17·3

÷ 0·1 _____

x 100 _____

÷ 100 _____

÷ 0·01 _____

_____ x 0·01

x 1000 _____

÷ 10 _____

_____ x 10

÷ 1000 _____

x 0·1 _____

468

x 1000 _____

÷ 0·01 _____

÷ 1000 _____

x 100 _____

_____ x 0·01

x 10 _____

÷ 10 _____

_____ ÷ 0·1

x 0·1 _____

÷ 100 _____

Name _____

Dice numerators

Roll a dice to give each numerator.
Calculate the product.

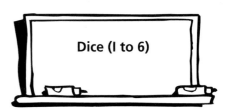

Dice (1 to 6)

1. $\dfrac{\square}{6} \times 12 =$ ☁

2. $15 \times \dfrac{\square}{5} =$ ☁

3. $\dfrac{\square}{4} \times 16 =$ ☁

4. $21 \times \dfrac{\square}{3} =$ ☁

5. $\dfrac{\square}{7} \times 28 =$ ☁

6. $40 \times \dfrac{\square}{8} =$ ☁

7. $63 \times \dfrac{\square}{7} =$ ☁

8. $\dfrac{\square}{10} \times 110 =$ ☁

9. $\dfrac{\square}{15} \times 75 =$ ☁

10. $\dfrac{\square}{12} \times 72 =$ ☁

11. $13 \times \dfrac{\square}{2} =$ ☁

12. $120 \times \dfrac{\square}{20} =$ ☁

13. $11 \times \dfrac{\square}{4} =$ ☁

14. $9 \times \dfrac{\square}{5} =$ ☁

9

Fractions to decimals

Complete this chart to show decimal equivalents of fractions.

Do as much as you can without a calculator, then use a calculator for the rest.

Write the decimal numbers correct to three decimal places.

Numerator

	1	2	3	4	5	6	7	8	9	10
1	1	2	3		5					
2			1·5							
3			1							
4			0·75							
5							1·4			
6										
7						0·857	1			
8										
9	0·111									
10										

Denominator

Name ______________________________

Halfway numbers

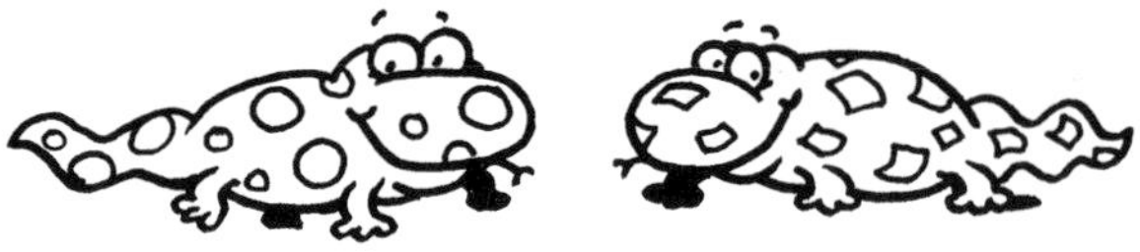

Write the numbers that are halfway between these numbers.

1. 7, ________ , 8
2. 5, ________ , 4
3. 13, ________ , 14
4. 2·4, ________ , 2·5
5. 13·8, ________ , 13·7
6. 6·71, ________ , 6·72
7. 8·34, ________ , 8·35
8. 9·4, ________ , 9·41
9. 7·39, ________ , 7·4
10. 3·24, ________ , 3·236
11. 6·476, ________ , 6·48
12. 5·1, ________ , 5·06
13. 4·8, ________ , 5·1
14. 6·2, ________ , 5·9
15. 7·39, ________ , 7·42
16. 8·71, ________ , 8·68
17. 2, ________ , 2·12
18. 3·4, ________ , 3·54
19. 4·68, ________ , 4·692
20. 5·36, ________ , 5·374
21. $^{-}2$, ________ , $^{+}3$
22. $^{-}5$, ________ , $^{+}2$

Addition game

Game I

```
[   ] · [   ][   ][   ]

+ [   ] · [   ][   ][   ]
  _____
```

score [   ]

Game 2

```
[   ] · [   ][   ][   ]

+ [   ] · [   ][   ][   ]
  _____
```

score [   ]

Game 3

```
[   ] · [   ][   ][   ]

+ [   ] · [   ][   ][   ]
  _____
```

score [   ]

Game 4

```
[   ] · [   ][   ][   ]

+ [   ] · [   ][   ][   ]
  _____
```

score [   ]

Total score [   ]

Instructions

A game for two or more players, each with a copy of this scoresheet.
Roll a dice eight times each. After each roll, write your dice score in one of the boxes.
After the eighth roll, find the total of your two decimal numbers. Score the amount you need to add to your total to make the next whole number. For example, a total of 9·573 gives a score of 0·427. The player with the largest total score after four rounds, wins.

Materials
A dice (1 to 6)

Name _____

Place the digits

The two numbers in each subtraction contain all the digits 1 to 8. Find the missing digits in each.

1.

$$6 \cdot \square\,\square\ 8$$
$$-\ 1 \cdot \square\,\square\,\square$$
$$4 \cdot 9\ 1\ 1$$

2.

$$8 \cdot \square\,\square\,\square$$
$$-\ 5 \cdot \square\,\square\ 7$$
$$2 \cdot 7\ 1\ 4$$

3.

$$\square \cdot 5\ \square\,\square$$
$$-\ 2 \cdot \square\ 3\ 4$$
$$4 \cdot 7\ 2\ 7$$

4.

$$4 \cdot \square\,\square\ 8$$
$$-\ \square \cdot \square\ 7\ \square$$
$$3 \cdot 1\ 9\ 6$$

5.

$$\square \cdot 4\ \square\,\square$$
$$-\ 5 \cdot \square\,\square\ 1$$
$$0 \cdot 6\ 5\ 2$$

6.

$$\square \cdot 7\ \square\,\square$$
$$-\ 1 \cdot \square\,\square\ 4$$
$$7 \cdot 4\ 7\ 1$$

7.

$$\square \cdot \square\ 5\ \square$$
$$-\ 2 \cdot \square\,\square\,\square$$
$$2 \cdot 1\ 8\ 9$$

8.

$$\square \cdot \square\,\square\,\square$$
$$-\ \square \cdot 6\ \square\ 4$$
$$1 \cdot 9\ 0\ 8$$

9.

$$\square \cdot \square\,\square\ 3$$
$$-\ \square \cdot 6\ \square\,\square$$
$$2 \cdot 4\ 6\ 5$$

10.

$$\square \cdot \square\ 5\ \square$$
$$-\ 4 \cdot \square\,\square\,\square$$
$$2 \cdot 5\ 3\ 5$$

11.

$$6 \cdot \square\,\square\ 1$$
$$-\ \square \cdot \square\,\square\,\square$$
$$2 \cdot 6\ 3\ 6$$

12.

$$\square \cdot 3\ \square\,\square$$
$$-\ \square \cdot \square\ 6\ \square$$
$$0 \cdot 5\ 5\ 3$$

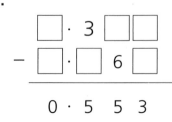

PHOTOCOPY MASTERS

Name _____

Power substitution

If $a = 1$, $b = 2$, $c = 3$, $d = 4$, $e = 5$, write the value of these:

1. $b^2 =$ _____

2. $c^2 =$ _____

3. $d^2 - 4 =$ _____

4. $a^3 =$ _____

5. $c^3 =$ _____

6. $c^2 + 5 =$ _____

7. $b^3 =$ _____

8. $a^2 =$ _____

9. $c^4 =$ _____

10. $d^3 =$ _____

11. $e^3 =$ _____

12. $b^4 =$ _____

13. $a^9 =$ _____

14. $b^6 =$ _____

15. $b^5 =$ _____

16. $a^{27} =$ _____

17. $a^2 + b^2 =$ _____

18. $b^2 + c^2 =$ _____

19. $c^3 - b^2 =$ _____

20. $c^3 - d^2 =$ _____

21. $b^7 =$ _____

22. $5d^2 =$ _____

23. $6a^3 =$ _____

24. $\dfrac{d^2}{4} =$ _____

25. $\dfrac{c^2}{3} =$ _____

26. $\dfrac{b^5}{2^3} =$ _____

Missing numbers

Write the missing numbers.

1. ⟨ ⟩ add ⁻4 = ⁺1

2. ⟨ ⟩ add ⁺3 = ⁻2

3. ⁺5 add ⟨ ⟩ = ⁻1

4. ⁻3 add ⟨ ⟩ = ⁺4

5. ⁺2 add ⟨ ⟩ = ⁻7

6. ⟨ ⟩ add ⁻5 = ⁻6

7. ⟨ ⟩ + (⁺5) = (⁻2)

8. (⁻3) + ⟨ ⟩ = (⁻1)

9. (⁺4) + (⁻2) + ⟨ ⟩ = (⁺3)

10. (⁻2) + ⟨ ⟩ + (⁻5) = (⁺7)

11. (⁺4) + (⁻2) = (⁺5) + ⟨ ⟩

12. (⁻3) + (⁻2) = ⟨ ⟩ + (⁺2)

13. ⁺6 subtract ⟨ ⟩ = ⁺3

14. ⁺1 subtract ⟨ ⟩ = ⁻2

15. ⁻3 subtract ⟨ ⟩ = ⁺2

16. ⁻5 subtract ⟨ ⟩ = ⁺1

17. ⟨ ⟩ subtract ⁻1 = ⁺1

18. ⟨ ⟩ subtract ⁺7 = ⁻4

19. (⁺8) − ⟨ ⟩ = (⁻1)

20. (⁻3) − ⟨ ⟩ = ⁺2

21. ⟨ ⟩ − (⁺4) = (⁻3)

22. ⟨ ⟩ − (⁻2) = ⁺5

23. ⟨ ⟩ − (⁺5) = (⁺2)

24. ⟨ ⟩ − (⁺4) = 0

Italian decimal multiplication

Use this multiplication method to multiply 35·8 x 4·6.

Draw a 2 x 3 grid (to match the numbers of digits), with diagonals in each square. Write the numbers, with decimal points, in position as shown.

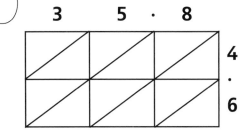

Multiply each row heading by each column heading. Write the tens digit of the answer above the diagonal, and the units digit below.

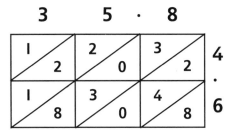

Add the numbers in each diagonal row of the grid, starting from the bottom right. Carry numbers up to the next diagonal if necessary.

Locate the position of the decimal point in the answer by finding where the two decimal points from outside the grid intersect on the grid, then sliding down the diagonal line.

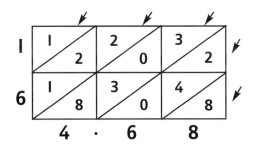

Write the answer.

35·8 x 4·6 = 164·68

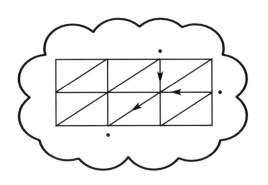

Use the Italian method to find these products.
Check each answer with a calculator.

1. 2·74 x 3·6   2. 31·5 x 2·7   3. 42·3 x 4·5

4. 63·7 x 1·9   5. 53·4 x 4·8   6. 27·9 x 5·6

Can you explain how it works?

16

Name _____

Dividing, then checking by multiplying

Complete each written division on another piece of paper, then check the answers by written multiplication.

1. 68·96 ÷ 16 = ⬭   16 x ⬭ = ⬭

2. 75·14 ÷ 17 = ⬭   17 x ⬭ = ⬭

3. 86·10 ÷ 15 = ⬭   15 x ⬭ = ⬭

4. 54·88 ÷ 14 = ⬭   14 x ⬭ = ⬭

5. 54·15 ÷ 19 = ⬭   19 x ⬭ = ⬭

6. 44·98 ÷ 26 = ⬭   26 x ⬭ = ⬭

7. 63·18 ÷ 27 = ⬭   27 x ⬭ = ⬭

8. 90·75 ÷ 33 = ⬭   33 x ⬭ = ⬭

9. 53·94 ÷ 29 = ⬭   29 x ⬭ = ⬭

10. 93·16 ÷ 34 = ⬭   34 x ⬭ = ⬭

Percentage chart

Complete this percentage chart, without using a calculator.

When you have finished, use your calculator to check how many correct answers you have.

	£2800	£3600	£5400	£450	£18 000
21%					
16%					
49%					
89%					
131%					
61%					
36%					
109%					
7%					

Dice percentages

Write what percentage of all the dice are:

1. ones _____

2. twos _____

3. fives _____

4. fours _____

5. sixes _____

6. threes _____

7. even numbers _____

8. odd numbers _____

9. numbers more than 2 _____

10. numbers less than 5 _____

11. numbers in the first row which are odd _____

12. numbers in the fourth row which are twos _____

13. numbers in the fifth column which are even _____

14. numbers in the top two rows which are odd _____

15. numbers in the top three rows which are fives _____

Names

Make a list of the first names of children in your class.

Write these proportions as percentages of all the names.

1. Short names (6 letters or fewer) _____

2. Long names (more than 6 letters) _____

3. Names with between 5 and 8 letters inclusive _____

4. Names with more than 2 vowels _____

Write the ratio of:

5. Short names to long names _____

6. Names which contain the letter 'o' to names that don't _____

Collect data from another class, calculate the same proportions and ratios and compare.

Name _____

Explaining errors

There is a mistake in each calculation.

Explain how you can tell there is a mistake in each one without doing the calculation.

I. Jenny has £23·72 in her purse. She buys a top costing £15·49 and calculates that she has £8·84 left.

2. Jamal's dad promises to double the money he saves for their holiday. Jamal has saved £3·76. He calculates that he will have £7·54 for the holiday.

3. On a game show, Katie is asked give the square root of 441. She gives the answer 23.

4. In a half-price sale, Susie saw a video camera. The original price was £368·20. Susie calculates that in the sale she would pay £184·40.

5. The train fare from Chesterlea to Potley is £1·48. Sian calculates that to pay for herself and her sister, she will need £3·16.

6. At a restaurant, John orders fish and chips for £2·36, Jamie orders a salad for £1·78, and Ayesha orders a pizza for £5·29. They calculate that their bill will come to £9·54.

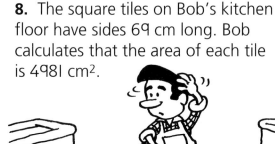

7. Betty works Monday to Friday every week. She calculates that since starting work, she has worked for 765 days, which is the same as 156 weeks or 3 years.

8. The square tiles on Bob's kitchen floor have sides 69 cm long. Bob calculates that the area of each tile is 4981 cm².

PHOTOCPY
MASTERS

Number investigations

Patterns with triangular numbers

These are the first four triangular numbers.

1   3   6   10

Write the first ten triangular numbers.

Investigate the totals of pairs of consecutive triangular numbers. Describe any patterns you notice.

Patterns with odd numbers

Copy, continue and describe this pattern.

Write the total of the first ten odd numbers.

$$1 = 1$$
$$1 + 3 = 4$$
$$1 + 3 + 5 =$$

Copy and continue this pattern. Describe the pattern and why it is formed.

$$1 = 1$$
$$3 + 5 =$$
$$7 + 9 + 11 =$$

Name _____

Powers and brackets with algebra

If $a = 1$, $b = 2$, $c = 3$ and $d = 4$, write the value of these:

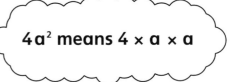

$4a^2$ means $4 \times a \times a$

1. $b^2 =$ _____

2. $3b^2 =$ _____

3. $2c^2 =$ _____

4. $4d^2 =$ _____

5. $6a^2 =$ _____

6. $5(a + b)^2 =$ _____

7. $6(b + c)^2 =$ _____

8. $2(d - a)^3 =$ _____

9. $3c^3 - 1 =$ _____

10. $2b^3 + 3 =$ _____

11. $100 - 2c^2 =$ _____

12. $50 - 3d^2 =$ _____

13. $(a + b)^2 + (b + c)^2 =$ _____

14. $(d - b)^3 + (c - a)^3 =$ _____

15. $3(b + d)^2 - 7 =$ _____

16. $4(c + b)^2 =$ _____

17. $3(2a + c)^2 =$ _____

18. $\dfrac{5(a + b + c)}{6} =$ _____

19. $\dfrac{4(a + 3b)^2}{7} =$ _____

20. $\dfrac{15(2d - 3b)^3}{4} =$ _____

Combining letters

Simplify each expression.

Remember to write numbers before letters when multiplying. For example, b × 4 is written as 4b and not b4.

I. 2 × z = _____

2. b × 3 = _____

3. I × q = _____

4. z × I = _____

5. b × c = _____

6. p × t = _____

7. 5 × b × c = _____

8. p × 3 × q = _____

9. 2 × a × 3 = _____

10. 3 × b × 4 = _____

II. a × y × y = _____

12. p × q × r = _____

13. a × a = _____

14. p × p × p = _____

15. 3 × a × b × a = _____

16. 2 × q × q = _____

17. I0 ÷ b = _____

18. c ÷ 5 = _____

19. (5 × c) ÷ b = _____

20. (4 × b) ÷ 3 = _____

Missing terms

Write the missing expressions.

1. $3d +$ ⬭ $+ 6d = 13d$

2. $5y + 4y -$ ⬭ $= 6y$

3. $3w -$ ⬭ $+ 2 = 2w + 3$

4. $4z +$ ⬭ $- 6 = 7z - 6$

5. $5 + 2c +$ ⬭ $= 2c + 6$

6. $3 + 4y + 5 +$ ⬭ $= 10y + 8$

7. ⬭ $+ 3y - 2y - 1 = 7 + y$

8. $2a +$ ⬭ $+ 5a + 4 = 10a + 4$

9. $6b - 2b -$ ⬭ $- 1 = 7b - 1$

10. $7g +$ ⬭ $+ 4 - 6g = 4 + 4g$

11. $4z + 5 +$ ⬭ $- 2 = z - 3$

12. $8q - q + 3 -$ ⬭ $= 3 + q$

13. $6 + 7c -$ ⬭ $- 5c = 6 - 2c$

14. $3t + 5 - 2t -$ ⬭ $= 5 - 3t$

Removing brackets

Write each expression without brackets.

Combine terms where possible.

1. $3(a + 4) + 2a$ = __$3a + 12 + 2a$__ = __$5a + 12$__

2. $5(b - 2) - 3b$ = _____ = _____

3. $6(z + 3) + z$ = _____ = _____

4. $7(p + 1) - 6p$ = _____ = _____

5. $4(2 + g) + 3g$ = _____ = _____

6. $3(a + b) + 2a$ = _____ = _____

7. $4(b + c) - 3c$ = _____ = _____

8. $5(d + 4) - 19$ = _____ = _____

9. $5a + 3(a + 1)$ = _____ = _____

10. $4q + 2(3 + q)$ = _____ = _____

11. $6g + 7(g - 1)$ = _____ = _____

12. $2(f + 4) + 3(f + 1)$ = _____ = _____

13. $3(a + 4) + 2(a - 1)$ = _____ = _____

14. $4(z - 3) + 3(z - 2)$ = _____ = _____

15. $4(3 + n) + 2(5 + n)$ = _____ = _____

Addition pyramids

Complete these pyramids.

Each brick number is found by adding the two below.

	10	
3		7

1.
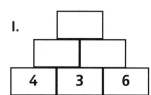
| 4 | 3 | 6 |

2.
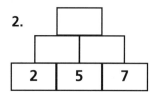
| 2 | 5 | 7 |

3.
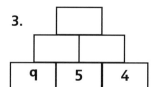
| 9 | 5 | 4 |

4.
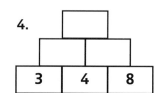
| 3 | 4 | 8 |

Write a formula to calculate the top number of the pyramid from the bottom numbers.

Let the bottom numbers be unknowns a, b and c.

Use the pyramids above to check your formula.

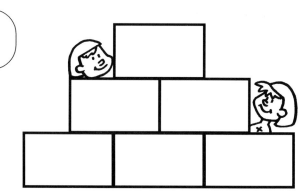

Write a formula to calculate the top number of this larger pyramid from the bottom numbers.

Let the bottom numbers be unknowns a, b, c and d.

Test your formula on these pyramids.

5.
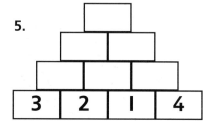
| 3 | 2 | 1 | 4 |

6.
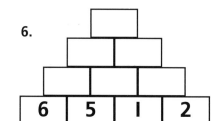
| 6 | 5 | 1 | 2 |

7.
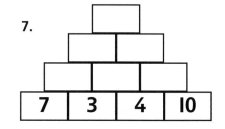
| 7 | 3 | 4 | 10 |

PHOTOCOPY MASTERS

Equations practice

Solve these equations.

1. $3a + 2 = 17$
    $3a =$
    $a =$

2. $5b - 3 = 12$
    $5b =$
    $b =$

3. $4y + 7 = 19$
    $4y =$
    $y =$

4. $3p - 8 = 25$
    $=$
    $=$

5. $6q + 3 = 27$
    $=$
    $=$

6. $2z - 9 = 43$
    $=$
    $=$

7. $3c + 4 = 19$
    $=$
    $=$

8. $2a - 5 = 13$
    $=$
    $=$

9. $5b + 3 = 18$
    $=$
    $=$

10. $9m - 11 = 25$
    $=$
    $=$

11. $2n + 14 = 30$
    $=$
    $=$

12. $4p - 3 = 25$
    $=$
    $=$

13. $9q + 22 = 40$
    $=$
    $=$

14. $3s - 17 = 1$
    $=$
    $=$

15. $7t + 13 = 20$
    $=$
    $=$

16. $5f - 9 = 6$
    $=$
    $=$

17. $2g + 3 = 4$
    $=$
    $=$

18. $4h + 2 = 3$
    $=$
    $=$

Meeting points

Use the tables to write four points which lie on each line.

Plot them on the grid and draw their lines.

Write the coordinates of the point where the two lines meet.

I.

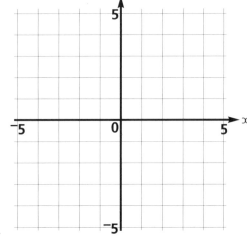

$y = x$

x				
y				

$y = 3$

x				
y				

Meeting point 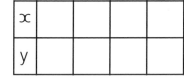 (,)

2.

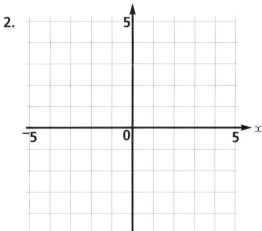

$y = ^-1$

x				
y				

$y = 2x$

x				
y				

Meeting point  (,)

3.

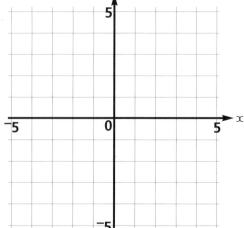

$y = x + 1$

x				
y				

$y = 3 - x$

x				
y				

Meeting point (,)

Electricity charges

Draw lines to complete the graph to show the electricity charges from Super Power Electricity Company.

They charge 10p per unit for the first 1000 units, then 5p per unit for any more units used after that.

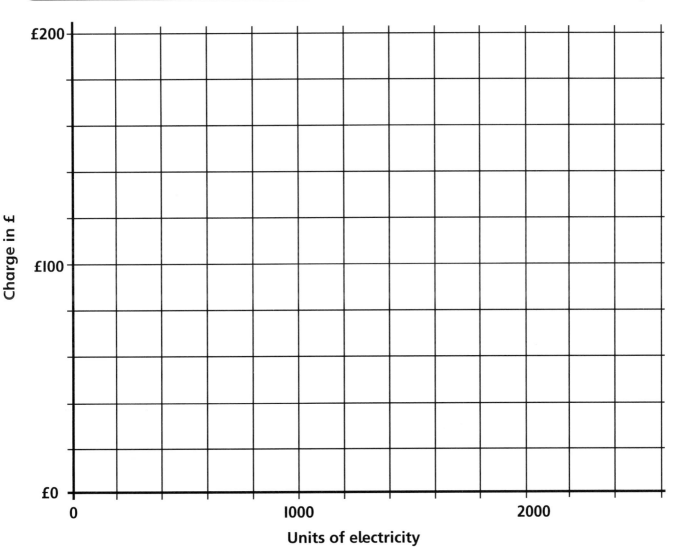

Charge in £

£200

£100

£0

0   1000   2000

Units of electricity

Use the graph to work out the charge for families who use:

1. 1200 units _____

2. 2000 units _____

3. 800 units _____

4. 2400 units _____

Write how many units of electricity have been used if a bill comes to:

5. £80 _____

6. £180 _____

7. £65 _____

8. £150 _____

Name _____

What's the rule?

Spot the rule, describe the function, then write the missing numbers in each table.

1. $x \rightarrow$ _____

IN	OUT
3	6
5	8
2	5
4	7
6	
9	

2. $x \rightarrow$ _____

IN	OUT
4	20
7	35
2	10
5	25
1	
8	

3. $x \rightarrow$ _____

IN	OUT
1	⁻4
3	⁻2
7	2
5	0
9	
2	

4. $x \rightarrow$ _____

IN	OUT
4	9
10	21
5	11
3	7
7	
2	

5. $x \rightarrow$ _____

IN	OUT
6	16
4	10
8	22
7	19
3	
2	

6. $x \rightarrow$ _____

IN	OUT
5	19
9	35
4	15
7	27
3	
6	

7. $x \rightarrow$ _____

IN	OUT
8	25
5	16
2	7
7	22
3	
9	

8. $x \rightarrow$ _____

IN	OUT
7	13
9	17
1	1
3	5
2	
8	

9. $x \rightarrow$ _____

IN	OUT
6	29
4	21
7	33
3	17
9	
2	

10. $x \rightarrow$ _____

IN	OUT
5	26
8	65
7	50
3	10
4	
9	

11. $x \rightarrow$ _____

IN	OUT
10	97
5	47
4	37
3	27
8	
7	

12. $x \rightarrow$ _____

IN	OUT
6	35
9	80
10	99
5	24
4	
8	

Fibonacci sequences

A sequence where each number is made by adding the last two numbers in the sequence is called a Fibonacci sequence.

1, 1, 2, 3, 5, 8, 13, 21, 34, 55, ...

Use the same rule to continue these sequences.

1, 3, ____, ____, ____, ____, ____, ____, ____, ____, ____

2, 5, ____, ____, ____, ____, ____, ____, ____, ____, ____

4, 1, ____, ____, ____, ____, ____, ____, ____, ____, ____

If only the units digits from the first sequence are written, it looks like this:

1, 3, 4, 7, 1, 8, 9, 7, 6, 3, 9, ...

Continue the sequence further and look at the units digits. The pattern of units digits repeats itself.

Investigate the pattern of units digits for Fibonacci sequences starting with these pairs of numbers.

2, 2, ...

3, 2, ...

4, 2, ...

Now try with some sequences of your own.

Squares and spots

Write the number of white squares in each sequence, then write the number of squares there would be in the nth term.

1.
  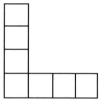

Term	Ist	2nd	3rd	nth
Squares				

2.
  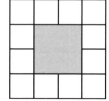

Term	Ist	2nd	3rd	nth
Squares				

3.
  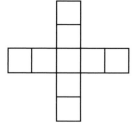

Term	Ist	2nd	3rd	nth
Squares				

4.
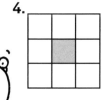 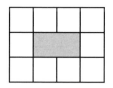 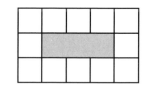

Term	Ist	2nd	3rd	nth
Squares				

Write the number of spots in each sequence, then write the number of spots there would be in the nth term.

Term	Ist	2nd	3rd	nth
Spots				

5.
 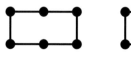 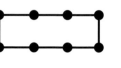

6.
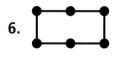 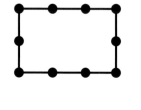 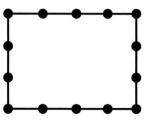

Term	Ist	2nd	3rd	nth
Spots				

Units of length

> Complete each statement.

I. 2·35 m = _____ cm

2. 0·46 m = _____ cm

3. 19 cm = _____ m

4. 340 cm = _____ m

5. 8 cm = _____ m

6. 35 mm = _____ cm

7. 600 mm = _____ cm

8. 450 mm = _____ m

9. 10 500 m = _____ km

10. 3 ft = _____ inches

II. 7 yards = _____ ft

12. 30 inches = _____ feet

13. 1 ft 8 inches = _____ inches

14. 15·5 cm = _____ m

15. 4·3 m = _____ cm

16. 7·35 km = _____ m

17. 0·0006 km = _____ m

18. 0·367 km = _____ m

19. 3·7 cm = _____ mm

20. 15·9 cm = _____ mm

21. 87·5 mm = _____ cm

22. 2·5 mm = _____ cm

23. 2 km = _____ cm

24. 3 450 000 mm = _____ km

25. 6550 cm = _____ km

26. 7·325 km = _____ mm

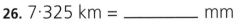

Name _____

Cube buildings

Each of these models is made from 6 cubes of the same size.
Estimate which have the largest and smallest surface areas.

largest surface area _____ smallest surface area _____

Use centimetre cubes to build the models, then find the surface area of each.

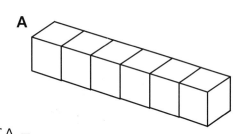

A

SA = _____

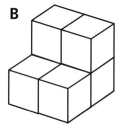

B

SA = _____

C

SA = _____

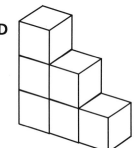

D

SA = _____

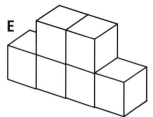

E

SA = _____

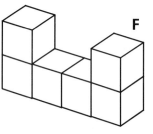

F

SA = _____

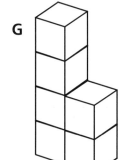

G

SA = _____

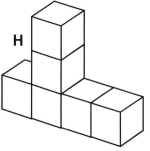

H

SA = _____

Were your estimates right?

Make some different models using 6 cubes. Find their surface areas.

Name _____

Missing parts

Write the missing lengths.

1.

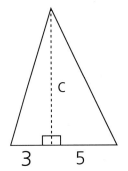

3   5

Area = 60 cm²

c = ☐ cm

2.

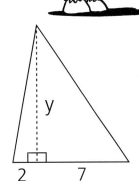

2   7

Area = 45 cm²

y = ☐ cm

3.

6   3

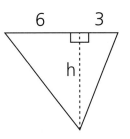

Area = 36 cm²

h = ☐ cm

4.

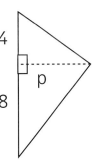

Area = 30 cm²

p = ☐ cm

5.

5   5

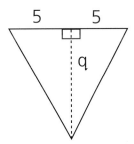

Area = 45 cm²

q = ☐ cm

6.

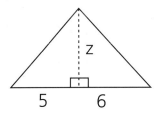

5   6

Area = 33 cm²

z = ☐ cm

7.

b   4

Area = 15 cm²

b = ☐ cm

8.

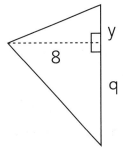

Area = 48 cm²

y = ☐ cm

9.

7   3

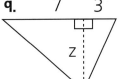

Area = 35 cm²

z = ☐ cm

Describing angles

∠ ABC means the angle made by tracing A to B to C.

Write the size of these angles.

1.

∠ ABC _____

2.

42°

∠ DEF _____

3.

96°

63°

∠ GIJ _____

4.

246°

∠ LMN _____

5.

44°

∠ QRS _____
∠ PRQ _____
∠ OSR _____

6.

96°

146°

∠ XVT _____
∠ TXV _____
∠ XTW _____

7.

51°

63°

∠ CBA _____
∠ ABZ _____
∠ ABD _____

PHOTOCOPY MASTERS

Drawing shapes

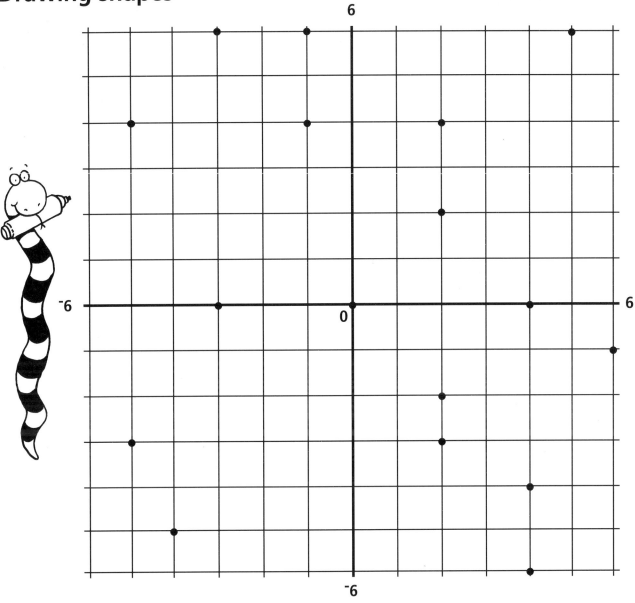

Using only points marked on the grid,
write the coordinates of these shapes.

I. A square   (,)(,)(,)(,)

2. A rectangle   (,)(,)(,)(,)

3. A right-angled triangle   (,)(,)(,)

4. An isosceles triangle   (,)(,)(,)

5. A parallelogram   (,)(,)(,)(,)

6. A kite   (,)(,)(,)(,)

7. An arrowhead   (,)(,)(,)(,)

8. An isosceles trapezium   (,)(,)(,)(,)

q. A right-angled trapezium   (,)(,)(,)(,)

Reflections

Write the coordinates of these points after:

1. reflection in the x-axis.

(3, 2) ⟶ (   )   (⁻1, 4) ⟶ (   )

(5, ⁻3) ⟶ (   )   (⁻4, ⁻2) ⟶ (   )

2. reflection in the y-axis.

(⁻1, 4) ⟶ (   )   (2, 0) ⟶ (   )

(3, ⁻1) ⟶ (   )   (⁻4, ⁻5) ⟶ (   )

3. reflection in one axis followed by reflection in the other.

(0, 4) ⟶ (   )   (⁻3, 1) ⟶ (   )

(⁻1, ⁻6) ⟶ (   )   (2, $\frac{1}{2}$) ⟶ (   )

4. reflection in the line x = 2.

(0, 3) ⟶ (   )   (1, 2) ⟶ (   )

(⁻4, ⁻1) ⟶ (   )   (⁻2, 3) ⟶ (   )

5. reflection in the line y = 1.

(3, ⁻1) ⟶ (   )   (4, 1) ⟶ (   )

(1, 0) ⟶ (   )   (⁻2, ⁻5) ⟶ (   )

6. reflection in the line y = x.

(1, ⁻4) ⟶ (   )   (⁻5, 2) ⟶ (   )

(3, 3) ⟶ (   )   (⁻3, ⁻3) ⟶ (   )

PHOTOCOPY MASTERS

Name _____

Rotations

Draw the new position of each shape after
these rotations about the centre of the circle.

I. 90° clockwise

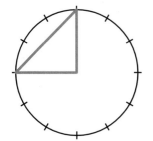

2. 90° anticlockwise

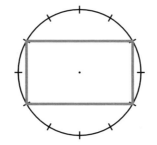

3. 180°

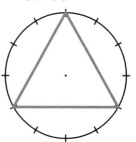

4. 60° clockwise

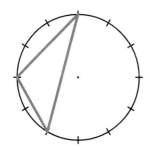

5. 120° anticlockwise

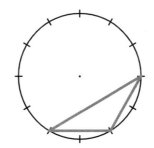

6. 270° anticlockwise

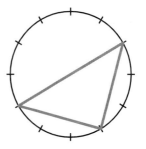

7. 150° clockwise

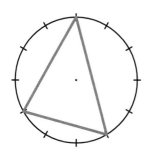

8. 330° clockwise

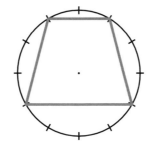

9. 210° anticlockwise

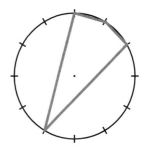

10. 330° anticlockwise

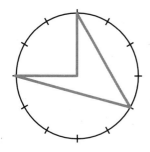

II. 240° clockwise

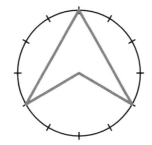

12. 150° anticlockwise

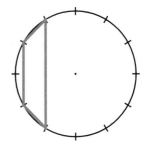

Congruent halves

Divide the geoboard into two congruent halves.
How many different ways can you find?

Extend to dividing it into four congruent quarters.

1.

2.

3.

4.

5.

6.

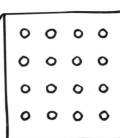

7.

8.

9.

10.

11.

12.

13.

14.

15.

16.

Name that shape

Name the mystery shape.

I. It has a circular base, one vertex and two faces.

2. It has 6 square faces, and 12 edges.

3. It has 2 identical circular faces, and one more curved face.

4. Its faces are all rectangles. It has 8 vertices.

5. It has 5 faces, 6 vertices, and 9 edges.

6. It has no edges or vertices.

7. It has one circular face and one face which is half the surface of a sphere.

8. It has 4 faces which are congruent triangles.

9. It has 7 faces, 10 vertices, and 15 edges.

10. It has 8 congruent equilateral triangles as faces. It has 6 vertices.

II. It has 12 congruent faces, which are regular pentagons.

12. It has 20 congruent equilateral triangles as faces.

Name _____

Types of triangle

Draw different triangles by joining three dots on the grid.
If one triangle can be matched directly to another (even by rotation or reflection) they are not different. They are congruent.

Can you find 18 different triangles?

Label each one as acute-angled, obtuse-angled or right-angled.

Rotating ring of tetrahedra

The net below is made from equilateral triangles. The shaded parts are the tabs.

Copy the net onto card, cut it out, crease along the lines, then glue the tabs.

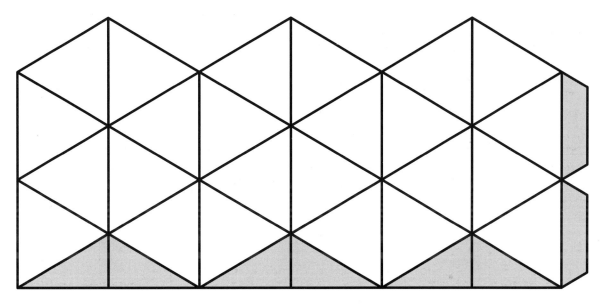

The result is a ring of six rotating tetrahedra.

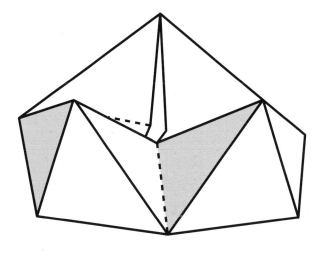

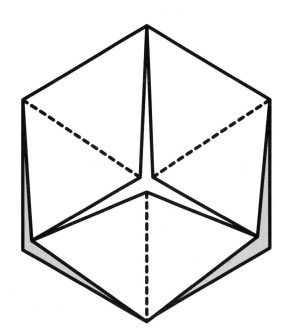

Name _____

Football survey

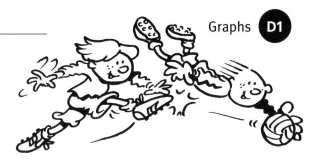

These are the results and positions of football teams after the 2000–2001 season.

Choose ways of comparing the different data. Construct graphs to show the results, then write about any conclusions, for example:

Are more goals scored at home than away?

Do Premier League teams average more goals than Division 1 teams?

Are there more draws in the higher leagues?

How do the average number of goals scored per game compare across the different divisions?

English Premier Division

	P	W	D	L	F	A	Pt	GD
Man. Utd	38	24	8	6	79	31	80	48
Arsenal	38	20	10	8	63	38	70	25
Liverpool	38	20	9	9	71	39	69	32
Leeds U	38	20	8	10	64	43	68	21
Ipswich T	38	20	6	12	57	42	66	15
Chelsea	38	17	10	11	68	45	61	23
Sunderland	38	15	12	11	46	41	57	5
Aston Villa	38	13	15	10	46	43	54	3
Charlton Ath.	38	14	10	14	50	57	52	-7
Southampton	38	14	10	14	40	48	52	-8
Newcastle U.	38	14	9	15	44	50	51	-6
Tottenham H.	38	13	10	15	47	54	49	-7
Leicester C.	38	14	6	18	39	51	48	-12
Middlesbro	38	9	15	14	44	44	42	0
West Ham U.	38	10	12	16	45	50	42	-5
Everton	38	11	9	18	45	59	42	-14
Derby Co.	38	10	12	16	37	59	42	-22
Man. City	38	8	10	20	41	65	34	-24
Coventry C.	38	8	10	20	36	63	34	-27
Bradford C.	38	5	11	22	30	70	26	-40

English Division 3

	P	W	D	L	F	A	Pt	GD
Brighton &HA.	46	28	8	10	73	35	92	38
Cardiff C.	46	23	13	10	95	58	82	37
Chesterfield	46	25	14	7	79	42	80	37
Hartlepool U.	46	21	14	11	71	54	77	17
Leyton O.	46	20	15	11	59	51	75	8
Hull C.	46	19	17	10	47	39	74	8
Blackpool	46	22	6	18	74	58	72	16
Rochdale	46	18	17	11	59	48	71	11
Cheltenham T.	46	18	14	14	59	52	68	7
Scunthorpe U.	46	18	11	17	62	52	65	10
Southend U.	46	15	18	13	55	53	63	2
Plymouth Arg.	46	15	13	18	54	61	58	-7
Mansfield T.	46	15	13	18	64	72	58	-8
Macclesfield	46	14	14	18	51	62	56	-11
Shrewsbury T.	46	15	10	21	49	65	55	-16
Kiddrminster	46	13	14	19	47	61	53	-14
York C.	46	13	13	20	42	63	52	-21
Lincoln C.	46	12	15	19	58	66	51	-8
Exeter	46	12	14	20	40	58	50	-18
Darlington	46	12	13	21	44	56	49	-12
Torquay U.	46	12	13	21	52	77	49	-25
Carlisle U.	46	11	15	20	42	65	48	-23
Halifax T.	46	12	11	23	54	68	47	-14
Barnet	46	12	9	25	67	81	45	-14

English Division 1

	P	W	D	L	F	A	Pt	GD
Fulham	46	30	11	5	90	32	101	58
Blackburn R.	46	26	13	7	76	39	91	37
Bolton Wan.	46	24	15	7	76	45	87	31
Preston NE	46	23	9	14	64	52	78	12
Birmingham C.	46	23	9	14	59	48	78	11
West Brom.	46	21	11	14	60	52	74	8
Burnley	46	21	9	16	50	54	72	-4
Wimbledon	46	17	18	11	71	50	69	21
Watford	46	20	9	17	76	67	69	9
Sheff. Utd.	46	19	11	16	52	49	68	3
Nottm Forest	46	20	8	18	55	53	68	2
Wolves	46	14	13	19	45	48	55	-3
Gillingham	46	13	16	17	61	66	55	-5
Crewe Alex.	46	15	10	21	47	62	55	-15
Norwich C.	46	14	12	20	46	58	54	-12
Barnsley	46	15	9	22	49	62	54	-13
Sheff. Wed.	46	15	8	23	52	71	53	-19
Grimsby T.	46	14	10	22	43	62	52	-19
Stockport Co.	46	11	18	17	58	65	51	-7
Portsmouth	46	10	19	17	47	59	49	-12
Crystal P.	46	12	13	21	57	70	49	-13
Huddersfield	46	11	15	20	48	57	48	-9
QPR	46	7	19	20	45	75	40	-30
Tranmere R.	46	9	11	26	46	77	38	-31

Scottish Premier Division

	P	W	D	L	F	A	Pt	GD
Celtic	38	31	4	3	90	29	97	61
Rangers	38	26	4	8	76	36	82	40
Hibernian	38	18	12	8	57	35	66	22
Kilmarnock	38	15	9	14	44	53	54	-9
Hearts	38	14	10	14	56	50	52	6
Dundee	38	13	8	17	51	49	47	2
Aberdeen	38	11	12	15	45	52	45	-7
Motherwell	38	12	7	19	42	56	43	-14
Dunfermline	38	11	9	18	34	54	42	-20
St.Johnstone	38	9	13	16	40	56	40	-16
Dundee U.	38	9	8	21	38	63	35	-25
St. Mirren	38	8	6	24	32	72	30	-40

English Division 2

	P	W	D	L	F	A	Pt	GD
Millwall	46	28	9	9	89	38	93	51
Rotherham U.	46	27	10	9	79	55	91	24
Reading	46	25	11	10	86	52	86	34
Walsall	46	23	12	11	79	50	81	29
Stoke C.	46	21	14	11	74	49	77	25
Wigan Ath.	46	19	18	9	53	42	75	11
Bournemouth	46	20	13	13	79	55	73	24
Notts Co.	46	19	12	15	62	66	69	-4
Bristol C.	46	18	14	14	70	56	68	14
Wrexham	46	17	12	17	65	71	63	-6
Port Vale	46	16	14	16	55	49	62	6
Peterborough	46	15	14	17	61	66	59	-5
Wycombe Wan.	46	15	14	17	46	53	59	-7
Brentford	46	14	17	15	56	70	59	-14
Oldham Ath.	46	15	13	18	53	65	58	-12
Bury	46	16	10	20	45	59	58	-14
Colchester U.	46	15	12	19	55	59	57	-4
Northampton	46	15	12	19	46	59	57	-13
Cambridge U.	46	14	11	21	61	77	53	-16
Swindon T.	46	13	13	20	47	65	52	-18
Bristol R.	46	12	15	19	53	57	51	-4
Luton T.	46	9	13	24	52	80	40	-28
Swansea	46	8	13	25	47	73	37	-26
Oxford U.	46	7	6	33	53	100	27	-47

Name _____

Sponsored walk

These are the distances walked by a group of people on a sponsored walk.

Complete a frequency table below to show how many people walked each distance. Use the table to calculate the mean distance walked.

5 km   6 km   8 km   6 km
8 km   10 km   10 km   5 km
9 km   9 km   7 km
11 km   7 km   10 km   8 km
6 km
9 km   5 km   6 km
7 km   9 km   8 km   7km
10 km
8 km   10 km
7 km   9 km   7 km
8 km   9 km
11 km   9 km
9 km   6 km
8 km   7 km   7 km
10 km   9 km

distance	tallies	frequency	

mean distance = _____

Dice throwing

Complete the grid to show all the possible totals when these two dice are thrown.

red

	2		
1	5	4	5
	3		

green

	0		
4	4	1	2
	3		

green

		0	I	2	3	4	4
red	I						
	2						
	3						
	4						
	5						
	5						

Write the probability for each total.

total	chance	probability
0	in 36	$\overline{36}$
I	in	
2	in	
3	in	
4	in	
5	in	
6	in	
7	in	
8	in	
q	in	
10	in	

PHOTOCOPY MASTERS

6 Group Activities

Purpose

The activities in this section are intended as a follow-up to the material in the introductory teaching. They are practical activities, ideal for paired or group work, as well as providing opportunities for investigational work.

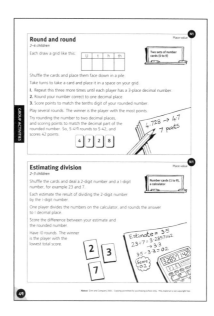

Structure

Two Group Activities are provided for each unit of teaching and these are clearly referenced on the matching Teacher Card.

The Group Activities are photocopiable, so can be presented directly to the children. This encourages language development by allowing children to interpret instructions themselves.

It is assumed that the Group Activity work will follow the introductory teaching from the appropriate Teacher Card unit.

Using the Group activities

The activities can be attempted in class by groups of children, or be set as homework for children to share with parents/carers at home. Each activity includes the following information:

- appropriate number of children/people
- a list of relevant materials and 'specialist resources' (included as Resource Masters on pages 121–127 of this book)
- clear instructions that can easily be interpreted by children, allowing the teacher to focus on other groups.

We suggest that after spending some time working independently on the group activities in class or as homework, the topic should be rounded off with a discussion about what the children have learned and any difficulties they encountered.

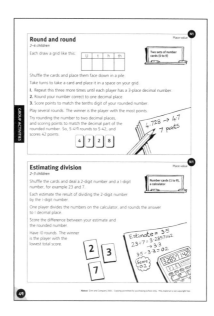

Round and round

2–4 children

Each draw a grid like this:

U	t	h	th

Two sets of number cards (0 to 9)

Shuffle the cards and place them face down in a pile.

Take turns to take a card and place it in a space on your grid.

I. Repeat this three more times until each player has a 3-place decimal number.

2. Round your number correct to one decimal place.

3. Score points to match the tenths digit of your rounded number.

Play several rounds. The winner is the player with the most points.

Try rounding the number to two decimal places, and scoring points to match the decimal part of the rounded number. So, 5·419 rounds to 5·42, and scores 42 points.

4·728 → 4·7
7 points

4 7 2 8

Estimating division

2–3 children

Shuffle the cards and deal a 2-digit number and a I-digit number, for example 23 and 7.

Number cards (1 to 9), a calculator

Each estimate the result of dividing the 2-digit number by the I-digit number.

One player divides the numbers on the calculator, and rounds the answer to I decimal place.

Score the difference between your estimate and the rounded number.

Have I0 rounds. The winner is the player with the lowest total score.

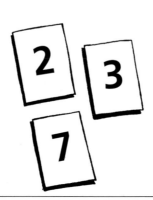

2 3
7

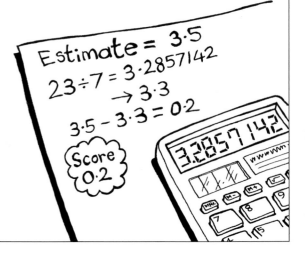

Estimate = 3·5
23 ÷ 7 = 3·2857142
→ 3·3
3·5 − 3·3 = 0·2
Score 0·2

Time trial

2 children

Each player writes five 2-digit decimal numbers, in a list, together with the double.

The first player starts the stopwatch, then reads the numbers, one at a time, whilst the second player has to say the double. If correct, the next number is read.

Stop the watch after the fifth number is doubled correctly and record the time.

Now swap roles. Who took the shortest time?

Repeat for different numbers.

A sheet of paper each, a stopwatch

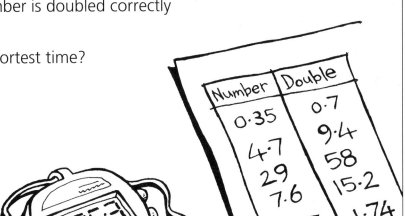

Number	Double
0·35	0·7
4·7	9·4
29	58
7·6	15·2
0·87	1·74

GROUP ACTIVITIES

Doubling and halving

2 children

Each player draws a place-value board as shown, large enough to contain number cards.

Each deal two cards face down. Secretly place them on your board, cover them and write the double of the decimal number on a sheet of paper.

Take turns to reveal your double. The other player must say the matching 'half'. Remove the cover from your place-value board to check. If your partner is correct, they collect a counter.

Play eight rounds then check to see who has collected the most counters.

Try dealing three cards, and making a 3-digit decimal number.

Number cards (1 to 9), sheets of paper, counters

double 0·38 = 0·76

Multiplying using factors

2 children or 2 pairs

2 dice, paper

Dice throws						
Numbers to be multiplied	4·3	5·4	7·6	6·2	1·9	3·7
Numbers to multiply by	30	24	12	18	20	36

Roll a dice to select the number to be multiplied, and another to select the multiplier (number to multiply by).

Each choose a different pair of factors of the multiplier. So, for a multiplier of 24, you could choose 3 and 8, or 4 and 6.

Multiply the numbers together, by making notes on paper, then compare. Check each other's calculations.

Repeat several times.

$$5.4 \times 20$$
$$= 5.4 \times 10 \times 2$$
$$= 54 \times 2 = 108$$

Multiplying by doubling and halving

2–3 children

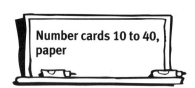

Number cards 10 to 40, paper

Shuffle the cards and make two piles face down. Reveal the top two cards for numbers which must be multiplied together.

Work on your own to double one number and halve the other before multiplying.

First try to calculate the answer in your head and write it down.

Next make notes to do the calculation and write this down. Are the answers the same?

Compare each other's answers. Score I point for a correct answer by making notes, and a bonus point if your mental calculation is also correct.

Play six rounds and see who wins the most points.

14   27

$$14 \times 27 =$$
$$7 \times 54 =$$

GROUP ACTIVITIES

Ordering fractions

2–3 children

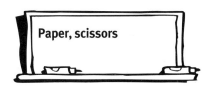

Paper, scissors

Cut out the fraction blocks.

Put each set in order, from smallest to largest, by changing them into a set which have a common denominator.

What are the two words spelt by the letters?

Y	M	I	P	A	D	R
$\frac{1}{4}$	$\frac{7}{10}$	$\frac{3}{4}$	$\frac{3}{20}$	$\frac{1}{2}$	$\frac{4}{5}$	$\frac{2}{5}$

T	H	R	D	O	E	N	C	A	O
$\frac{1}{4}$	$\frac{5}{12}$	$\frac{3}{4}$	$\frac{2}{3}$	$\frac{5}{6}$	$\frac{1}{2}$	$\frac{11}{12}$	$\frac{1}{6}$	$\frac{1}{3}$	$\frac{1}{12}$

Comparing fractions

2 children

Fraction cards
(Resource Master 1)

Shuffle the fraction cards and place them face down.
Take turns to reveal two cards, and put the smaller on the left and larger on the right.

Game 1 Say the smallest common denominator of the two fractions.

Game 2 Convert them both into equivalent fractions with the same denominator, and put them in order.

Game 3 Convert them both into equivalent fractions with the same denominator, and add them.

Game 4 Convert them both into equivalent fractions with the same denominator, and find the difference.

Discuss and check each other's answers.

If correct immediately, score 2 points. If correct after some help, score 1 point.

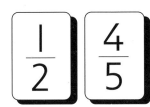

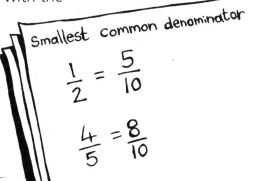

Smallest common denominator

$\frac{1}{2} = \frac{5}{10}$

$\frac{4}{5} = \frac{8}{10}$

Adding by doubling

3 children

2 dice

Dice throws						
Easy	4·3	5·4	7·6	6·2	1·9	3·7
Hard	30	24	12	18	20	36

Play the easier version first, then try the harder version.

Throw two dice to choose two numbers to be added, using doubling.

Each player, in turn, has to say the answer using a different double.

So, if you choose 5·8 and 6·1, you could say:

A   double 5·8 + 0·3 = 11·6 + 0·3 = 11·9

B   double 6·1 − 0·3 = 12·2 − 0·3 = 11·9

C   double 6 + 0·1 − 0·2 = 12 + 0·1 − 0·2 = 11·9

Repeat the activity for different additions,
taking turns to go first.

$5·8 + 6·1 =$

Differencing

2–3 children

Shuffle the cards and create two decimal numbers,
for example 4·36 and 8·72.

Place-value cards
(U, t, h), a stopwatch,
paper

Start the stopwatch. Players have one minute to calculate
the difference between the numbers mentally. Do not use jottings,
just write down the answer.

Next, all players check the answer by using jumps along a number line, on paper.
Each correct answer scores 1 point.

Play several rounds to see who scores the most points.

For an easier version, only use
units and tenths place-value
cards.

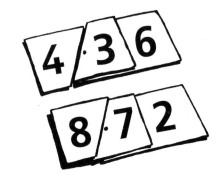

4·36

8·72

difference =

GROUP ACTIVITIES

Prime number game

2 children

Take turns to throw the two dice, and arrange them to make a 2-digit number.

If your number is prime, then you score points to match the number.

The winner is the first player to reach 150 points.

Investigate how many different prime numbers can be made by throwing the two dice.

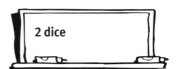

2 dice

Score 31

Factor chart

2–3 children

Draw a chart which shows all the factors of numbers.

Large sheets of squared paper

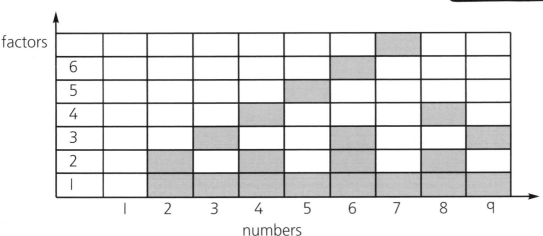

factors

numbers

Shade squares to indicate that the numbers are factors.

Look for and describe patterns.

Multiplying and dividing
2–4 children

Deal out three cards. One player arranges them to make a whole number or decimal number, using a counter as a decimal point.

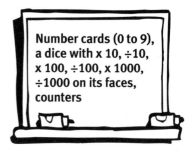

Number cards (0 to 9), a dice with x 10, ÷10, x 100, ÷100, x 1000, ÷1000 on its faces, counters

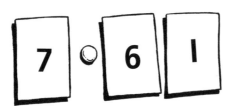

Take turns to roll the dice and change the number to match the dice throw. Say the answer. If correct, take a counter.

After the first round, another player selects three cards and makes a new number. Repeat the activity.

Have several rounds and see who collects the most counters.

Three in a row
2–4 children

Take turns to roll the red and blue dice and find the matching number in the chart.

Roll the x/÷ dice and change the number to match. Say the answer. If correct, cover the number with one of your counters.

A red and blue dice (1 to 6), a dice with x 10, ÷10, x 0·1, ÷0·1, x 0·01, ÷0·01 on its faces, a set of counters each of your own colour

The winner is the first to have three counters in a row.

blue \ red	•	••	•••	::	:•:	:::
•	2·7	0·36	1·45	1·9	16·2	135
••	13	216	1·8	0·5	26	7·3
•••	0·3	5·6	27·3	2·9	172	9·3
::	8·6	0·03	17	7·3	39·5	15
:•:	58	184	6·9	0·08	43	0·8
:::	2·1	0·7	5·4	19	0·8	48·6

Fraction game

2 children

Shuffle the fraction cards and the number cards (I to I0) and place them face down in two separate piles.

Take turns to reveal one card from each pile.

Multiply the two numbers together.

Check each other's calculations. If correct, score points to match the whole number part of the answer.

Have I0 turns each, reshuffling if necessary. The winner is the player with the most points.

Try a game with number cards I0 to 20, or I to 20.

Fraction cards (Resource Master 1), number cards (1 to 20)

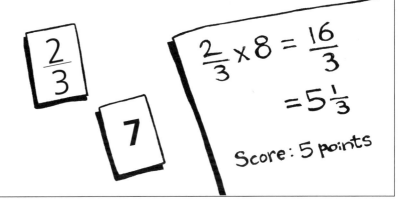

$$\frac{2}{3} \times 8 = \frac{16}{3}$$
$$= 5\frac{1}{3}$$

Score: 5 points

Fraction multiplying

2–3 children

Cover each spot with a counter. Take turns to remove a counter and try to do the calculation mentally, or on paper, and say the answer.

Counters, paper

Give the answer as simply as possible. So, for ' $\frac{3}{5} \times 4$ ' say 'twelve fifths which is two and two-fifths'.

Check each other's calculations. If correct keep the counter. If not, give it to your opponent. When they have all been removed, who has collected the most?

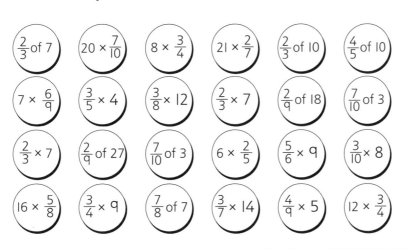

$\frac{2}{3}$ of 7 $20 \times \frac{7}{10}$ $8 \times \frac{3}{4}$ $21 \times \frac{2}{7}$ $\frac{2}{3}$ of 10 $\frac{4}{5}$ of 10

$7 \times \frac{6}{9}$ $\frac{3}{5} \times 4$ $\frac{3}{8} \times 12$ $\frac{2}{3} \times 7$ $\frac{2}{9}$ of 18 $\frac{7}{10}$ of 3

$\frac{2}{3} \times 7$ $\frac{2}{9}$ of 27 $\frac{7}{10}$ of 3 $6 \times \frac{2}{5}$ $\frac{5}{6} \times 9$ $\frac{3}{10} \times 8$

$16 \times \frac{5}{8}$ $\frac{3}{4} \times 9$ $\frac{7}{8}$ of 7 $\frac{3}{7} \times 14$ $\frac{4}{9} \times 5$ $12 \times \frac{3}{4}$

Ninths and elevenths

2–3 children

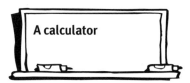

A calculator

Change each of these fractions into decimals, using a calculator, noting any patterns.

Investigate similar patterns in elevenths.

Find a denominator of your own which produces patterns like this.

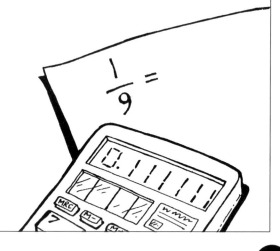

Calculator game

2–4 children

Shuffle the cards and place them face down.

One person reveals a fraction card.

All players try to write it as a decimal by dividing the numerator by the denominator.

Check answers with the calculator.

Score I point for each correct answer.

The winner is the player with the highest score out of 10.

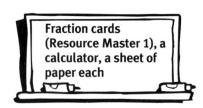

Fraction cards (Resource Master 1), a calculator, a sheet of paper each

GROUP ACTIVITIES

Get between them
2 children

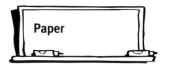

The first player starts by writing two numbers.

The second player writes any number between them, and crosses out one of the two 'outside' numbers.

The first player now writes a number between these two, and crosses out one of the 'outside' numbers.

Continue like this taking turns for a few rounds.

Repeat for different starting numbers.

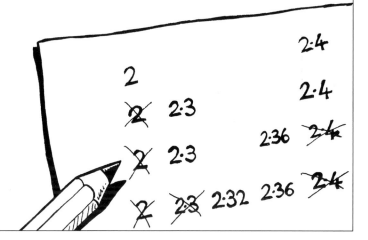

Adding and subtracting 0·1 and 0·01
2–4 children

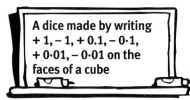

A dice made by writing + 1, – 1, + 0.1, – 0.1, + 0·01, – 0·01 on the faces of a cube

Choose any one of these circled numbers.

Take turns to roll the dice, and say the result of changing the number to match the dice.

Check each other's answers. If correct, write the answer as your score.

Play six rounds, one for each circled number. Add up your six scores.

The winner is the player with the largest total.

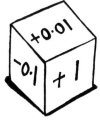

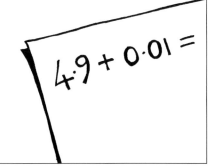

GROUP ACTIVITIES

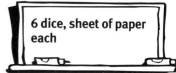

6 dice, sheet of paper each

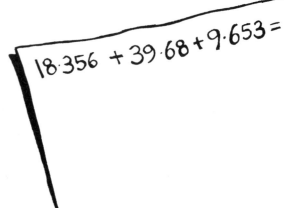

Dice roll

2–4 children

18·356   142·7   39·68   15·4   0·8379   0·653

One player rolls three dice.

Match the dice numbers to the decimal numbers.

Each player adds the three numbers together.

Compare answers, and check for errors.
Score 1 point for each correct total.

Have three rounds.

Extend to rolling four dice,
then five dice and then
six dice.

18·356 + 39·68 + 9·653 =

Digit total of totals

3 children

Place value cards
(U, t, h, th)

Take turns to choose three cards from each set to make
three 3-place decimal numbers.

Find the total of your three numbers.

Check each other's totals.

Your score is the digit total
of the answer. So, a total
of 8·736 scores 24 points,
because 8 + 7 + 3 + 6 = 24.

Play three rounds each to
see who scores the most
points.

8·817

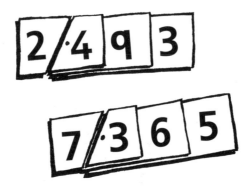

2·493

7·365

7·365 + 2·493 + 8·817 =

GROUP ACTIVITIES

Big difference

2–4 children

Place-value cards (U, t, h, th), sheet of paper each

Spread out the place-value cards, face down.

One player takes two cards from each set to create two decimal numbers each with 3 decimal places.

All subtract the smaller number from the larger, then check that you agree the answer.

The first player scores points to match the digital root of the answer. To find the digital root add the digits, then add the digits of the total until you reach a 1-digit number.

So, if the answer is 3·568 the digital root is:

$3 + 5 + 6 + 8 = 24$, $2 + 4 = 6$
Score 6 points.

Play three rounds. Who scores the most points?

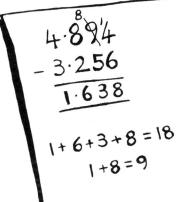

$$4.8\overset{8}{9}\overset{1}{4}$$
$$- 3.256$$
$$\overline{1.638}$$

$1 + 6 + 3 + 8 = 18$
$1 + 8 = 9$

Subtraction game

2–3 children

Two sets of number cards (0 to 9)

Each player draws the outline of a subtraction, like this:

Shuffle the cards, and place them in a pile face down.

Turn over eight cards, one at a time. After each card, write the number in one of your boxes, before the next card is revealed.

Make sure the top number is larger than the bottom number, otherwise you will score 0 points.

When the two numbers are complete, subtract your bottom number from your top number. Score points to match each digit in the answer which is greater than 6.

So, for 3·848, score $8 + 8 = 16$ points.

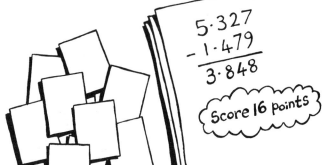

$$5.327$$
$$- 1.479$$
$$\overline{3.848}$$

Score 16 points

Power game

2 children

Take turns to throw the two dice.

Choose one number to be the power, and the other to be the base number, e.g. 2^3.

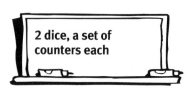

2 dice, a set of counters each

If the answer appears on the board, cover it with one of your counters.

Remember that 4^1 is 4, 6^1 is 6.

The winner is the first to have four counters in a straight line.

9	2	64	125	1
16	25	1	64	6
1	3	729	4	27
32	36	256	1	5
1	1024	81	216	16
243	1	8	4	625

Powers and primes

2–3 children

Odd numbers 1 19 3 17 71 5

Prime numbers 2 13 3 5 11 17

Powers of 2 2 4 8 16 32 64

Choose any odd number, for example 15.

Can it be written as the total of a prime number and a power of 2?

Here are three ways of doing this:

$15 = 13 + 2^1$ $15 = 11 + 2^2$ $15 = 7 + 2^3$

$$15 = 13 + 2^1$$
$$15 = 11 + 2^2$$
$$15 = 7 + 2^3$$

Investigate for other odd numbers.

See-saw balancing
2–3 children

Number cards (⁻4 to ⁺4), paper

Draw a large see-saw like this:

Position any three cards to make the see-saw balance.

To balance the see-saw, the total on each side must be the same.

How many different ways can you find to balance the see-saw?

Investigate for a see-saw with three numbers on one side and one number on the other, or two numbers on each side.

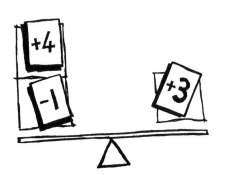

Addition and subtraction tables
2–3 children

Complete these addition and subtraction tables.

In the addition table add the top number and side number in each row and column.

In the subtraction table subtract the top number from the side number.

Make two of your own tables. Include some positive and negative I-place decimals, or simple fractions.

+	⁺3	⁻4	⁺2	⁻5	⁺4
⁻6					
⁺7					
⁻1					
⁺10					
⁻4					

−	⁻6	⁺7	⁺1	⁻7	⁺4
⁺5					
⁻4					
0					
⁻7					
⁺2					

GROUP ACTIVITIES

Nearest to 200 game

2–4 children

Each deal five cards from your shuffled pack.

Arrange the cards to make two numbers: one with digits TU·t and one with U·t.

Use counters for the decimal points. Try to make numbers with a product as close as possible to 200.

Do your calculations separately, then check together using the calculator

The player whose answer is closest to 200 wins the round.

The winner is the first player to win four rounds.

A set of number cards each (1 to 9), a calculator, a sheet of paper each, counters

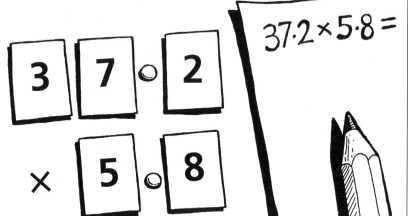

Calculator game

2–4 children

Choose a 2-digit multiplying number, for example 23. Shuffle and deal out the cards to make three decimal numbers with digits U·th. Use counters for the decimal points.

Complete three multiplications by multiplying each of the decimal numbers by the chosen 2-digit number.

Check each other's answers. Collect a counter for each correct answer.

Repeat five times, choosing different multiplying numbers and making different decimal numbers each time. Who collects the most counters?

Number cards (1 to 9), counters, paper

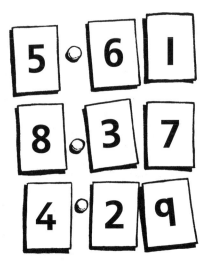

$5 \cdot 61 \times 23 =$

$8 \cdot 37 \times 23 =$

$4 \cdot 29 \times 23 =$

GROUP ACTIVITIES

Five divisions

2–4 children

Spread out the place-value cards, and make five different I-place decimal numbers.

Shuffle the number cards and deal one each. Each player then divides each of the five numbers by their card number, correct to one decimal place.

Check each other's answers with a calculator, scoring one point for each correct answer.

Repeat for a different set of decimal numbers and different number cards.

Who scores the most points?

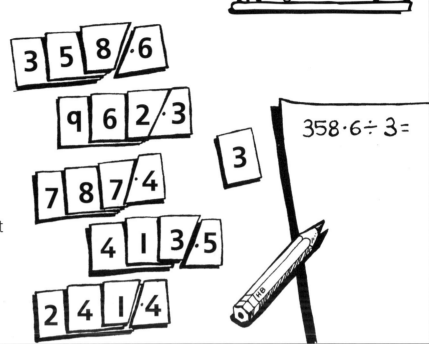

358·6÷3=

Decimal divisions

2–4 children

Write down any 3-digit number.

Shuffle the number cards, and deal them out to make four 2-digit numbers, each with one decimal place. Use counters for the decimal points.

Divide the 3-digit number by each of the decimal numbers. (Start by changing the divisions to contain whole numbers only).

Write answers correct to one decimal place.

Check each other's answers using a calculator.

Place-value cards (H, T, U, t), number cards (3 to 9), a calculator, a sheet of paper each

Number cards (1 to 9), counters, paper, a calculator

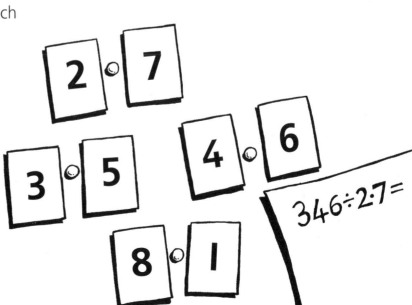

346÷2·7=

Percentage game

2–4 children

£1400   £800   £950   £6800   £7300   £5200

A dice, number cards (10 to 100), a calculator, a sheet of paper each

Shuffle the cards, and place them face down in a pile.

Roll the dice and choose the matching amount. Reveal a card to give a percentage.

Each player calculates the percentage of the amount, for example 23% of £7300, and records their answer.

Check your answers together using the calculator. If correct, score points to match the number of hundreds in the answer. So, for an answer of £1679, score 16 points.

Play several rounds, and see who scores the most points.

23% of £7300

Calculator percentages

4 children

Number cards (10 to 100), a calculator

Shuffle the cards and place them face down in a pile. Choose a percentage together, for example 14%.

Select a number card, for example 72.

Each player calculates 14% of 72 using a different method.

Player A changes the percentage to a decimal.

Player B changes the percentage to a fraction.

Player C finds 1% of the number then multiplies.

Player D uses the percentage key and multiplies.

Player B is allowed ten key presses on the calculator, the other three players only seven.

Check answers, then swap roles. Play several rounds.

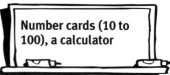

14% of 72 =

With or without a calculator
2–4 children

Number cards (1 to 12), a
calculator each, paper

Shuffle the cards, and place them face down in a pile.
Choose two cards and place the smaller as the numerator
of a fraction, and the larger as the denominator.

Each try to write the fraction as a decimal and as a
percentage, without using a calculator.

If you are unsure, use a calculator
to help you.

If you find the correct answer
without using a calculator, score
2 points. If you use a calculator,
score I point.

Repeat for different fractions.

Who scores the most points?

GROUP ACTIVITIES

Fractions to percentages
2 children

Fraction cards (Resource
Master 1), a calculator

Game I
Shuffle the fraction cards and place them face down
in a pile.

Take turns to select a card, and change it into a percentage,
correct to one
decimal place, without using the calculator. Use the calculator to check. If
correct, keep the card. If not, replace it.

Game 2

Deal out five cards in a straight line. Put them in estimated order, from smallest
to largest. Check the order by changing each fraction to a percentage, with or
without the calculator. Is your order correct?

Reshuffle and repeat several times.

$\frac{1}{5}$ $\frac{1}{4}$ $\frac{2}{5}$ $\frac{3}{8}$ $\frac{3}{10}$ $\frac{1}{2}$ $\frac{11}{20}$ $\frac{7}{12}$ $\frac{3}{4}$ $\frac{7}{8}$

Card proportions

2–4 children

Shuffle the cards, and place them face down in a pile.
Split the pack and spread roughly half the cards on the table.

All players have to find six different proportions each,
and write them in decimal form, correct to
one decimal place. Try to do this without using a calculator.

The categories are:

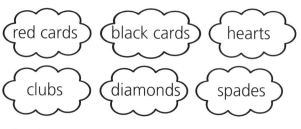

A pack of playing cards, a calculator each, paper

Check each other's answers, scoring one
point for each correct proportion.

Replace the cards, reshuffle, split them again,
and repeat.

Dice ratios

2 children

Roll the dice 24 times, and record each score.

Find how many of each dice number appeared.

Write the ratio of ones to each of the other numbers.
Then write the ratio of twos to each of the others,
threes to each of the others, ... and so on.

Simplify each ratio as much as you can.

Repeat the activity, rolling the
dice a different number of times.

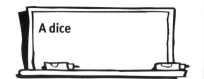

A dice

Ratios

Mystery numbers
2–4 children

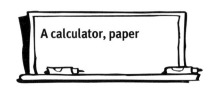

A calculator, paper

Each player writes an addition of two decimal numbers, including the answer. Do not show your addition to the other players.

Take turns to say your answer and one of your numbers. The others must do an inverse calculation (i.e. subtraction) to work out the mystery missing number. Are they are correct? Check using a calculator.

Repeat the activity for a subtraction of two decimal numbers, then a multiplication of a decimal number and a 1-digit number.

$$43 \cdot 2 + \bigcirc = 513 \cdot 74$$

Different methods of calculating
2–3 children

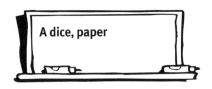

A dice, paper

Take turns to roll a dice. Find the calculation below that matches the dice number you roll.

Write the calculation and a method of doing it.

If you roll a number that has already appeared, try to write a different method of doing the calculation.

Continue for several rounds, looking for different methods for each calculation.

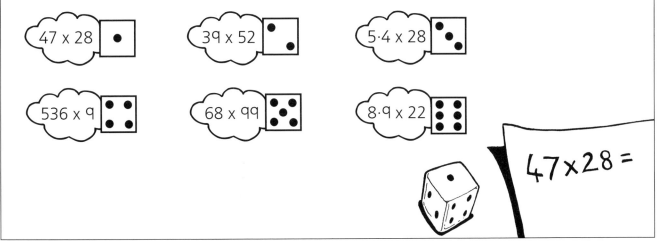

47 x 28 •

39 x 52 ⚁

5·4 x 28 ⚂

536 x 9 ⚃

68 x 99 ⚄

8·9 x 22 ⚅

$$47 \times 28 =$$

GROUP ACTIVITIES

Estimating squares

2–4 children

Shuffle the cards and place them in a pile. Deal two cards to make a 2-digit number.

Each estimate the square of the number as close as you can. No jottings allowed!

Check the answer with a calculator. The player with the nearest estimate collects a counter.

Repeat several times, reshuffling each time. The winner is the first to get five points.

Try these variations:

I. Deal two cards to make a decimal number U·t.

2. Deal three cards to make a 3-digit number.

Number cards (0 to 9), paper, a calculator, counters

Card squares

2–3 children

Use the cards to make square numbers. Each card may be used once only.

Number cards (0 to 9)

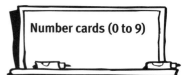

This arrangement makes 3 square numbers:

This arrangement makes 4 square numbers:

   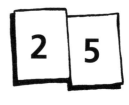

Investigate different possible arrangements. How many of the cards can you use?

Five minute challenge

2–4 children

Shuffle the cards and place them in a pile.

Deal out four cards.

Each make a calculation using the four digits without showing the other players.

Show your answer to the others, but keep the calculation hidden. The others have five minutes, timed on the stopwatch, to find your calculation.

If, after five minutes your calculation is not discovered, you collect a counter.

Repeat several times, using different sets of four cards.

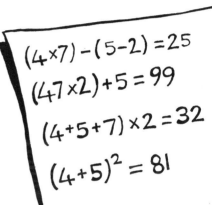

Number cards (0 to 9), paper, counters, stopwatch

$(4 \times 7) - (5 - 2) = 25$

$(47 \times 2) + 5 = 99$

$(4 + 5 + 7) \times 2 = 32$

$(4 + 5)^2 = 81$

Ten calculation challenge

2–3 children

Use the digits 2, 3, 4, 5 only, to make calculations with answers from 21 to 30.

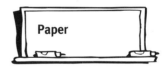

Paper

Make a table with ten entries from 21 to 30, and try to make calculations for each answer, using each digit no more than once in each calculation.

After 20 minutes calculate your score. For each correct calculation, score:

- 5 points for each use of a bracket
- 3 points for each use of a power
- 2 points for each x and ÷ sign
- 1 point for each + and – sign.

Who scores the most points?

Repeat for different sets of digits, and ranges of answers.

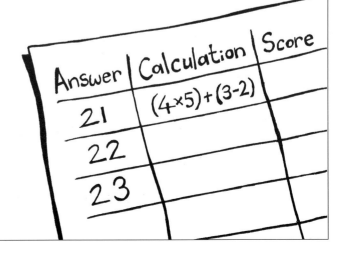

Answer	Calculation	Score
21	$(4 \times 5) + (3 - 2)$	
22		
23		

GROUP ACTIVITIES

Longhand

2–3 children

Shuffle the cards and place them face down.

Reveal one card.

Write down a longhand version of the expression on the card.

Check each other's answers.

Collect a counter for each correct answer.

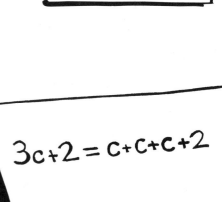

Algebra cards 1 (Resource Master 2), paper, counters

Algebraic expressions

2–3 children

Shuffle both sets of cards, and place them face down in two piles.

Take turns to reveal two algebra cards and one sign card.

Write an expression based on the chosen cards, in the simplest form possible.

Check each other's work.

Try choosing three algebra cards, and two sign cards.

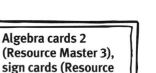

Algebra cards 2 (Resource Master 3), sign cards (Resource Master 5)

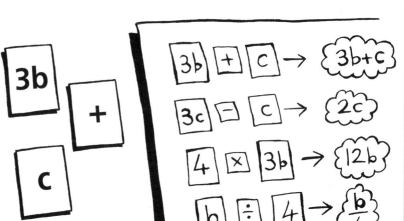

Combine the terms

2 children

Shuffle the cards which contain an 'a' and spread them out face down.

Take turns to choose two cards and say the result of combining the algebraic terms in them.

Write down the expression.

Repeat for all cards containing 'b', then for all cards containing 'c'.

Repeat the activity using all the cards together.

Remember: You can only combine like terms.

Algebra cards 1
(Resource Master 2)

$3a + 4$

$2a - 3$

$3a + 4 + 2a - 3 = 5a + 1$

Patterns in grids

2–3 children

Use algebra to explore patterns in a grid with 6 rows and 6 columns.

Start with 3 x 3 square within the grid.

Demonstrate that these pairs of totals made by adding the numbers in the shaded squares are the same.

Explore other patterns.

1	2	3	4	5	6
7	8	9	10	11	12
13	14	15	16	17	18
19	20	22	22	23	24
25	26	27	28	29	30
31	32	33	34	35	36

Squared paper

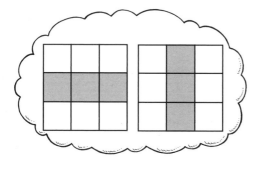

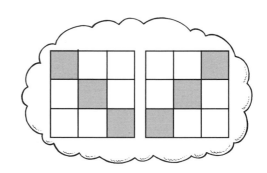

Substitution game

2–3 children

Shuffle both sets of cards and place them face down in two piles.

Deal one algebra card to each player.

Reveal the top number card. This is the value to be substituted.

Each player substitutes the value on the number card for x in the expression on their algebra card.

The player with the highest value collects 3 counters, the player with the next highest score collects 2 counters, and third place collects one counter.

Continue until all the cards have been used. Who has the most counters?

Repeat the game by reshuffling the algebra cards, and choosing a new number card.

| $3x + 2$ | $5x$ | $4x + 5$ |

Multiplying brackets

2–3 children

Shuffle both sets of cards and place them face down in two piles.

Reveal one algebra card, and one number card. Each player multiplies these together and writes the answer. All reveal your answers together.

If correct, collect a counter.

Play 20 rounds, using each algebra card once, and reshuffling the number cards when needed.

The winner is the player who collects the most counters.

$c + 3$

$9c + 27$

9

Circles and squares

2–3 children

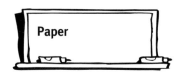

Draw two small circles on the left of a piece of paper, and three small squares on the right.

Join each circle to each square. Count the number of lines you have drawn.

Try this for different numbers of circles and squares.

Find a formula which connects the number of lines (L), the number of circles (C) and the number of squares (S).

Use the formula to find the number of lines needed for 10 squares and 15 circles.

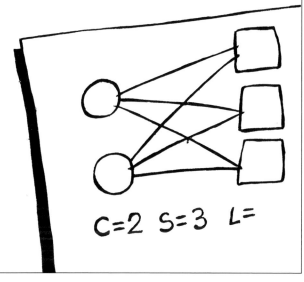

C=2 S=3 L=

Surface squares

2–3 children

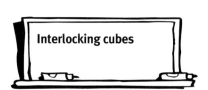

Build cubes of different sizes.

Count the number of square faces (f) that can be seen around the surface of each cube.

Find the length of the edge (l) of each cube.

Find a formula that links l and f.

l = 1
f = 6

l = 2
f =

Mystery track

2–4 children

Each place a counter at 'Start'. Throw the dice, and move your counter a matching number of spaces. Look at the space you land on. Write an equation using addition or subtraction that has this solution.

A dice, counters

If correct, collect counters to match the value of the letter in the space. The game ends when one player has moved round the track twice. Who collects the most counters?

Repeat the game, writing equations involving multiplication as well.

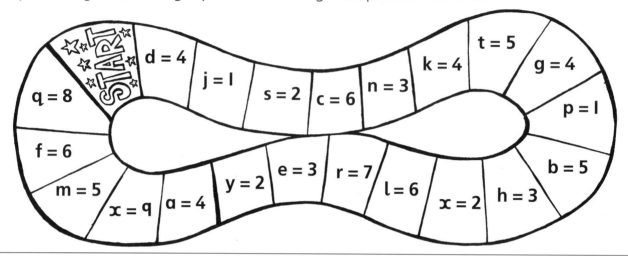

Equation cover-up

2–3 children

Take turns to throw the dice.

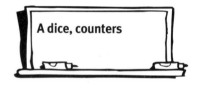

A dice, counters

If your dice number matches the solution to an equation, cover it with one of your counters.

Continue until all equations are covered. Who has placed the most counters?

$17 = 2g + 5$

$7 + 3p = 19$

$4 + 5d = 29$

$2p + 3 = 5$

$32 = 6x + 2$

$5g + 4 = 19$

$4z + 1 = 9$

$5t - 3 = 7$

$13 = 3x - 5$

$3q - 1 = 2$

$20 - 3c = 8$

$4h - 5 = 7$

GROUP ACTIVITIES

Multiplication graphs

2–3 children

Investigate the graphs of multiplication tables. For example, for the x4 table draw the graph of $y = 4x$.

Draw this coordinate grid, write a table of values, and plot the points.

Join them with a straight line.

Explore the graphs of other multiplication tables, drawing the lines on the same grid.

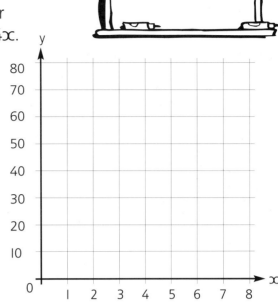

Squared paper

x	1	2	3	4	5	6	7	8
y								

Straw lines

2–3 children

Investigate the position of straight-line graphs on your grid using a drinking straw as your straight line.

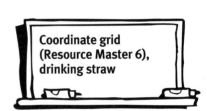

Coordinate grid (Resource Master 6), drinking straw

Start by showing the position of the lines $x = {}^-3$, $x = 4$, $x = 2$, $x = {}^-1$, and other vertical lines. Next show the position of horizontal lines, naming them each time.

Now start with the set of lines $y = x$, $y = x + 1$, $y = x + 2$, ... Also include $y = x - 1$, $y = x - 2$, ... Name each line as you show it.

Next show the lines $y = 2x$, $y = 2x + 1$, $y = 2x = 2$, ... as well as $y = 2x - 1$, $y = 2x - 2$, $y = 2x - 3$, ...

Extend to showing other straight lines, for example $y = 3x$, ...

How many different lines can you show on your grid?

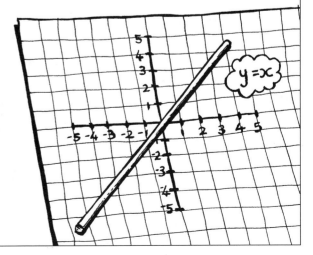

Mobile phones

3 children

Each person chooses one of each of these mobile phone companies.

Squared paper

Company	Charges
'Ring-ring'	£15 rental, calls charged at 10p per minute
'Hear-say'	£10 rental, calls charged at 15p per minute
'Cell-mate'	Free rental, calls charged at 20p per minute

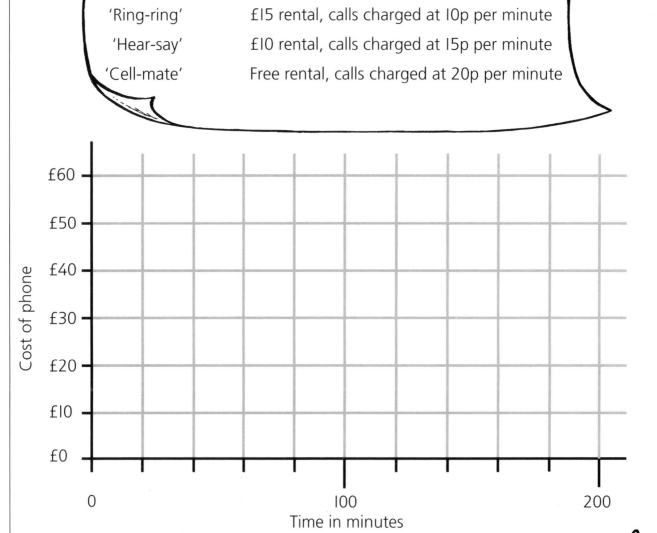

Cost of phone (£0 – £60) vs Time in minutes (0 – 200)

Each person draws a straight line on this graph to show the charges.

Whose company is the cheapest if you make total calls of:

 100 minutes?   120 minutes?   150 minutes?

How many minutes of phone time can you get for:

£20?   £25?   £30?

GROUP ACTIVITIES

Function cards

2–3 children

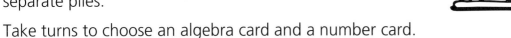

Shuffle the cards, and place them face down in two
separate piles.

Take turns to choose an algebra card and a number card.

Use the number card as the input and calculate the value of
the output for your chosen algebra card. This is your score.

Check each other's calculations and write your scores in a table.

When all algebra cards have been used,
the winner is the player with
the highest score.

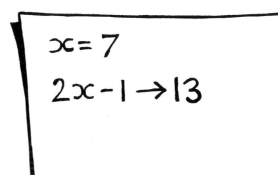

Triple machines

2–3 children

This is a triple machine – it has three operations.

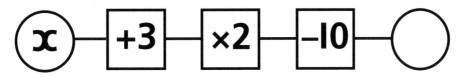

Find the outputs from the machine for the input
numbers 5, 10 and 3.

Invent your own triple machines and try them out
on the same numbers.

Describe each triple machine using algebra.

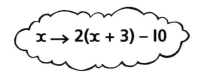

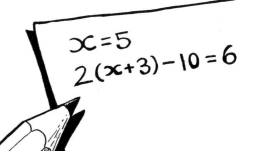

Diagonals

2–3 children

Paper

Look at these circles. The number of points on them increases by I each time. The points are joined to draw all the diagonals for each circle.

Write the number of diagonals on these three circles.

2 points

3 points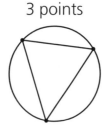

4 points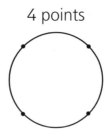

I diagonal

Draw two more circles with 5 points and 6 points. Draw all the diagonals and count them.

Complete and continue the sequence for the number of diagonals.

I, 3, ___, ___, ___

Sequence cover-up

2 children

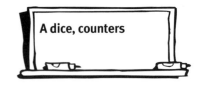

A dice, counters

One player writes a sequence of six numbers, hidden from the other player.

The other player throws a dice. The first player says the matching term in the sequence. For example, if a '3' is thrown, say the third number in the sequence.

Continue throwing the dice to find more numbers in the sequence. Your score is the number of throws you need before you can say the full sequence.

Swap roles and repeat.

The winner of the round is the player who needs fewest dice throws to say their partner's whole sequence.

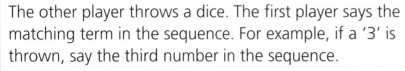

19, 16, 13, 10, 7, 4

GROUP ACTIVITIES

Surrounds

2–3 children

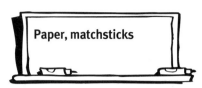

Paper, matchsticks

Make different sequences of 'surrounding' patterns.

Start with a shape, then surround it with a larger shape, and so on.

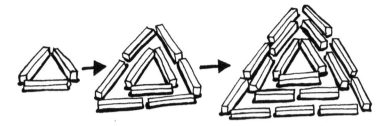

Make a sequence from the number of sticks used for each shape.

Find how many sticks in the 10th shape, then the nth shape.

Here are some ideas for starting shapes:

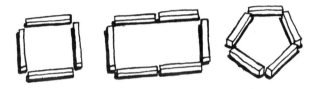

GROP ACTIVITIES

Joins

2–3 children

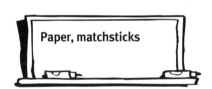

Paper, matchsticks

Make different sequences of 'joining' patterns.

Start with a shape, then join on another of the same shape, and so on.

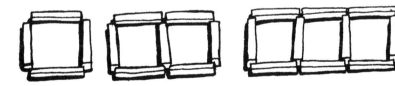

Make a sequence from the number of sticks used for each shape.

Find how many sticks in the 10th shape, then the nth shape.

Here are some ideas for starting shapes:

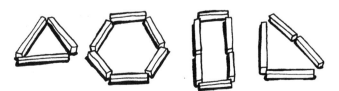

Recipes

2–3 children

Cake recipe

4 oz butter	1 tbsp bicarbonate of soda
8 oz sugar	
12 oz flour	3 eggs
6 oz nuts	2oz cocoa

A recipe book

Rewrite this recipe, using grams instead of ounces.

Copy out five recipes from a recipe book, and write each twice, once using grams, and once using ounces.

Parcels

2–3 children

Choose a parcel, and write down its weight in grams, kilograms, pounds and ounces.

Find out how much it would cost to send.

Write a list of the weights and postage costs for each parcel.

Repeat for each parcel.

Information about postage prices, several 'pretend parcels' with weights marked in different units

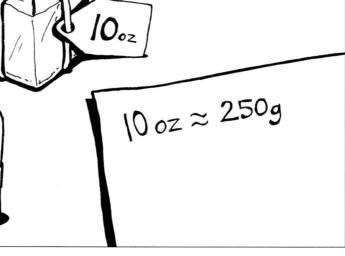

10oz

2·3 Kg

10 oz ≈ 250g

Surface areas of cuboids

2–3 children

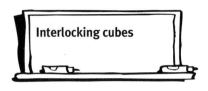

Interlocking cubes

Investigate patterns in the surface areas
of l x l x n cuboids.

Start by finding the surface areas of l x l x l,
l x l x 2, l x l x 3, ... cuboids. Use the answers
to find a formula for the surface area of
a l x l x n cuboid.

Extend the investigation
to l x 2 x n, then
l x 3 x n cuboids.

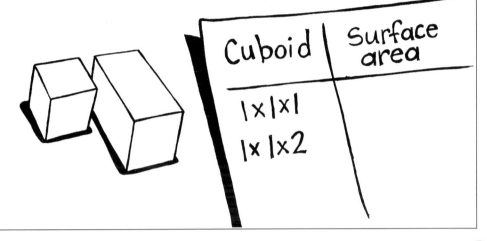

Cuboid	Surface area
l x l x l	
l x l x 2	

The Cuboid Club

2–3 children

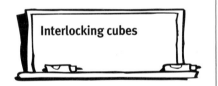

Interlocking cubes

Cuboids that belong to the Cuboid Club must have
surface areas between 50 cm^2 and 70 cm^2.

Check that this cuboid belongs to the Club.

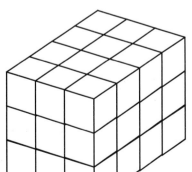

How many different cuboids you can find which belong to the Club?

Build models from cubes to help you investigate.

Areas of non-right-angled triangles

2–3 children

Squared paper, rulers, scissors

Draw rectangles on squared paper.

Find the area of your rectangle and write it down.

Mark a point on the longest side of the rectangle, and join it with a straight line to the two opposite corners.

Cut along these lines to leave a triangle. Find the area of the two right-angled triangles you have cut off.

Place them on top of the larger triangle. What do you notice?

Compare their areas with the area of the rectangle. What do you notice?

Repeat for different-sized rectangles.

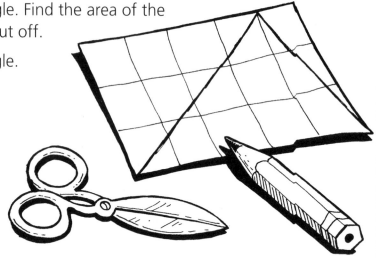

Area game

2 children

One player creates any shape on the geoboard, says its area, and draws it on the dotty paper.

4 x 4 geoboards, elastic bands, square dotty paper

The other player creates a different shape with the same area, and draws this on the same dotty paper.

Continue like this until a player draws a shape which is congruent to any already drawn. That player loses.

Repeat for different shapes.

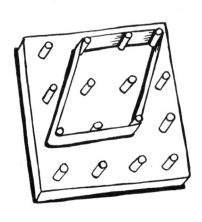

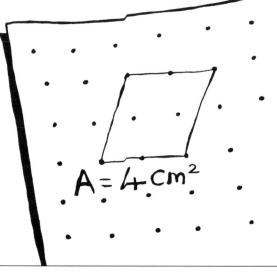

$A = 4 \text{ cm}^2$

GROUP ACTIVITIES

Measuring angles

2–3 children

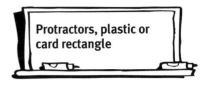

Protractors, plastic or card rectangle

Use a rectangle to draw a pair of parallel lines.

Draw an intersecting line.

Use your protractor to measure each angle, extending the lines if necessary.

Write the angles on the diagram and colour any equal angles.

Repeat for two pairs of intersecting parallel lines.

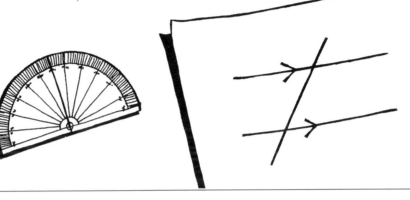

Clock angles

2–3 children

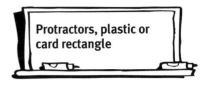

An analogue clock face with movable hands

Take turns to move the hands of a clock to show a time.

Start with the minute hand on a 10-minute interval, for example 6:20, 10:50.

Write down the two angles (one reflex angle, one acute or obtuse angle) made by the hands of the clock.

Calculate the angle made by the minute and hour hand for each interval of 10 minutes. (**Remember** if the minute hand moves 20 minutes, then the hour hand moves for one third of an hour.)

Write down the time and angle.

Repeat for different times.

Extend to times that are not on 10-minute intervals.

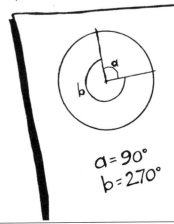

$a = 90°$
$b = 270°$

Making squares

2 children

Plot these points on the coordinate grid.

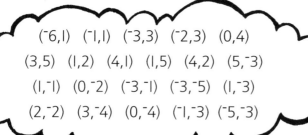

(⁻6,1) (⁻1,1) (⁻3,3) (⁻2,3) (0,4)
(3,5) (1,2) (4,1) (1,5) (4,2) (5,⁻3)
(1,⁻1) (0,⁻2) (⁻3,⁻1) (⁻3,⁻5) (1,⁻3)
(2,⁻2) (3,⁻4) (0,⁻4) (⁻1,⁻3) (⁻5,⁻3)

Different coloured pencils, coordinate grid (Resource Master 6)

Take turns to join a set of four coordinates to make a square.

How many different squares can you draw?

You may use a point as the vertex of more than one square.

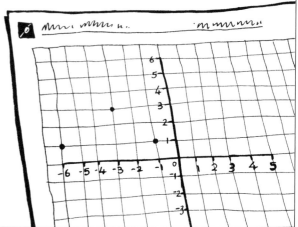

Making trapezia

2–3 children

Shuffle the cards and take turns to deal two.

Choose one for the x-coordinate, and one for the y-coordinate.

Plot the point on the grid, using your own colour.

If you have four points which are the vertices of a trapezium, draw it and score 1 point.

If you can draw a right-angled trapezium score 2 points.

If you can draw an isosceles trapezium score 3 points.

Continue playing and drawing trapezia until one person has scored 10 points.

Coordinate grid (Resource Master 6), 2 sets of number cards (⁻5 to 5), different coloured pencils

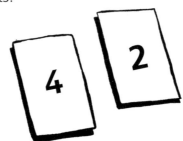

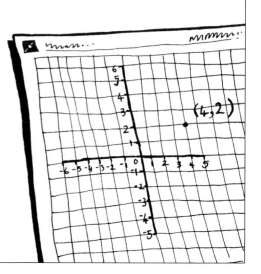

(4,2)

GROUP ACTIVITIES

Parallel mirrors

2–3 children

Draw a set of parallel mirror lines, each the same distance apart.

Draw a shape to be reflected in the first mirror.

Draw its image after reflection. Reflect this image in the next mirror, and so on.

Discuss any patterns created.

Investigate for different starting shapes, and at different positions in relation to the first mirror line.

GROUP ACTIVITIES

Letter reflections

2–3 children

Investigate the reflection of capital letters in a vertical mirror line.

Which have an identical image?

Repeat for reflections in a horizontal mirror line.

Explore any words which have identical images.

The L-Game

2 children

Place the pieces in this position.

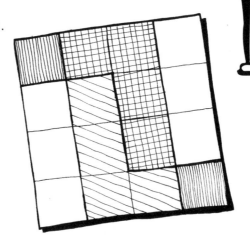

A 4 x 4 grid, 2 square pieces, 2 L-shaped pieces (red and blue) to fit the grid

Choose an L-piece each.

Take turns to pick up your own L-piece and place it in a new position. Then, if you wish, move one of the square pieces.

You may move your L-piece by a translation, reflection or rotation. After moving it describe the transformation.

You win the game if your opponent is unable to move.

Transforming points

2–3 children

Shuffle each set of cards and place them in two piles.

In turn draw one card from each pile to give horizontal and vertical coordinates of a point. Mark the point on the grid.

Two sets of positive and negative number cards (⁻6 to 6), a dice, coordinate grid (Resource Master 6)

Throw the dice and match the number to the transformations below. Say the coordinates of your point after this transformation. Check each other's answers. Score I point if correct.

Play 8 rounds, reshuffling if necessary. Who scores the most points?

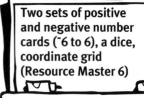

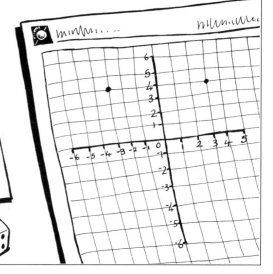

⚀	reflection in x-axis
⚁	rotation 180° about (0,0)
⚂	reflection in y-axis
⚃	rotation 90° clockwise about (0,0)
⚄	reflection in y = x
⚅	translation 3 left, 4 down

Symmetrical shapes
2–3 children

Build shapes with line symmetry on the geoboard.

Copy them onto spotty paper, and draw the line of symmetry.

Build shapes with rotational symmetry.

Copy them onto spotty paper, and mark the centre of rotation.

Geoboards, elastic bands, spotty paper

Order of rotational symmetry
3–4 children

Draw round the outside of these shapes:

square   rectangle   parallelogram

rhombus   regular hexagon   regular octagon

2-d shapes with rotational symmetry (square, rectangle, parallelogram, rhombus, regular hexagon, regular octagon), pins, a pinboard

Find the centre of each shape by drawing diagonals.

Cut out the shapes. Pin each one to the board, through its centre.

Turn them, testing for rotational symmetry.

Write the order of rotational symmetry for each shape.

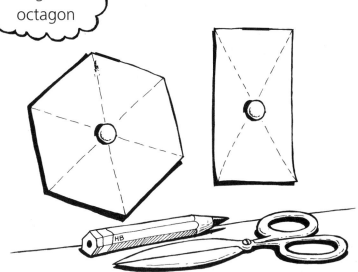

Build the model

2 children

Interlocking cubes, squared paper

Each build a model made from six cubes, without letting your partner see.

Draw four views of your model: front view, right-side view, left-side view and top view.

Keeping your model hidden, show your drawings to your partner, who tries to build the model from the drawings.

When completed, compare them with the hidden models.

Repeat several times, extending to models made from eight cubes.

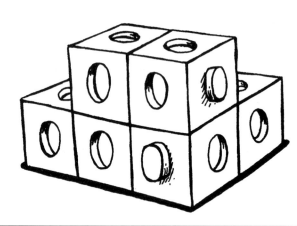

Cube challenge

2–3 children

Card, rulers, pencils, glue, scissors

Draw three of these nets on card. Make sure the measurements are accurate.

Cut them out and score along the lines.

Fold and glue the tabs to make three congruent shapes.

Try to arrange the three models to make a cube.

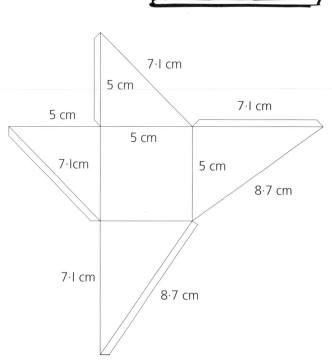

7·1 cm

5 cm

7·1 cm

5 cm

5 cm

7·1cm

5 cm

8·7 cm

7·1 cm

8·7 cm

GROUP ACTIVITIES

Congruency game

2–4 children

Geoboards (3 x 3 or
4 x 4), spotty paper,
counters

Choose a shape, for example 'isosceles triangle' and make it
on your geoboard, unseen by the others.

All reveal your shapes. If your shape is not congruent to any
of the others, collect a counter. Repeat several times, choosing
a different shape each time. Who collects the most counters?

Examples of shapes might be:

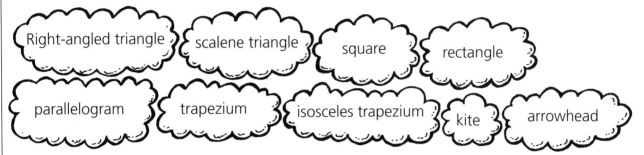

Right-angled triangle   scalene triangle   square   rectangle

parallelogram   trapezium   isosceles trapezium   kite   arrowhead

Can you explain why 'equilateral triangle' and
'rhombus' not included?

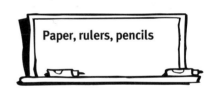

Joining mid-points

2–3 children

Paper, rulers, pencils

Draw several large quadrilaterals of different types.

Use the ruler to mark accurately the mid-points of
each side.

Join adjacent mid-points.

Write about any patterns you notice.

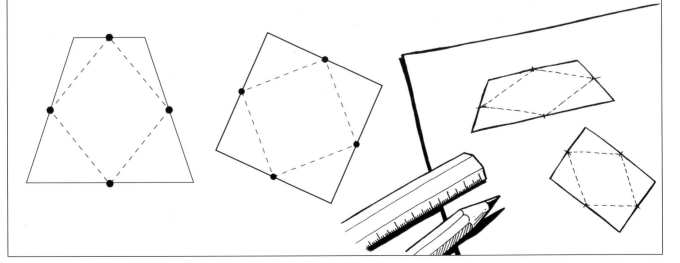

GROUP ACTIVITIES

Regular polygons

2–3 children

Pencils, rulers, protractors, plain paper circles

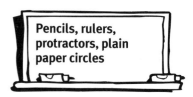

Here is a method of constructing a regular pentagon.

1. Find the centre of the circle by folding it in half, then half again.

2. Draw one radius of the circle.

3. Construct this pattern using a ruler and protractor. (Each interior angle of a pentagon is $360° \div 5 = 72°$).

4. Join the points on the boundary of the circle to create a regular pentagon.

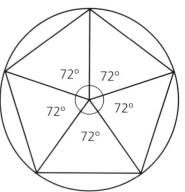

Use the same method to construct a regular hexagon and a regular octagon.

You will need to calculate the interior angles first.

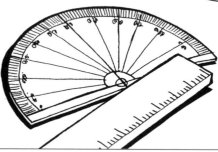

Constructing an octahedron

2–3 children

Pencils, rulers, protractors, card, glue, scissors

Using a ruler and protractor, construct this net on card. It is the net of an octahedron, which is made from eight equilateral triangles.

Put some tabs on the outside edges. (Start by drawing a tab on any edge, then go round the net putting a tab on alternate edges).

Cut out the net and score along the lines. Glue the tabs, and build your octahedron.

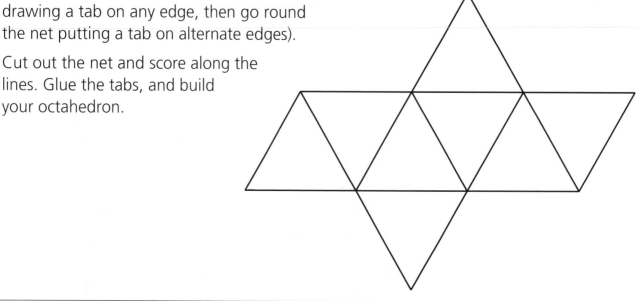

Reaction test

2–3 children

Ask some people you know if you can test their reactions.

Each person should place their wrist on the edge of a table, holding their first finger and thumb the width of a ruler apart.

Hold the bottom of a ruler just above their hand.

When you let go of the ruler, they have to catch it by bringing their finger and thumb together. Look at the position of the ruler in their grip to measure how many centimetres the ruler fell before being caught.
Record this as a measure of reaction time.

Give each person three attempts using their right hand, and three using their left hand. Find the mean for each set.

Collect data from different people, and represent the results graphically.

A ruler, paper, pencil, graph paper

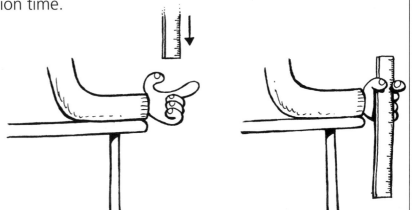

GROUP ACTIVITIES

Coin study

2–4 children

How old are coins?

Are Ip coins older than I0p coins?

Survey as many different coins as you can. Look at Ip, 2p, 5p, I0p, 20p, 50p, £I and £2 coins.

Record data based on the year each coin was made.

Show your results graphically, then write about any conclusions.

Lots of coins, ruler, pencil, paper, graph paper

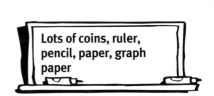

Photographs

2–3 children

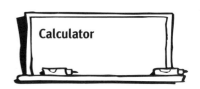

Look at this chart which shows the cost of developing
photographs at 'Supasavers Photos'.

Use a calculator to
investigate the mean
cost for developing
one photograph.

Is it cheaper to use
24 exposure film or
36 exposure film?

SIZE	Economy 7 days	Standard 3 days	Express Next day	Extra Set
Super 6" x 4"	£3·09	£3·39	£3·69	£1·99
Giant 7" x 5"	N/A	£4·39	£4·99	£2·99
Super 6" x 4"	£2·39	£2·69	£2·99	£1·99
Giant 7" x 5"	N/A	£3·69	£4·29	£2·99

An average challenge

2–4 children

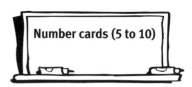

Shuffle the cards and place them face down in a pile. Turn
over the top card, for example 7.

Each write:

I. a list of 10 different numbers which has a mean of 7

2. a list of 10 different numbers which has a mode of 7

3. a list of 10 different numbers which has a median of 7.

Compare your lists. Now try to create a list
of 10 numbers which has all three
averages equal to 7.

Try the challenge for a different
card number.

Cubes

2–3 children

Put 2 yellow, 2 green, I blue and I red cube in a bag.

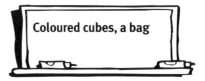

Coloured cubes, a bag

If a cube is taken out and put back 24 times, how many cubes do you estimate will be:

I. red?   **2.** green?   **3.** blue?   **4.** yellow?

Take out and put back a cube 24 times, and draw a tally chart to show the colours of the cubes.

Compare the results with your estimates.

Decide how many times you estimate the cube will be yellow if it is taken out and put back:

5. 42 times?

6. 90 times?

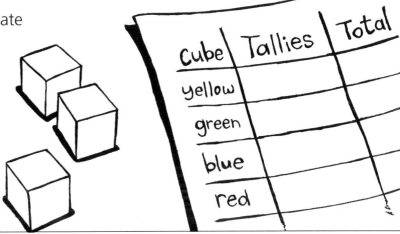

Menus

2–4 children

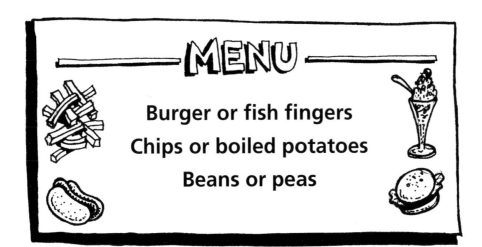

Choose one item from each line of the menu, for example:

Burger, chips and peas

Can you find I2 different choices from the menu?

7 Assessment

How and when to assess

This assessment section provides teacher's notes and a photocopiable pupil assessment sheet on key topics covered in Abacus 7. Links are given to relevant Teacher Card units in which the material is covered. This structure gives flexibility to the teacher over how and when to assess.

You may decide to use the tests as a check-up as each topic is completed, or to use several sheets to make a 'mini-test' for the end of each half term.

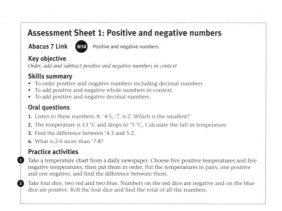

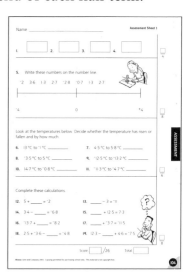

Administering the tests

Within each teacher's section, the notes are organised as follows:
- **Key objective**, making explicit which key objective from the NNS Year 7 Framework is being assessed.
- **Skills summary**, giving details of the exact mental and written skills covered in the test.
- **Oral questions**, several questions that should be read out by the teacher at the start of the test. Answer boxes are provided on the photocopiable assessment sheets. Read each question twice, allowing about ten seconds between each reading.
- **Practice activities**, further practical activities focusing on the key skills, for children who need some extra reinforcement.

Each assessment sheet has a margin on the right to record a pupil's score for each question. The total can be transferred to the foot of the page, and carried over to the next sheet, if appropriate. Where pupils have answered incorrectly, but shown some understanding or relevant working, you may decide to award half a mark. All answers are included at the back of this book in the section starting on page 143.

The style of administration, e.g. formal timed, or informal untimed, is entirely up to the individual teacher. Before starting remind the pupils to read each question carefully, and check their work at the end.

National Curriculum levels

These assessment sheets test what it would be reasonable to assume the most able children can achieve during Year 6 (P7) if studying material from the Year 7 Framework (i.e. consolidating level 5, starting on level 6; or consolidating level E, starting on level F in Scotland).

Assessment Sheet 1: Positive and negative numbers

Abacus 7 Link   **N14** Positive and negative numbers

Key objective
Order, add and subtract positive and negative numbers in context

Skills summary
- To order positive and negative numbers including decimal numbers
- To add positive and negative whole numbers in context
- To add positive and negative decimal numbers

Oral questions
1. Listen to these numbers: 8, ⁻4·5, ⁻7, 6·2. Which is the smallest?
2. The temperature is 13 °C and drops to ⁻5 °C. Calculate the fall in temperature.
3. Find the difference between ⁻4·3 and 5·2.
4. What is 2·6 more than ⁻7·8?

Practice activities
1 Take a temperature chart from a daily newspaper. Choose five positive temperatures and five negative temperatures, then put them in order. Put the temperatures in pairs, one positive and one negative, and find the difference between them.

2 Take four dice, two red and two blue. Numbers on the red dice are negative and on the blue dice are positive. Roll the four dice and find the total of all the numbers.

Assessment Sheet 2: Fractions, decimals, percentages

Abacus 7 Links   **N4** Fractions   **N18** Fractions, decimals, percentages   **N19** Ratio and proportion

Key objective
Use the equivalence of fractions, decimals and percentages in describing proportions

Skills summary
- To find equivalent fractions by cancelling
- To compare and order fractions by converting them to a common denominator
- To convert a fraction to a percentage and vice versa
- To convert a decimal to a percentage and vice versa
- To use direct proportion in simple contexts

Oral questions
1. Listen to these numbers: $\frac{2}{7}$, $\frac{3}{8}$, $\frac{4}{10}$, $\frac{3}{15}$. Which is equivalent to $\frac{2}{5}$?
2. Which is the largest fraction: $\frac{3}{4}$, $\frac{5}{12}$, $\frac{5}{6}$?
3. Write 45% as a fraction in its simplest form.
4. Write 0·125 as a percentage.

Practice activities
1 Roll two 10-sided dice. Make a fraction by writing the smallest number as the numerator and the largest number as the denominator. Write the fraction in its simplest from, as a decimal and as a percentage (use a calculator if necessary). Repeat several times.

2 Put 50 counters of different colours in a bag. Write the proportion of each colour as a fraction, as a decimal and as a percentage.

Assessment Sheet 3: Order of operations

Abacus 7 Link Order of operations

Key objective
Know and use the order of operations

Skills summary
- To know and use the order of operations including brackets and indices
- To calculate with mixed operations, including with a calculator

Oral questions
1. (Write $3 + 4^2$ on the board.) Which part of this calculation would you do first?
2. (Write $3 \times 4 + 7 = 33$ on the board.) Write out the calculation putting the brackets in the correct place.
3. (Write $(4 + 9) \times 3 + 4 =$ on the board.) Calculate the answer.
4. (Write $4 \times 12 + (21 \div 3)$ on the board.) Calculate the answer.

Practice activities

1 Choose four numbers and three operations, e.g. $4 \times 3 + 7 - 2$. Using the same numbers and operations with brackets, how many different answers can be found?

2 Using three or four numbers, two or three operations and a calculator work out a calculation. Give the numbers, the operations and the answer to a partner. Can they work out the order that numbers and operations were put into the calculator? Repeat several times swapping roles.

Assessment Sheet 4: Mental methods

Abacus 7 Links Multiplication/division Addition/subtraction **N8** Fractions Percentages

Key objective
Extend mental methods of calculation to include decimals, fractions and percentages

Skills summary
- To use partitioning or factors for multiplying and dividing (including decimal numbers)
- To add by partitioning, adjusting or using near doubles as appropriate
- To multiply a fraction by a whole number or a whole number by a fraction
- To calculate percentages of numbers or quantities without using a calculator

Oral questions
1. What is 7·3 multiplied by 6?
2. Find the total of 23·4, 23·5 and 19·6.
3. What is 16 lots of $\frac{1}{5}$? Write the answer as a mixed number.
4. In a sale there is 15% off. Find how much will be taken off a shirt that cost £28.

Practice activities

1 Take a set of decimal place-value cards and choose two numbers to form a 1-place decimal number. Roll a 10-sided dice to generate a multiplier and multiply the first number by the second. Record the method. Repeat several times.

2 Look at advertisements in newspapers with percentage discounts advertised. Work out the new price of each advertised item without using a calculator.

ASSESSMENT

Assessment Sheet 5: Written methods

Abacus 7 Links Multiplication Division

Key objective
Refine written methods of multiplication and division of whole numbers to ensure efficiency, and extend to decimals with two decimal places

Skills summary
- To use a standard written method to multiply HTU × TU, TU·t × U·t and U·th × TU
- To use a standard written method to divide HTU ÷ TU, HTU·t ÷ U, TU·th ÷ TU

Oral questions
1. Multiply 0·6 by 0·9.
2. What is 20 lots of 0·7?
3. Divide 17·5 by 5.
4. A number divided by 4 gives the answer 2·35. What is the number?

Practice activities
1 Form a 2-place decimal number by using place-value cards, e.g. 2·53. Pick a 2-digit number from a set of 2-digit number cards. Use a written method to multiply the two numbers together. Repeat several times.

2 Form a 1-place decimal number using place-value cards, e.g. 347·4. Roll a 10-sided dice to generate a divisor. Use a written method to divide the first number by the second. Repeat several times.

ASSESSMENT

Assessment Sheet 6: Checking results

Abacus 7 Links Checking results

Key objective
Judge whether an answer is reasonable and check results, including using knowledge of the number system, rounding to approximate and inverse operations

Skills summary
- To use rounding to approximate the size of an answer
- To check by using the inverse operation
- To check using knowledge of the number system
- To check a calculation by doing an equivalent calculation

Oral questions
1. What is 28 multiplied by 102 approximately?
2. Will 267 add 375 have an odd or even answer?
3. Approximately how many lots of 2·7 are there in 55?
4. A number multiplied by 1·5 gives 36. What is the number?

Practice activities
1 Put a multiplication or division into a calculator, e.g. 46·1 × 3·8, and find the answer. Use the inverse operation to work backwards. Record calculations, e.g. 175·18 ÷ 3·8 = 46·1. Repeat.

2 Take a dice with +, × and − signs on. Form two 3-digit numbers using place-value cards. Roll the dice to decide on the operation. Write down the calculation 572 − 361 and whether the answer will be odd or even. Repeat several times.

Assessment Sheet 7: Appropriate methods

Abacus 7 Links Addition Subtraction Multiplication Division

Key objective
Choose and justify the use of an appropriate and efficient method for solving a problem

Skills summary
- Choose the appropriate operation(s) to solve word problems
- Decide whether calculations can be done mentally, with a pencil and paper or a calculator
- Explain and record how a problem was solved
- Make up problems to reflect statements

Oral questions
1. Which operation is carried out on 345 and 27 to give 9315?
2. The distance around a regular hexagon is 75 cm. What is the distance along one side?
3. Write down a calculation to match the previous question.
4. The sum of two odd numbers is 20, the difference between them is 6 and their product is 91. What are the two numbers?

Practice activities

1 Play with a partner. Make two numbers with place-value cards. Decide whether to add, subtract, multiply or divide them. Write down an approximate answer. Check on the calculator. The person who is closest to the answer scores a point. First to five points wins.

2 Take a set of calculations (about 5) written on card without the answers and write a problem to match each calculation.

Assessment Sheet 8: Letters or symbols

Abacus 7 Links   Algebra

Key objective
Use letters or symbols to represent unknown numbers or variables

Skills summary
- Know that letters are used to stand for numbers
- Use the equals sign appropriately and correctly
- Use letter symbols to write statements
- Substitute values of letters in expressions

Oral questions
1. If n is 6 what is 2n?
2. If b = 6 find the value of 3b – 7.
3. Write 2 times 'n' as an algebraic expression.
4. Write an expression for 3 lots of 'a' divided by 2.

Practice activities

1 Use Algebra cards 1 (Resource Master 2). Pick one of the cards and roll a dice to stand for the unknown number, find the total value of the expression. Repeat several times.

2 Use Algebra cards 1 (Resource Master 2). Pick a card and write down what the expression means, e.g. 2b – 3 means 'two lots of an unknown number, b, subtract three'.

Assessment Sheet 9: Algebraic operations

Abacus 7 Links Algebra

Key objective
Know that algebraic operations follow the same conventions and order as arithmetical operations

Skills summary
- To recognise algebraic conventions
- To use simple expressions with brackets
- To simplify linear algebraic expressions by collecting terms
- To solve simple equations

Oral questions
1. Simplify the expression $a + a + a + a$.
2. (Write $2(a + 3)$ on the board). Rewrite the expression without the brackets.
3. If $a + 3 = b$, write a value for a in terms of b.
4. If $2a + 5 = 11$, what is the value of a?

Practice activities

1 Take a dice with sides labelled: a, b, c, $2a$, $2b$, $2c$. Roll the dice six times. Write down the total, e.g. $2a + 2b + b + b + 2c + 2a$, then simplify, i.e. $4a + 3b + 2c$. Repeat several times.

2 Take a selection of algebra cards (those with the letter a and the 1-digit numbers) from Resource Master 2. Pick one of each type of card. Also pick a 2-digit number card from a set (10 to 20). Write the equation formed, e.g. $a + 5 = 12$. Find the value of the unknown, a.

Assessment Sheet 10: Sequences

Abacus 7 Links   Algebra

Key objective
Generate terms of a sequence given a rule

Skills summary
- To generate given terms of a sequence given a rule
- To describe a rule for a sequence
- To describe the general term of a sequence using words, and using symbols
- To calculate a number in the sequence given the general term

Oral questions
1. Listen to these numbers: 64, 60, 56, 52. Describe the rule for the sequence.
2. Listen to these numbers: 1, 3, 6, 10. What is the next number in the sequence?
3. The rule for a sequence of numbers is: Double the last number and subtract 3. The first number in the sequence is 5, what will the next number be?
4. The nth term in a sequence is as $3n - 2$. What is the value of the 4th term?

Practice activities

1 Work with a partner. Write down the first four terms of a sequence. Ask your partner to describe the sequence in words. Repeat, swapping roles.

2 Use a selection of cards from Algebra cards 3 (Resource Master 4) in the form $mx + c$. Change x to n to form a sequence rule. Write down the first five numbers in the sequence, e.g. $2n + 3$ (5, 7, 9, 11, 13).

Assessment Sheet 11: Coordinates

Abacus 7 Links Algebra

Key objective
Find coordinate pairs that satisfy a given rule and plot these on a coordinate grid

Skills summary
- To recognise coordinates that satisfy a rule
- To complete a table of values, find the y coordinate from the x-coordinate and a given rule
- To recognise that a function such as $y = 3x + 1$ corresponds to a straight line

Oral questions
1. Which of these points is not on the line $y = 2x$? (2,4), (3,5), (3,6), (5,10).
2. A point lies on the line $y = 3x - 1$. If the x-coordinate is 1, what is the y-coordinate?
3. Write down the coordinates of a point on the line $y = 5 - x$.
4. (Write the coordinates (1,3), (2,6), (3,9), (4,12) on the board). All these points lie on the same line, what is the rule for the line?

Practice activities
1 An activity for pairs. The first person decides on a rule and writes down three pairs of coordinates that satisfy the rule. The second person has to guess the rule. If they guess correctly, they score 2 points; if they need extra pairs of coordinates they score 1 point. Repeat, swapping roles.

2 Use the first three rows of Algebra cards 3 (Resource Master 4). Pick a card and write down three coordinates that satisfy the rule. Repeat several times.

Assessment Sheet 12: Lines and angles

Abacus 7 Links Lines and angles

Key objective
Recognise and use parallel lines and the sum of angles at a point, on a straight line and in triangles

Skills summary
- To recognise vertically opposite angles and adjacent angles
- To recognise corresponding angles and alternate angles
- To recognise that parallel lines are always equidistant
- To use knowledge that the sum of the three interior angles of a triangle is 180°
- To recognise and use exterior angles of a triangle as the sum of two opposite interior angles

Oral questions
1. Look at the shape A on the sheet. Mark any pairs of parallel sides.
2. Look at the triangle. What is the size of the missing interior angle?
3. Look at the triangle. What is the size of angle X?
4. Look at the triangle. Calculate the size of angle Y.

Practice activities
1 Draw a pair of intersecting lines. Measure one of the angles. Use it to work out the other three angles. Repeat several times.

2 Draw a triangle. Measure two of the angles and calculate the size of the third. Use the information to calculate the size of the exterior angles.

Assessment Sheet 13: Converting metric units

Abacus 7 Links Measures

Key objective
Convert from one metric unit to another

Skills summary
- To convert from a metric unit of capacity to another
- To convert from a metric unit of weight to another
- To convert from a metric unit of length to another

Oral questions
1. What is 75 centilitres in millilitres?
2. Simon runs 2·85 km of a 3 km race. How much has he left to run in metres?
3. How many grams in 1·45 kg?
4. A container holds 650 cm³. What is this in centilitres?

Practice activities
1. Look at a range of different food packets labelled with weights. Write down the weight of each one in grams and kilograms. Find the total weight of all the packets and write this in tonnes.

2. Use a calculator to find how much a range of different cuboid containers will hold by measuring length, breadth, height and multiplying them together. Write the answer in cubic centimetres, then in millilitres and litres.

Assessment Sheet 14: Reading and interpreting scales

Abacus 7 Link Measures

Key objective
Read and interpret scales on a range of measuring instruments

Skills summary
- Read and interpret scales for a range of measures including length, weight, capacity, time, temperature, speed
- Read and interpret horizontal, vertical and circular scales

Oral questions
1. Look at scale A. What measurement does the arrow represent?
2. On scale A, mark 1275 g.
3. Look at scale B. How fast is the car going in kilometres per hour?
4. On scale B, indicate 34 miles per hour.

Practice activities
1. On a range of different weighing scales measure the weight of an object. Discuss with a partner how the weight is shown on the different scales. Repeat with different objects.

2. Look at a range of different measuring jugs. Mark on each jug where 375 ml would be. Decide which would be the best jug to use. Repeat with 55 ml, 1.2 l.

Assessment Sheet 15: Averages

Abacus 7 Link Averages

Key objective
Compare two simple distributions using the range and one of the measures of average

Skills summary
- To find the mean, median or mode of a set of data
- To find the range of a set of data
- To compare two sets of data

Oral questions
1. (Write the numbers 3, 4, 7, 6 on the board.) What is the mean of this set of numbers?
2. Look at the numbers again. What is the range?
3. (Write 7, 7, 8, 8, 9, 9, on the board.) These are the scores of a set of children in a spelling test. What did the seventh child score if the mode for this set of data is 9?
4. (Write 6, 7, 5, 8, 8, 9, 4.) These are scores from a mental arithmetic test. Find the median.

Practice activities
1 Find the range and average age (decide which sort of average to use) of 10 children from a class list of dates of birth. Repeat the exercise with 10 different children, then compare the average age and the range.

2 Collect data about temperature over 14 days (this can be found on the internet or from newspapers). Find the range and average for the set of data. Repeat for a different two-week period. Compare the information.

Assessment Sheet 16: Probability

Abacus 7 Link Probability

Key objective
Know that probabilities lie between 0 and 1, and calculate probabilities based on equally likely outcomes in simple contexts

Skills summary
- To place probabilities on a scale from 0 to 1
- To list all the possible outcomes of an event
- To calculate probabilities based on equally likely outcomes of a single event

Oral questions
1. What is the probability of not rolling a 6 on a 6-sided 1 to 6 dice?
2. What is the probability of rolling a prime number on a 6-sided 1 to 6 dice?
3. In a bag there are 5 red counters, 3 yellow counters and 2 blue counters. What are the probabilities of choosing and not choosing a yellow counter?
4. A yellow counter is removed from the bag. What is the probability of choosing a yellow counter now?

Practice activities
1 Predict the most likely when tossing two coins: 2H, 2T or H + T. Toss the coins 30 times and record the results. How many of each would you expect in 60 throws? Try it, then compare.

2 Roll two dice. Find the difference between the numbers rolled. Repeat 30 times. What difference occurs most frequently? Explain why.

I.    2.   3.    4.

$\frac{\boxed{}}{4}$

5.   Write these numbers on the number line.

$^-2$ 3·6   1·3   2·7 $^-2$·8 $^-0$·7   1·3   2·7

$^-4$ 0 $^+4$

$\frac{\boxed{}}{8}$

Look at the temperatures below. Decide whether the temperature has risen or fallen and by how much.

6.   13 °C to $^-$1 °C _____

7.   4·5 °C to 5·8 °C _____

8. $^-$3·5 °C to 5 °C _____

9. $^-$12·5 °C to $^-$13·2 °C _____

10.   14·7 °C to $^-$0·8 °C _____

II. $^-$11·3 °C to $^-$4·7 °C _____

$\frac{\boxed{}}{6}$

Complete these calculations.

12.   5 + _____ = $^-$2

13.   _____ − 3 = $^-$11

14.   3·4 − _____ = $^-$6·8

15.   _____ + 12·5 = 7·3

16. $^-$13·7 + _____ = $^-$8·2

17.   _____ + $^-$3·7 = $^-$11·5

18.   2·5 + $^-$3·6 − _____ = $^-$4·8

19.   12·3 − _____ + 4·6 = $^-$7·5

$\frac{\boxed{}}{8}$

Score: $\boxed{}$/26   Total: $\boxed{}$

ASSESSMENT

Name _____

I. [ ]   2. [ ]   3. [ ]   4. [ ]

$\dfrac{\square}{4}$

5. Complete these equivalent fractions.

a $\dfrac{6}{9} = \dfrac{2}{\square}$ **b** $\dfrac{8}{20} = \dfrac{2}{\square}$ **c** $\dfrac{9}{12} = \dfrac{\square}{4}$ **d** $\dfrac{21}{24} = \dfrac{\square}{8}$

e $\dfrac{20}{28} = \dfrac{5}{\square}$ **f** $\dfrac{14}{20} = \dfrac{\square}{10}$ **g** $\dfrac{32}{40} = \dfrac{4}{\square}$ **h** $\dfrac{63}{108} = \dfrac{\square}{12}$

$\dfrac{\square}{8}$

Change each set of fractions so they have a common denominator. Write them in order from smallest to largest.

6. $\dfrac{2}{3}$ $\dfrac{1}{6}$ $\dfrac{3}{4}$ $\dfrac{7}{12}$ _____

7. $\dfrac{1}{2}$ $\dfrac{13}{20}$ $\dfrac{3}{4}$ $\dfrac{2}{5}$ $\dfrac{7}{10}$ _____

$\dfrac{\square}{9}$

8. Complete the table to show equivalent fractions (in their simplest form), decimals and percentages.

Fraction	$\dfrac{3}{10}$	$\dfrac{7}{20}$			$\dfrac{21}{25}$
Decimal	0·3		0·42		
Percentage	30%			37·5%	

$\dfrac{\square}{8}$

9. Stephen receives £5 per week pocket money. Each week he saves half. Of the money left he spends 20% on sweets and 30% on comics. What fraction of the original amount does he have left?

_____

10. Butter comes in 250 g packets. A recipe needs 75 g of butter. How much of the packet of butter is left as a percentage?

_____

$\dfrac{\square}{2}$

Score: [ ] / 31   Total: [ ]

ASSESSMENT

Name _____

1. [ ]   **2.** [ ]   **3.** [ ]   **4.** [ ]

$$\frac{\boxed{}}{4}$$

Circle the part of the calculation you would do first.

5. $27 + (4^2 \times 2)$

6. $18 \div 3 \times (27 - 17)$

7. $23 + 7 \times 4$

8. $48 - 27 \div 3$

9. $17 \times 4 - 3^2$

10. $10 \times 7 - (4 \times 6)$

$$\frac{\boxed{}}{6}$$

Tick the calculations that are correct.

11. $12 \times (3 + 4) = 40$ [ ]

12. $(3^2 + 7) \times 3 = 48$ [ ]

13. $(4 \times 7) + 8 \div 4 = 30$ [ ]

14. $13 + 4 \times 6 = 102$ [ ]

15. $4^3 \div (9 + 7) = 4$ [ ]

16. $(14 + 7) \times (42 \div 14) = 63$ [ ]

$$\frac{\boxed{}}{6}$$

Put brackets in these calculations to make them correct.

17. $12 \times 7 + 3 = 120$

18. $120 \div 47 - 35 = 10$

19. $34 + 7 \times 2 = 82$

20. $24 - 8 \times 15 \div 5 = 48$

21. $3 \times 4 + 48 - 25 = 35$

22. $6^2 + 4 \times 7 = 280$

$$\frac{\boxed{}}{6}$$

Score: [ ] /22   Total: [ ]

Name _____

I.	2.	3.	4. 

$$\frac{\Box}{4}$$

Calculate the answer to each question. Show your working in the spaces.

5. 14 x 7·2	**6.** 3·7 x 15	**7.** 666 ÷ 18	**8.** 271 ÷ 13

$$\frac{\Box}{4}$$

Complete these calculations.

9. 2·7 + 2·71 = _____

10. 5·6 – 2·9 = _____

II. 12·3 – 10·7 = _____

12. 4·53 + 2·98 = _____

13. 5·35 – _____ = 3·36

14. 7·8 + _____ = 15·62

15. _____ + 3·97 = 8·43

16. _____ – 2·4 = 8·71

$$\frac{\Box}{8}$$

17. Join pairs that give the same answer.

a	15% of 40	**e**	$\frac{7}{8}$ x 32
b	35% of 80	**f**	$\frac{3}{7}$ x 14
c	8% of 200	**g**	$\frac{1}{5}$ x 100
d	12·5% of 160	**h**	$\frac{4}{9}$ x 36

$$\frac{\Box}{4}$$

Score: [   ] /20   Total: [   ]

ASSESSMENT

Name _____

1. [　　　]　　2. [　　　]　　3. [　　　]　　4. [　　　]

$\dfrac{\square}{4}$

Find the answer to each calculation.

5. 347 x 46	**6.** 28·6 x 2·77	**7.** 3·84 x 73
8. 738 ÷ 36	**9.** 315·3 ÷ 6	**10.** 50·68 ÷ 14

$\dfrac{\square}{6}$

Tick the calculations that are correct.

11.
```
      5 1 2
   ×     3 4
   ---------
   2 0 4 8
   1 5 3 6
   ---------
   3 5 8 4
```
[　]

12.
```
      6 3 · 4
   ×     2 · 9
   -----------
       5 7 · 0 6
     1 2 8 · 8
   -----------
     1 8 5 · 0 6
```
[　]

13.
```
      6 · 4 8
   × 1  7
   -----------
     4 5 · 3 6
     6 4 · 8
   -----------
   1 1 0 · 1 6
```
[　]

14.
```
27) 8 6 4
    8 1 0     27 × 30
    -----
      5 4
      5 4     27 × 2
    -----
        0
```
864 ÷ 27 = 32   [　]

15.
```
7) 3 3 3 · 2
   2 8 0        7 × 40
   -------
   4 3 · 2
   4 2           7 × 6
   -------
     1 · 2
     0 · 7       7 × 0·1
   -------
     0 · 5
     0 · 4 9     7 × 0·07
   -------
     0 · 0 1
```
333·2 ÷ 7 = 46·17   [　]

$\dfrac{\square}{5}$

Score: [　　] / 15　　　　Total: [　　　]

Abacus Ginn and Company 2001. Copying permitted for purchasing school only. This material is not copyright free.

Name _____

1. [ ] 2. [ ] 3. [ ] 4. [ ]

$\frac{\square}{4}$

5. Join each calculation to its approximate answer.

a	431 x 28		**e**	40
b	357 ÷ 0·2		**f**	1750
c	42·8 x 0·9		**g**	50
d	987 ÷ 19		**h**	12000

$\frac{\square}{4}$

Sandra says 'Each of these answers is wrong'. Without working out the correct answer, how could you check Sandra if is right?

6. 1457 ÷ 8 = 183 _____

_____

7. 283 x 27 = 7639 _____

_____

8. 52·9 x 1·8 = 256·22 _____

_____

$\frac{\square}{3}$

Write an equivalent calculation for each of these.

9. 347 x 9 = _____ **10.** 24·6 ÷ 0·3 = _____

11. 594 ÷ 8 = _____ **12.** 47·3 x 0·9 = _____

$\frac{\square}{4}$

Score: [ ] /15   Total: [ ]

ASSESSMENT

Name _____

I. [ ]   **2.** [ ]   **3.** [ ]   **4.** [ ]

$\frac{\square}{4}$

Complete the calculations below by writing in the correct operation(s).

5. 609 [ ] 7 = 87

6. 245 [ ] 47 = 11 515

7. (23 [ ] 16) [ ] 174 = 542

8. (657 [ ] 0·25) [ ] 122·25 = 42

$\frac{\square}{4}$

Find the answer to each question below. You can do it mentally, using a written method or with a calculator. Record how you did each one.

9. 27 x 34

10. 324 ÷ 2·72

II. 618 ÷ 3

12. 231 x 0·1

$\frac{\square}{4}$

---

13. A school hall has area 864 m². The length of the hall is one and a half times the width. What is the length of the hall?

_____

14. One odd number divided by the next odd number gives the answer 0·8̇66̇. What are the two numbers?

_____

Score: [ ] /14   Total: [ ]

$\frac{\square}{2}$

Name _____

1. [ ]   **2.** [ ]   **3.** [ ]   **4.** [ ]

$\frac{\square}{4}$

Find two possible values for the unknowns in each question.

5.  + ● = 17

◆ = _____ and ● = _____

◆ = _____ and ● = _____

6. ■ – ○ = 12

■ = _____ and ○ = _____

■ = _____ and ○ = _____

$\frac{\square}{8}$

Write these statements using numbers and letter symbols.

7. 6 add c _____

8. 3 lots of d _____

9. 7 subtract 2 lots of n _____

10. e multiplied by 4 _____

11. b times 7 subtract 2 _____

12. 3 divided by a add 2 _____

$\frac{\square}{6}$

Find the value of each expression.

 $a = 3$ $b = 7$ $c = 4$  $d = 2$

13. $2a + 4 =$ _____

14. $10 - 2c =$ _____

15. $3(5 + d) =$ _____

16. $a(c - 1) =$ _____

17. $d(b + c) =$ _____

18. $\dfrac{c}{d} + b =$ _____

$\frac{\square}{6}$

Score: [ ] /24   Total: [ ]

Name _____ **Assessment Sheet 9**

1.   2. [   ] 3. [   ] 4. [   ]

$\frac{\square}{4}$

Simplify the expressions below.

5. b + b + a _____ 6. a + a + a + c _____

7. 3p + 4q – p _____ 8. 5a – 2a + 3c _____

9. 7f + 2 – 3f _____ 10. 4e + 3 – 3e _____

$\frac{\square}{6}$

---

11. Join expressions that are equivalent.

f   10a – 15

a   3(a + 4)

g   10a – 3

b   5(2a –3)

h   3ac + 12

c   a(2 + a)

i   2a + a²

d   3a(c + 4)

j   3a + 12

k   3ac + 12a

$\frac{\square}{4}$

Find the value of the unknown in each equation.

12. 2a = 14 a = _____ 13. b – 3 = 8 b = _____

14. 3c – 5 = 10 c = _____ 15. 3(d + 2) = 18 d = _____

16. (e ÷ 3) x 7 = 14 e = _____ 17. 2(f² + 7) = 112 f = _____

$\frac{\square}{6}$

Score: [   ] /20   Total: [   ]

Name _____

1.   2.   3.   4.

$\frac{}{4}$

Write the tenth term in each sequence. Write the rule for each.

5.   3, 7, 11, 15   ☐   _____

6.   2·5, 3, 3·5, 4   ☐   _____

7.   43, 36, 29, 22   ☐   _____

$\frac{}{6}$

Given these rules work out the next four terms in each sequence.

8.   3, ___, ___, ___, ___   add 5 to the last number

9.   13, ___, ___, ___, ___   subtract 4 from the last number

10.   4, ___, ___, ___, ___   add 1 and double the last number

$\frac{}{12}$

---

11.   Match the rule to the sequence.

a	2, 4, 6, 8	**e**	2 − n
b	2, 5, 8, 11	**f**	2n + 1
c	3, 5, 7, 9	**g**	2n
d	1, 0, ⁻1, ⁻2	**h**	3n − 1

$\frac{}{4}$

Given these rules, find the value of term shown.

12. $n^2 + 1$ 8th term = ___   **13.** $3n − 5$ 10th term = ___

14. $8 − 2n$ 6th term = ___   **15.** $2n^2 + n$ 4th term = ___

$\frac{}{4}$

Score: ☐ /30   Total: ☐

ASSESSMENT

Name _____

I. 　2. 　3. [ ]　4. [ ]

$\dfrac{}{4}$

Use the points on the grid to answer these questions.

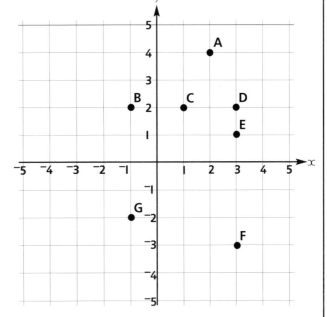

5. Which points lie on the
line $x = 3$?

6. Which points lie on the
line $y = 2$?

7. Which point lies on both the lines
$y = 2x$ and $y = x + 1$?

8. Which point lies on both the lines
$y = 4 - x$ and $y = x - 2$?

$\dfrac{}{8}$

Write the equation for each line.

9.　(1,4)　(2,5)　(3,6)　(4,7)　　_____

10.　(3,1)　(2,0)　(1,⁻1)　(0,⁻2)　　_____

II.　(2,6)　(3,9)　(4,12)　(5,15)　　_____

12.　(1,4)　(2,3)　(3,2)　(4,1)　　_____

$\dfrac{}{4}$

Complete these sets of coordinates which lie on each line.

13.　$y = 2x + 1$　(3, ____)　(____ , 11)　(____ , 17)　(12, ____)

14.　$y = 7 - x$　(⁻1, ____)　(____ , 6)　(____ , 4)　(0, ____)

15.　$y = 3x - 4$　(⁻2, ____)　(____ , ⁻4)　(3, ____)　(____ , 11)

$\dfrac{}{12}$

Score: [ ] /28　　　　Total: [ ]

ASSESSMENT

Name _____

1. [ ]   **2.** [ ]

3. [ ]   **4.** [ ]

 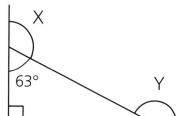

A

X

63°

Y

▢/4

Use the known angle to work out the missing angles.

5.

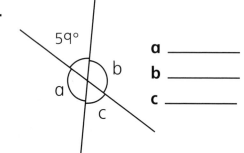

59°

a _____
b _____
c _____

6.

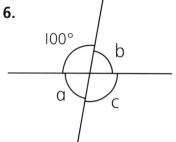

100°

a _____
b _____
c _____

7.

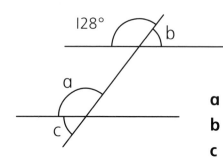

128°

a _____
b _____
c _____

8.

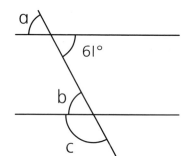

61°

a _____
b _____
c _____

▢/12

Work out the unknown angles on these shapes.

9.

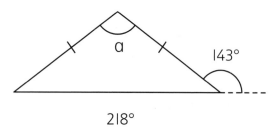

143°

10.

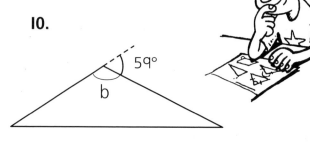

59°

180°...

11.

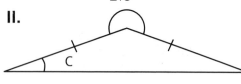

218°

12.

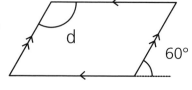

d

60°

▢/4

Score: [ ] /20   Total: [ ]

ASSESSMENT

1. 　　2. 　　3. 　　4.

☐/4

Circle all the measurements that are equivalent to the measurement in the box.

5. | 35 cm |　　3500 mm　　350 mm　　0·35 m　　0·035 m

6. | 560 ml |　　0·56 l　　5·6 cl　　56 cl　　560 cm³

7. | 4.7 kg |　　47 g　　470 g　　4700 g　　0·0047 tonnes

8. | 370 cl |　　3·7 l　　37 l　　3700 ml　　3700 cm³

☐/10

Put these sets of measurements in order from smallest to largest.

9.　　25 cm　　0·015 m　　1·8 cm　　230 mm　　0·2 m

10.　　3·8 l　　250 cl　　3500 ml　　325 cl　　2750 cm³

11.　　0·04 tonnes　　37 kg　　38500 g　　38·2 kg　　0·039 tonnes

☐/15

---

12. Maria buys 2 tonnes of gravel for a garden path. She uses 1·68 tonnes. How much gravel does she have left in kilograms?

_____

13. A container holds 7500 cm³. If 2·8 litres of water are added, how many more litres are needed to fill the container?

_____

☐/2

Score: ☐ /31　　Total: ☐

Name _____

I.

2.

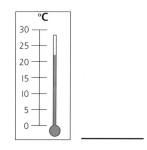

Scale A

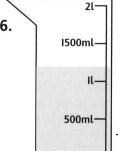

Scale B

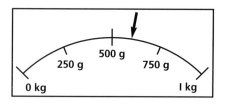

4

Look at these scales. Write each measurement shown including the unit.

5.

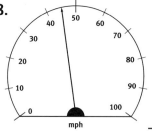 _____

6.

 _____

7.

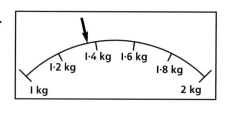 _____

8.

 _____

q. 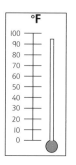 _____

10. 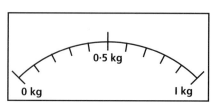 _____

6

Mark the amount shown on each scale.

II. 35 mph

12. 67 °F

13. 850 g

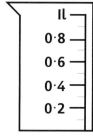

14. 0·73 l

15. 7:37 p.m.

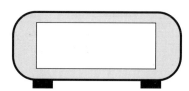

16. 125 mm

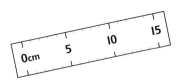

6

Score: [____] /16   Total: [____]

ASSESSMENT

Name _____

1. [ ]   2. [ ]   3. [ ]   4. [ ]

Fill in the missing number for each set so that the mean is correct.

5.   Mean = 7 | 6 | 10 | 5 | 8 | [ ] |

6.   Mean = 10 | 9 | 12 | 7 | 14 | 10 | [ ] |

7.   Mean = 15 | 8 | 10 | 9 | 20 | 18 | 16 | 13 | [ ] |

Find the range of each set of numbers above.

5a. _____   6a. _____   7a. _____

There are two football teams in a town – United and Rovers. These are the goals each team scores in ten matches.

United										Rovers									
5	0	1	0	6	3	0	1	0	4	1	2	0	2	2	2	1	1	2	1

Find the mean, median, mode and range for each team.

8. United: Mean _____   Median _____   Mode _____   Range _____

9. Rovers: Mean _____   Median _____   Mode _____   Range _____

10. David says 'United are the better team'. Explain which measure David might use to argue his point and why.

_____

_____

Score: [ ] /19   Total: [ ]

1. [ ]   2. [ ]   3. [ ]   4. [ ]

$\frac{\square}{4}$

5. Place the letter for each event on the probability scale.

0	$\frac{1}{2}$	1

A Rolling a number greater than 4 on a 6-sided dice.

B Picking a red cube from a bag containing 3 red cubes, 3 green cubes and 2 blue cubes.

C Picking a red card from a pack of cards.

D Rolling a number less than 7 on a 0 to 9 dice.

$\frac{\square}{4}$

6.   In a game number cards are placed in a bag.

Three [2] Two [3] Four [4] Two [5] One [6]

Join events which have the same probability.

a Picking an even number

b Picking a 4

c Picking a number greater than 4

d Picking a prime number

e Picking a 3 or a 5

f Picking a 2

g Picking a number greater than 2 and less than 6

h Picking a number greater than 3

$\frac{\square}{4}$

Score: [ ] / 12   Total: [ ]

Record-keeping grid

The record-keeping grid provides an opportunity to record scores achieved by children for each of the Assessment Sheets. Across the top there is room for up to twelve names. Recording their scores means that you can easily track children's progress over the course of the year.

Names												
Assessment Sheet 1												
Assessment Sheet 2												
Assessment Sheet 3												
Assessment Sheet 4												
Assessment Sheet 5												
Assessment Sheet 6												
Assessment Sheet 7												
Assessment Sheet 8												
Assessment Sheet 9												
Assessment Sheet 10												
Assessment Sheet 11												
Assessment Sheet 12												
Assessment Sheet 13												
Assessment Sheet 14												
Assessment Sheet 15												
Assessment Sheet 16												

$\dfrac{3}{4}$	$\dfrac{2}{3}$	$\dfrac{4}{5}$	$\dfrac{2}{5}$
$\dfrac{1}{3}$	$\dfrac{1}{4}$	$\dfrac{3}{8}$	$\dfrac{5}{8}$
$\dfrac{7}{8}$	$\dfrac{5}{6}$	$\dfrac{1}{12}$	$\dfrac{7}{12}$
$\dfrac{7}{10}$	$\dfrac{3}{10}$	$\dfrac{11}{20}$	$\dfrac{17}{20}$
$\dfrac{1}{5}$	$\dfrac{1}{8}$	$\dfrac{1}{6}$	$\dfrac{2}{7}$

RESOURCE MASTERS

2a − 3	3a + 4	2a	a − 2	a + 1
2b + 1	3b	b + 2	2a − 1	4a + 3
c + 3	2b − 3	3b + 4	3b − 1	b − 1
2c + 5	4c − 2	c − 4	3c + 2	2c

RESOURCE MASTERS

5	4	3	2	1
c	b	b	a	a
3b	3a	2b	2a	c
$\dfrac{c}{4}$	$\dfrac{b}{3}$	$\dfrac{a}{2}$	4c	3c

$2x + 3$	$3x$	$2x$	$2x - 1$	$x + 1$
$5x - 2$	$5 + 2x$	$10 - x$	$3x - 1$	$3x + 2$
$x + 2$	$5x$	$40 - 3x$	$100 - 5x$	$4x + 5$
$(1 + x)^2$	$x^2 + 3$	x^2	$x^2 - 1$	$x - 2$

⌣	⌣	⌢	⌢
+	+	+	+
|	|	|	|
✕	✕	✕	✕
•|•	•|•	•|•	•|•

RESOURCE MASTERS

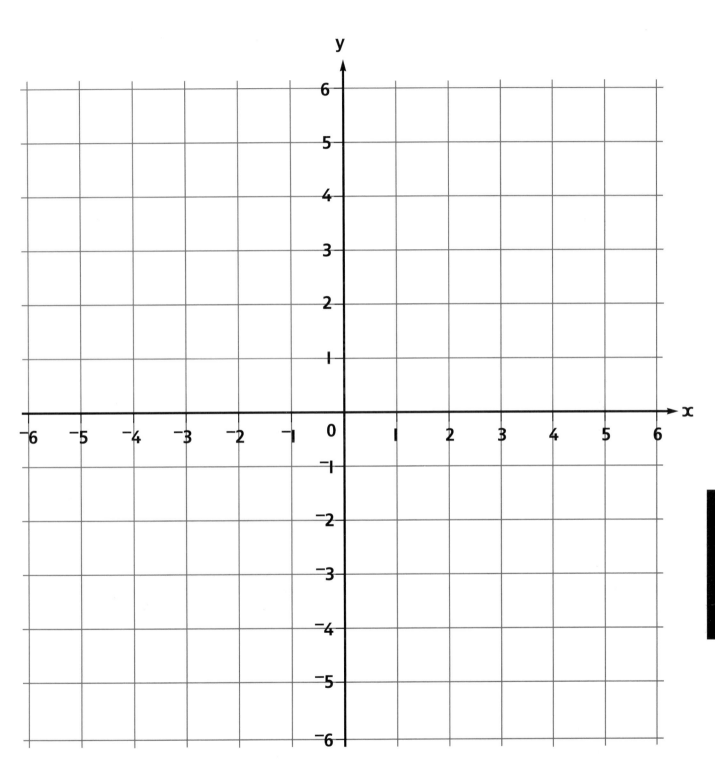

Red words	
cat	beach
dog	train
hut	peach
tin	stone

Green words	
pot	couch
bow	plate
fly	glove
man	arrow

Name															Total
cat															
dog															
hut															
tin															
beach															
train															
peach															
stone															
pot															
bow															
fly															
man															
couch															
plate															
glove															
arrow															
Total															

RESOURCE MASTERS

⑨ Planning

Framework matching charts

The chart on the following pages matches each unit from Abacus 7 to the 'primary' Year 7 Framework (published March 2000 and distributed to all Primary Schools in England and Wales), and Year 7 from the Key Stage 3 Framework for Teaching Mathematics using a code of abbreviations.

March 2000 Framework

Numbers and the number system (N)

Place-value, ordering and rounding	pv
Properties of numbers	pn
Fractions, decimals, percentages, ratio and proportion	fdp

Calculations (C)

Number operations and the relationships between them	nor
Mental methods and rapid recall of number facts	mm
Written methods	wm
Calculator methods	cm
Checking results	cr

Solving problems (SP)

Solving problems	sp

Algebra (A)

Equations and formulae	ef
Sequences and functions	sf
Graphs	g

Shape, space and measures (SSM)

Lines and angles	la
Properties of shapes	ps
Transformations	t
Coordinates	co
Construction	cn
Measures	m

Handling data (HD)

Specifying a problem, planning and collecting data	spc
Processing data	pd
Representing data, interpreting and discussing results	rd
Probability	pb

KS3 Framework

Using and applying mathematics to solve problems (UA)

Applying mathematics and solving problems	asp

Numbers and the number system (N)

Place-value, ordering and rounding	pv
Integers, powers and roots	ipr
Fractions, decimals, percentages, ratio and proportion	fdp

Calculations (C)

Number operations and the relationships between them	nor
Mental methods and rapid recall of number facts	mm
Written methods	wm
Calculator methods	cm
Checking results	cr

Algebra (A)

Equations, formulae and identities	efi
Sequences, functions and graphs	sfg

Shape, space and measures (SSM)

Geometrical reasoning: lines, angles	la
Transformations	t
Coordinates	co
Construction	cn
Measures and mensuration	m

Handling data (HD)

Specifying a problem, planning and collecting data	spc
Processing and representing data	prd
Interpreting and discussing results	idr
Probability	pb

Thus **SSM.t.1** indicates Shape, space and measures, Transformations, bullet 1, i.e. 'Understand and use the language and notation associated with reflections, translations and rotations.'

Exemplar planning grids

The tables on pages 132 to 137 show one way of matching the Abacus Units to the Numeracy Framework Planning Grids. They are arranged termly, in a suitable order for teaching alongside Abacus 6. However, you may wish to match them in a different order, or use your own planning grids. Clearly, whichever you use, your ongoing evaluation and assessment will inform the development of the scheme of work during the course of the year.

Abacus 7 National Numeracy Strategy Framework matching chart

Abacus 7 Unit	Objectives (March 2000 Framework)	Objectives (Key Stage 3 Framework)
N1 Place-value To round decimal numbers to the nearest whole number, tenth or hundredth To round decimal numbers to 1 or 2 decimal places To key in decimal numbers and read the calculator display	N.pv.1, 4, 5 SP.sp.1, 2, 3, 4	N.pv.1, 3 UA.asp.1, 2, 3, 4, 5
N2 Number facts To consolidate the rapid recall of addition pairs to 1 and 10, extending to decimals To derive quickly decimal complements to 1 and 10 To rehearse the doubles of 2-digit numbers including decimals, and corresponding halves To consolidate the rapid recall of doubles, and corresponding halves	C.mm.1 N.pv.3 SP.sp.1, 2, 3	C.mm.1, 2 UA.asp.1, 2, 3, 4
N3 Multiplication/division To consolidate and extend mental methods of calculation To extend the use of factors for multiplying and dividing To extend the use of partitioning for multiplying and dividing To rehearse and extend the use of doubling for multiplying To multiply by doubling one number and halving the other To multiply by partitioning the multiplier into combinations of 1, 2, 4, 8, 16	C.mm.1, 2 N.pn.2 SP.sp.1, 2, 3	C.nor.1 C.mm.1, 2 N.ipr.2 UA.asp.1, 2, 3, 4
N4 Fractions To find equivalent fractions by cancelling To compare and order sets of fractions by converting them to fractions with a common denominator To order fractions by positioning them on a number line	N.fdp.1 SP.sp.1, 2, 3, 4	N.fdp.1 UA.asp.1, 2, 3, 4, 5
N5 Addition/subtraction To rehearse strategies for adding mentally To add near doubles by doubling then adjusting To add by partitioning and dealing with the most significant digit first To add by adding too much then compensating To rehearse strategies for subtracting mentally To subtract by partitioning and dealing with the most significant digit first To subtract by subtracting too much then compensating	C.nor.1 C.mm.2 SP.sp.1, 2, 3	C.nor.1 C.mm.2 UA.asp.1, 2, 3, 4
N6 Factors and primes To rehearse tests for divisibility To recognise prime numbers, and to test by checking for divisibility To find the factors of a number by checking for divisibility by primes To find common factors of numbers To find the prime numbers up to 100	N.pn.2 SP.sp.1, 2, 3, 4	N.ipr.2 UA.asp.1, 2, 3, 4, 5
N7 Place-value To rehearse multiplying and dividing an integer by 10, 100 or 1000 To multiply and divide integers and decimals by 10, 100 or 1000 To multiply and divide by 0·1, 0·01 and 0·001 To recognise the equivalence of multiplying and dividing by 10/0·1, 100/0·01, 1000/0·001	N.pv.1 SP.sp.1, 2, 3	N.pv.1 UA.asp.1, 2, 3, 4
N8 Fractions To recognise equivalence between $\frac{1}{4}$ of 12, $\frac{1}{4}$ x 12, 12 x $\frac{1}{4}$ To multiply a fraction by a whole number or a whole number by a fraction To rehearse converting an improper fraction to a mixed number	N.fdp.2 SP.sp.1, 2, 3, 4	N.fdp.2 UA.asp.1, 2, 3, 4, 5
N9 Division To rehearse division, giving the quotient as a fraction To divide giving the quotient as a decimal, correct to 1 or 2 decimal places To interpret calculator displays after division, including recurring decimals To recognise when to round up or down after division To divide, giving the remainder as a fraction and as a decimal To recognise recurring decimals	N.fdp.1 C.nor.1 C.cm.1, 2 SP.sp.1, 2, 3, 4	N.fdp.1 C.mm.2 C.wm.2 C.cm.2 UA.asp.1, 2, 3, 4, 5
N10 Decimals To rehearse and extend understanding of decimal notation To compare and order decimals in different contexts To locate decimals numbers lying between two others To add 0·1 or 0·01 to any number To subtract 0·1 or 0·01 from any number	N.pv.1, 2 SP.sp.1, 2, 3, 4	N.pv.1, 2 UA.asp.1, 2, 3, 4, 5
N11 Addition To use standard written methods to add decimal numbers with three places of decimals To add numbers with different numbers of digits To use standard written methods to add decimals with different numbers of digits and decimal places	C.wm.1 SP.sp.1, 2, 3, 4	C.wm.1 UA.asp.1, 2, 3, 4, 5
N12 Subtraction To use standard written methods to subtract decimal numbers with three decimals places To subtract decimal numbers with different numbers of digits To use standard written methods to subtract decimals with different numbers of digits/decimal places	C.wm.1 SP.sp.1, 2, 3	C.wm.1 UA.asp.1, 2, 3, 4
N13 Powers To introduce index notation to write powers of small numbers To write numbers as the product of prime numbers using index notation	N.pn.3 SP.sp.1, 2, 3, 4	N.ipr.2, 3 UA.asp.1, 2, 3, 4, 5

PLANNING

Abacus 7 National Numeracy Strategy Framework matching chart (cont.)

Abacus 7 Unit	Objectives (March 2000 Framework)	Objectives (Key Stage 3 Framework)
N13 Powers (cont.) To recognise powers of 10 To interpret a million and a billion using powers of 10		
N14 Positive and negative numbers To rehearse the ordering of positive and negative numbers To add positive and negative whole numbers in context To add positive and negative decimal numbers To subtract positive and negative whole numbers in context	N.pv.3 SP.sp.2, 3, 4	N.ipr.1 C.nor.1 UA.asp.1, 3, 4, 5
N15 Multiplication To use informal written methods to multiply TU·t x U·t To use standard long multiplication to multiply TU·t x U·t To use standard long multiplication to multiply U·th x TU	C.wm.2 SP.sp.1, 2, 3, 4	C.wm.2 UA.asp.1, 2, 3, 4, 5
N16 Division To use standard written methods to divide HTU·t ÷ U To use standard written methods to divide TU·th ÷ TU To use standard written methods to divide HTU ÷ U·t To rehearse rounding decimals to 1 decimal place	C.wm.2 SP.sp.1, 2, 3	C.wm.2 UA.asp.1, 2, 3, 4
N17 Percentages To calculate percentages of numbers and quantities without using a calculator To calculate percentages of numbers and quantities using a calculator	N.fdp.2 C.cm.1 SP.sp.1, 2, 3, 4	N.fdp.3 C.cm.1,2 UA.asp.1, 2, 3, 4, 5
N18 Fractions, decimals, percentages To convert a fraction to a percentage with and without a calculator To convert a decimal to a percentage without a calculator To convert a percentage to a fraction and a decimal	N.fdp.1 C.cm.1, 2 C.mm.2 SP.sp.1, 2, 3	N.fdp.1,3 C.mm.2 C.cm.1,2 UA.asp.1, 2, 3, 4
N19 Ratio, proportion To consolidate links between ratio and proportion To use direct proportion in simple contexts To simplify ratios by cancelling	N.fdp.3 SP.sp.1, 2, 3	N.fdp.4 UA.asp.1, 2, 3, 4
N20 Checking results To use rounding to approximate the size of the answer To check by doing the inverse operation To check using knowledge of the number system To check a calculation by doing an equivalent calculation	C.cr.1 SP.sp.1, 2, 3	C.cr.1 UA.asp.1, 2, 3, 4
N21 Squares, cubes and roots To rehearse recognition of square numbers up to 12 x 12, and to extend to squares of larger numbers To understand the concept of square roots To estimate a square root To use a calculator to find squares and square roots To recognise cubes and cube roots	N.pn.1 C.mm.1 C.cm.1, 2 SP.sp.1, 2, 3, 4	N.ipr.3 C.mm.1 C.cm.1 UA.asp.1, 2, 3, 4, 5
N22 Order of operations To know and use the order of operations, including brackets and powers	C.nor.1 SP.sp.2, 3, 4	C.nor.1, 2 UA.asp.1, 3, 4, 5
A1 Algebra To use letters or symbols to represent unknowns To recognise algebraic conventions, e.g. 4n, 2x + 5, y² To begin to use simple expressions with brackets	A.ef.1, 2 SP.sp.1, 2, 3	A.efi.1, 2 UA.asp.1, 2, 3, 4
A2 Algebra To use algebra to generalise patterns To simplify linear algebraic expressions by collecting like terms	A.ef.3 SP.sp.2, 3, 4	A.efi.3 UA.asp.1, 3, 4, 5
A3 Algebra To substitute numbers in simple algebraic expressions To begin to multiply a single term over a bracket	A.ef.1, 4 SP.sp.2, 3, 4	A.efi.1, 5 UA.asp.1, 3, 4, 5
A4 Algebra To use mathematical formulae To substitute numbers in simple formulae To derive a formula	A.ef.4 SP.sp.1, 2, 3	A.efi.5 UA.asp.1, 2, 3, 4
A5 Algebra To solve simple equations To construct simple equations	A.ef.5 SP.sp.1, 2, 3, 4	A.efi.4 UA.asp.1, 2, 3, 4, 5
A6 Algebra To find coordinate pairs that satisfy a rule, e.g. y = 3x, and plot them on a coordinate grid To recognise that a function such as y = 3x + 1 corresponds to a straight-line graph To construct a table of values for a given equation before drawing a straight-line graph To recognise patterns in parallel straight-line graphs	A.g.1, 2 SP.sp.2, 3, 4	A.sfg.5 UA.asp.1, 3, 4, 5
A7 Algebra To recognise and interpret a distance-time graph To interpret and plot graphs of linear functions arising from everyday life	A.g.3 SP.sp.1, 2, 3, 4	A.sfg.6 UA.asp.1, 2, 3, 4, 5

PLANNING

Abacus 7 National Numeracy Strategy Framework matching chart (cont.)

Abacus 7 Unit	Objectives (March 2000 Framework)	Objectives (Key Stage 3 Framework)
A8 Algebra To explore simple function machines To express simple functions in words, then symbols To find outputs for given inputs and inputs for given outputs	A.sf.4 SP.sp.1, 2, 3	A.sfg.4 UA.asp.1, 2, 3, 4
A9 Algebra To generate terms of a sequence given a rule To describe a rule for a given sequence	A.sf.1, 2, 3 SP.sp.2, 3, 4	A.sfg.1, 2 UA.asp.1, 3, 4, 5
A10 Algebra To describe the general term of a sequence using words, and using symbols To calculate a number in a sequence given the general term To generate a sequence given the general term	A.sf.1, 2, 3 SP.sp.2, 3, 4	A.sfg.1, 2, 3 UA.asp.1, 3, 4, 5
M1 Measures To rehearse the units of capacity/weight To rehearse the relationship between metric and imperial units of capacity/weight To read and interpret scales To convert from one unit of capacity/weight to another To introduce the cubic centimetre, written cm³	SSM.m.1, 2, 3, 4 SP.sp.1, 2, 3, 4	SSM.m.1 UA.asp.1, 2, 3, 4, 5
M2 Area To rehearse the concept of surface area To derive and use a formula for finding the surface area of a cuboid To find the surface area of compound shapes made from cuboids	SSM.m.6 SP.sp.2, 3, 4	SSM.m.4 UA.asp.1, 3, 4, 5
M3 Area To derive and use the formula for the area of a right-angled triangle To find the area and perimeter of compound shapes To introduce the hectare as a large unit of area	SSM.m.5 SP.sp.1, 2, 3, 4	SSM.m.3 UA.asp.1, 2, 3, 4, 5
S1 Lines and angles To recognise vertically opposite angles, adjacent angles, corresponding angles and alternate angles To understand and use notation for labelling parallel sides To recognise exterior angles of triangles and recognise them as the sum of two opposite interior angles	SSM.la.1, 2 SSM.cn.1 SP.sp.2, 3, 4	SSM.gr.1, 2 SSM.m.2 SSM.cn.1 UA.asp.1, 3, 4, 5
S2 Coordinates To rehearse recognition of coordinates in all four quadrants To find coordinates of points determined by geometric information To recognise congruent shapes on a coordinate grid	SSM.co.1, 2	SSM.co.1
S3 Reflections To locate the image of an object which is reflected in different lines, including one side of the object To reflect a shape in a coordinate axis and extend to one coordinate axis, followed by another To reflect objects in mirror lines placed at different angles	SSM.t.1, 2	SSM.t.1, 2
S4 Rotations To rotate 2-d shapes about a given point, on or outside the shape To combine the transformations: rotation, reflection and translation	SSM.t.1, 4	SSM.t.1, 2
S5 Rotational symmetry To recognise rotational symmetry and recognise the 'order' of rotational symmetry To construct shapes and patterns with rotational symmetry	SSM.t.1, 4 SP.sp.2, 3, 4	SSM.t.1, 2 UA.asp.1, 3, 4, 5
S6 3-d shape To draw front views, side views and top views of 3-d shapes To construct a 3-d shape given drawings of its front, side, back and top views	SSM.ps.1, 3 SP.sp.2, 3, 4	SSM.gr.4 SSM.cn.2 UA.asp.1, 3, 4, 5
S7 Triangles and quadrilaterals To recognise congruency in triangles and quadrilaterals To rehearse the names of types of triangles and quadrilaterals To recognise an isosceles trapezium To rehearse the properties of kites and arrowheads To recognise symmetry and congruency in kites and arrowheads	SSM.la.2 SSM.ps.2 SP.sp.1, 2, 3, 4	SSM.gr.1, 2, 3 UA.asp.1, 2, 3, 4, 5
S8 Constructing shapes To construct a triangle, using a ruler and protractor, given two sides and the angle between them To construct a triangle using a ruler and protractor, given one side and two angles To construct a quadrilateral, using a ruler and protractor	SSM.cn.1, 2 SP.sp.2, 3, 4	SSM.cn.1, 2 UA.asp.1, 3, 4, 5
D1 Graphs To collect data from surveys and experiments To construct and interpret compound bar charts to represent data To construct and interpret pie charts to represent data	HD.spc.1, 2, 3 HD.rd.1, 2, 3 SP.sp.1, 2, 3, 4	HD.spc.1, 2, 3, 4 HD.prd.2 HD.idr.1, 2 UA.asp.1, 2, 3, 4, 5
D2 Averages To rehearse the types of average: mean, median, mode To find the mean of a simple frequency distribution To compare two sets of data using the mean and the range	HD.spc.1, 2, 3 HD.pd.1, 4 SP.sp.1, 2, 3, 4	HD.spc.1, 2, 3, 4 HD.prd.1 HD.idr.2, 3 UA.asp.1, 2, 3, 4, 5
D3 Probability To list all the outcomes of an event To assign probabilities to an event	HD.pb.1, 2, 3, 4, 5 SP.sp.1, 2, 3, 4	HD.pb.1, 2, 3, 4 UA.asp.1, 2, 3, 4, 5

PLANNING

Exemplar planning grid: autumn

Unit	Abacus 6 Unit	Abacus 7 Unit
1	**N1 Place-value** To rehearse rounding a number to its nearest 10, 100 or 1000 To rehearse rounding a decimal number (1-place, 2-place) to the nearest whole number To round a decimal number to the nearest tenth **N2 Place-value** To rehearse dividing whole numbers by 10 and 100 to obtain decimal numbers (1-place, 2-place)	**N1 Place-value** To round decimal numbers to the nearest whole number, tenth or hundredth To round decimal numbers to 1 or 2 decimal places To key in decimal numbers and read the calculator display
2–3	**N3 Multiplication/division** To rehearse the mental recall of multiplication facts up to 10 x 10, and mentally derive corresponding division facts To rehearse multiplying by zero **N4 Multiplication/division** To rehearse the recall or derivation of doubles of numbers 10 to 100, multiples of 10 to 1000, multiples of 100 to 10 000, decimals To recognise halving as the inverse (reverse) of doubling To recall or derive quickly the corresponding halves of doubles **N5 Multiplication/division** To rehearse multiplying by multiples of 10 To multiply by near multiples of 10, 100 **N6 Multiplication/division** To use doubling and halving to help multiply To use a known multiplication fact to derive another To multiply two numbers by doubling one and halving the other To multiply by 50, or 25, by multiplying by 100 and halving (and halving again)	**N2 Number facts** To consolidate the rapid recall of addition pairs to 1 and 10, extending to decimals To derive quickly decimal complements to 1 and 10 To rehearse the doubles of 2-digit numbers including decimals, and corresponding halves To consolidate the rapid recall of doubles, and corresponding halves **A1 Algebra** To use letters or symbols to represent unknowns To recognise algebraic conventions, e.g. $4n$, $2x + 5$, y^2 To begin to use simple expressions with brackets **N3 Multiplication/division** To consolidate and extend mental methods of calculation To extend the use of factors for multiplying and dividing To extend the use of partitioning for multiplying and dividing To rehearse and extend the use of doubling for multiplying To multiply by doubling one number and halving the other To multiply by partitioning the multiplier into combinations of 1, 2, 4, 8, 16
4–5	**N7 Fractions/decimals** To find fractions of numbers or quantities **N8 Fractions/decimals** To rehearse recognition of equivalence of fractions To reduce a fraction to its simplest form by cancelling common factors **N9 Fractions/decimals** To order fractions by converting them to fractions with a common denominator To order fractions by positioning them on a number line	**N4 Fractions** To find equivalent fractions by cancelling To compare and order sets of fractions by converting them to fractions with a common denominator To order fractions by positioning them on a number line
6	**D1 Grouped data** To group discrete data in equal intervals To construct a grouped frequency table To draw and interpret a bar graph based on grouped data **D2 Pie charts** To introduce a pie chart to represent data To interpret a pie chart	**D1 Graphs** To collect data from surveys and experiments To construct and interpret compound bar charts to represent data To construct and interpret pie charts to represent data
7	**Assess and review**	**Assess and review**

PLANNING

Exemplar planning grid: autumn (cont.)

Unit	Abacus 6 Unit	Abacus 7 Unit
8–10	**S1 Angle** To rehearse measuring angles (acute and obtuse) using a protractor To rehearse drawing angles using a protractor To estimate an angle in degrees To measure and calculate angles at a point **S2 Angle** To explore the angle sum of a triangle To calculate one angle of a triangle, given the other two **M1 Length** To introduce imperial measures of length To rehearse the relationship between metric units of length To rehearse the relationship between imperial and metric units of length **M2 Weight** To introduce imperial measures of weight To rehearse the relationship between metric units of weight and to introduce tonnes To rehearse the relationship between imperial/metric units of weight and to use scales which show both types **M3 Capacity** To introduce imperial measures of capacity To rehearse the relationship between metric units of capacity and to introduce centilitres To rehearse the relationship between imperial/metric units of capacity and to use scales which show both types	**S1 Lines and angles** To recognise vertically opposite angles, adjacent angles, corresponding angles and alternate angles To understand and use notation for labelling parallel sides To recognise exterior angles of triangles and recognise them as the sum of two opposite interior angles **M1 Measures** To rehearse the units of capacity/weight To rehearse the relationship between metric and imperial units of capacity/weight To read and interpret scales To convert from one unit of capacity/weight to another To introduce the cubic centimetre, written cm^3 **A2 Algebra** To use algebra to generalise patterns To simplify linear algebraic expressions by collecting like terms
11	**N10 Addition/subtraction** To mentally recall addition pairs to 1, 10, 100 and 1000 To recognise what must be added to a decimal number to make the next whole number **N11 Addition/subtraction** To select and use an appropriate operation and strategy when solving a problem To rehearse adding three or more numbers To rehearse adding and subtracting near whole numbers **N12 Addition/subtraction** To recognise that there are several mental subtraction strategies To select an appropriate subtraction strategy to solve a given problem	**N5 Addition/subtraction** To rehearse strategies for adding mentally To add near doubles by doubling then adjusting To add by partitioning and dealing with the most significant digit first To add by adding too much then compensating To rehearse strategies for subtracting mentally To subtract by partitioning and dealing with the most significant digit first To subtract by subtracting too much then compensating
12	**N13 Properties of number** To rehearse recognition of the multiples of numbers to 10 up to the tenth multiple To find common multiples of two or three numbers To find the smallest common multiple of two or three numbers **N14 Properties of number** To rehearse tests for divisibility by 2, 3, 5, 6, 9, 10 To know and apply tests for divisibility by 8, 25	**N6 Factors and primes** To rehearse tests for divisibility To recognise prime numbers, and to test by checking for divisibility To find the factors of a number by checking for divisibility by primes To find common factors of numbers To find the prime numbers up to 100 **A3 Algebra** To substitute numbers in simple algebraic expressions To begin to multiply a single term over a bracket
13	**Assess and review**	**Assess and review**

Exemplar planning grid: spring

Unit	Abacus 6 Unit	Abacus 7 Unit
1	**N15 Place-value** To multiply decimal numbers by 10 and 100 To recognise that multiplying by 100 is equivalent to multiplying by 10, then by 10 again **N16 Place-value** To divide decimal numbers by 10 and 100 To recognise that dividing by 100 is equivalent to dividing by 10, then 10 again	**N7 Place-value** To rehearse multiplying and dividing an integer by 10, 100 or 1000 To multiply and divide decimals by 10, 100 or 1000 and numbers by 0·1, 0·01 and 0·001 To recognise the equivalence of multiplying and dividing by 10/0·1, 100/0·01, 1000/0·001 **A4 Algebra** To use mathematical formulae and to substitute numbers in simple formulae To derive a formula
2–3	**N17 Multiplication/division** To mentally multiply TU x U or HTU x U by partitioning To rehearse the use of rounding strategies when multiplying **N18 Multiplication/division** **N19 Multiplication/division** To multiply ThHTU x U and HTU x TU using standard written methods **N20 Multiplication/division** To recognise the relationship between multiplication and division To rehearse recognising that from one multiplication or division fact, three others are possible To rehearse division, giving the remainder as a fraction To divide, giving the quotient as a decimal	**N8 Fractions** To recognise equivalence between $\frac{1}{4}$ of 12, $\frac{1}{4}$ x 12, 12 x $\frac{1}{4}$ To multiply a fraction by a whole number or a whole number by a fraction To rehearse converting an improper fraction to a mixed number **A5 Algebra** To solve simple equations To construct simple equations **N9 Division** To rehearse division, giving the quotient as a fraction To divide giving the quotient as a decimal, correct to 1 or 2 decimal places To interpret calculator displays after division, including recurring decimals To recognise when to round up or down after division To divide, giving the remainder as a fraction and as a decimal To rehearse recurring decimals
4	**N21 Fractions/decimals** To rehearse converting a mixed fraction into an improper fraction and vice versa **N22 Fractions/decimals** To rehearse decimal notation for tenths and hundredths, and to introduce thousandths To know the value of each digit in a number up to three decimal places To order a set of decimal numbers or measures (up to three decimal places)	**N10 Decimals** To rehearse and extend understanding of decimal notation To compare and order decimals in different contexts To locate decimals numbers lying between two others To add 0·1 or 0·01 to any number To subtract 0·1 or 0·01 from any number
5	**S3 Coordinates** To rehearse reading and plotting points in the first quadrant of a coordinate grid To extend the coordinate grid to four quadrants **S4 Reflection** To rehearse the concept of reflection To draw the reflection of a shape in a mirror line To draw the reflection of a shape in two mirror lines	**S2 Coordinates** To rehearse recognition of coordinates in all four quadrants To find coordinates of points determined by geometric information To recognise congruent shapes on a coordinate grid **A6 Algebra** To find coordinate pairs that satisfy a rule, e.g. $y = 3x$, and plot them on a coordinate grid To recognise that a function such as $y = 3x + 1$ corresponds to a straight-line graph To construct a table of values for a given equation before drawing a straight-line graph To recognise patterns in parallel straight-line graphs **S3 Reflections** To locate the image of an object which is reflected in different lines, including one side of the object To reflect a shape in a coordinate axis and extend to one coordinate axis, followed by another To reflect objects in mirror lines placed at different angles

PLANNING

Exemplar planning grid: spring (cont.)

Unit	Abacus 6 Unit	Abacus 7 Unit
5	**S5 Rotation/translation** To rehearse the concept of rotation To draw the position of a shape after a 90° or 180° rotation about a vertex To draw the position of a shape after translations To rehearse the position of a shape after reflection in a line **S6 3-d shape** To rehearse names and properties of common 3-d shapes To rehearse polyhedron, tetrahedron, octahedron, and introduce dodecahedron To recognise parallel and perpendicular faces and edges	**S4 Rotations** To rotate 2-d shapes about a given point, on or outside the shape To combine the transformations: rotation, reflection and translation **S5 Rotational symmetry** To recognise rotational symmetry and recognise the 'order' of rotational symmetry To construct shapes and patterns with rotational symmetry **S6 3-d shape** To draw front views, side views and top views of 3-d shapes To construct a 3-d shape given drawings of its front, side, back and top views
6	**Assess and review**	**Assess and review**
7–8	**M4 Area** To calculate the area of a rectangle To calculate the area of compound shapes that can be split into rectangles To find the surface area of a box, where the faces are all rectangles **M5 Area** To find the area of a right angled triangle by considering it as half a rectangle **D3 Conversion graphs** To construct and interpret line graphs in which intermediate values have meaning To construct and interpret a conversion graph	**M2 Area** To rehearse the concept of surface area To derive and use a formula for finding the surface area of a cuboid To find the surface area of compound shapes made from cuboids **M3 Area** To derive and use the formula for the area of a right-angled triangle To find the area and perimeter of compound shapes To introduce the hectare as a large unit of area **A7 Algebra** To recognise and interpret a distance-time graph To interpret and plot graphs of linear functions arising from everyday life
9–10	**N23 Addition/subtraction** To rehearse adding ThHTU + ThHTU using informal and standard written methods **N24 Addition/subtraction** To add U·th + U·th using informal and standard written methods **N25 Addition/subtraction** To subtract ThHTU – ThHTU using standard written methods **N26 Addition/subtraction** To rehearse subtracting U·th – U·th using standard written methods	**N11 Addition** To use standard written methods to add decimal numbers with three places of decimals To add numbers with different numbers of digits To use standard written methods to add decimals with different numbers of digits and decimal places **N12 Subtraction** To use standard written methods to subtract decimal numbers with three places of decimals To subtract decimal numbers with different numbers of digits To use standard written methods to subtract decimals with different numbers of digits/decimal places
11	**N27 Properties of number** To list all the pairs of factors of a number up to 100 To recognise that a number with an odd number of factors is a square number **N28 Properties of number** To introduce the concept of a prime number To recognise prime numbers as numbers which have exactly two factors	**N13 Powers** To introduce index notation to write powers of small numbers To write numbers as the product of prime numbers using index notation To recognise powers of 10 To interpret a million and a billion using powers of 10
12	**Assess and review**	**Assess and review**

Exemplar planning grid: summer

Unit	Abacus 6 Unit	Abacus 7 Unit
1	**N29 Place-value** To find the difference between a positive and a negative number To rehearse the ordering of positive and negative numbers **N30 Place-value** To rehearse rounding a number To estimate by approximating, and to check the result of a calculation by estimating To use a calculator effectively	**N14 Positive and negative numbers** To rehearse the ordering of positive and negative numbers To add positive and negative whole numbers in context To add positive and negative decimal numbers To subtract positive and negative whole numbers in context
2–3	**N31 Multiplication/division** To mentally multiply (U·t x U or U·th x U by partitioning To rehearse the use of rounding strategies when multiplying **N32 Multiplication/division** To multiply U·th x U using standard written methods **N33 Multiplication/division** To rehearse dividing HTU ÷ U using standard written methods To divide HTU ÷ TU using standard written methods **N34 Multiplication/division** To divide TU·th ÷ U using standard written methods	**N15 Multiplication** To use informal written methods to multiply TU·t x U·t To use standard long multiplication to multiply TU·t x U·t To use standard long multiplication to multiply U·th x TU **N16 Division** To use standard written methods to divide HTU·t ÷ U To use standard written methods to divide TU·th ÷ TU To use standard written methods to divide HTU ÷ U·t To rehearse rounding decimals to 1 decimal place
4–5	**N35 Percentages** To rehearse the concept of a percentage as a fraction of 100, and find simple percentages of quantities To express simple fractions as percentages **N36 Fractions/decimals** To rehearse the equivalence between fractions, decimals and percentages To begin to use a calculator to convert a fraction to a decimal **N37 Ratio/proportion** To introduce the idea of proportion **N38 Ratio/proportion** To introduce the idea of ratio and relate this to proportion To solve simple problems involving ratio and proportion	**N17 Percentages** To calculate percentages of numbers and quantities without using a calculator To calculate percentages of numbers and quantities using a calculator **N18 Fractions, decimals, percentages** To convert a fraction to a percentage with and without a calculator To convert a decimal to a percentage without a calculator To convert a percentage to a fraction and a decimal **N19 Ratio and proportion** To consolidate links between ratio and proportion To use direct proportion in simple contexts To simplify ratios by cancelling
6	**D4 Averages** To rehearse the concept of average To rehearse the meaning of mode as one type of average To introduce mean and median as types of average To calculate different types of average for a set of data **D5 Probability** To recognise events which are equally likely To predict the outcomes of equally-likely events To introduce the probability scale of 0 to 1 on the number line	**D2 Averages** To rehearse the types of average: mean, median, mode To find the mean of a simple frequency distribution To compare two sets of data using the mean and the range **D3 Probability** To list all the outcomes of an event To assign probabilities to an event
7	Assess and review	Assess and review

Exemplar planning grid: summer (cont.)

Unit	Abacus 6 Unit	Abacus 7 Unit
8–10	**S7 2-d shape** To rehearse the names of 2-d shapes To introduce the parallelogram, rhombus and trapezium **S8 2-d shape** To introduce the kite To name and classify different quadrilaterals **S9 2-d shape** To rehearse the names of different polygons To construct polygons from the dissected pieces of another shape **M6 Perimeter** To rehearse finding the perimeter of a rectangle To find the perimeters of compound shapes that can be split into rectangles	**S7 Triangles and quadrilaterals** To recognise congruency in triangles and quadrilaterals To rehearse the names of types of triangles and quadrilaterals To recognise an isosceles trapezium To rehearse the properties of kites and arrowheads To recognise symmetry and congruency in kites and arrowheads **S8 Constructing shapes** To construct a triangle, using a ruler and protractor, given two sides and the angle between them To construct a triangle using a ruler and protractor, given one side and two angles To construct a quadrilateral, using a ruler and protractor
11	**N39 Addition/subtraction** To check the result of a calculation by using an equivalent calculation or an inverse operation or an inverse order To solve real-life problems and check solutions **N40 Addition/subtraction** To explore mathematical patterns, particularly using addition and subtraction To relate these patterns to arithmetical facts and operations **N41 Properties of number** To recognise square numbers up to 12 x 12, and to calculate the squares of larger numbers To derive the squares of multiples of 10 To find the number which has a given square, i.e. its square root	**N20 Checking results** To use rounding to approximate the size of the answer To check by doing the inverse operation To check using knowledge of the number system To check a calculation by doing an equivalent calculation **A8 Algebra** To explore simple function machines To express simple functions in words, then symbols To find outputs for given inputs and inputs for given outputs **N21 Squares, cubes, roots** To rehearse recognition of square numbers up to 12 x 12, and to extend to squares of larger numbers To understand the concept of square roots To estimate a square root To use a calculator to find squares and square roots To recognise cubes and cube roots
12	**N42 Properties of number** To recognise a sequence of numbers, to find its pattern and predict the next few terms **N43 Properties of number** To rehearse properties of the sums of odd and even numbers To recognise the properties of the products of odd and even numbers	**A9 Algebra** To generate terms of a sequence given a rule To describe a rule for a given sequence **A10 Algebra** To describe the general term of a sequence using words, and using symbols To calculate a number in a sequence given the general term To generate a sequence given the general term **N22 Order of operations** To know and use the order of operations, including brackets and powers
13	**Assess and review**	**Assess and review**

Abacus 7 and Scottish Mathematics 5–14

On the following pages the Abacus 7 units are listed for you to see clearly the mathematical content and progression, and where the content fits in with the targets and strands of Mathematics 5–14. There is an implicit commitment to the content of Mathematics 5–14 and its aim 'to develop confidence in using and applying mathematics' throughout Abacus. The Abacus 7 material is set at a level that it is reasonable to assume that the highest achievers can attain in P7, i.e. mainly Level E, starting on Level F.

Abacus does not contain a separate self-contained section of problems and investigations, as the exploratory approaches reflected in problem-solving and investigational work, which is fundamental to the 5–14 programme, are basic to Abacus. The Abacus approach gives pupils ample opportunity to use and apply mathematics in practical tasks, explain their reasoning and take some responsibility for their learning.

To provide a quick reference between the targets of 5–14 and the content of the units of Abacus 7, a summary of the targets and strands appears below. For each unit in the grid there appears a code of abbreviations to match it to a particular strand. The codes used are as follows:

Information Handling		**Shape, Position and Movement**	
Collect	c	Range of shapes	rs
Organise	o	Position and movement	pm
Display	d	Symmetry	sy
Interpret	i	Angle	a
Probability	pr		

Number, Money and Measurement	
Range and type of numbers	rtn
Money	m
Add and subtract	as
Multiply and divide	md
Round numbers	rn
Fractions, percentages and ratio	fpr
Patterns and sequences	ps
Functions and equations	fe
Algebra	al
Measure and estimate	me
Time	t
Perimeter, formulae and scales	pfs

Each of the items or activities in the strand has then been given a number which will help identify the particular aspect in the strand to which the unit matches. The code has three parts – an indication of level (usually E or F), an abbreviation for the strand followed by a number.

Thus **E rtn 1** means Level E, Range and Type of Numbers, item 1, i.e. 'Negative numbers'.

PLANNING

Abacus 7 and the Northern Ireland Curriculum

On the following pages the Abacus 7 units are listed for you to see clearly the mathematical content and progression, and where the content fits in with the programmes of study of the Northern Ireland Curriculum. The units have been matched to the Key Stage 3 Programme of Study as the material covered is an extension from Abacus 6, which covers all of the Key Stage 2 content from the Northern Ireland Curriculum. The Abacus 7 material is set at a level that it would be reasonable to assume that the highest achievers can attain in P7, i.e. mainly level 5, starting on level 6.

There is an implicit commitment to Attainment Target: Processes in Mathematics throughout Abacus. The exploratory approaches reflected in problem-solving and investigational work are basic to Abacus. As well as Attainment Target: Processes in Mathematics, which is reflected and addressed throughout the whole programme, the Northern Ireland Key Stage 3 Curriculum has four other Attainment Targets: Number, Algebra, Shape, Space and Measures, and Handling Data.

The AT: Number (N) is divided into two strands:
- Understanding number and number notation   (n)
- Number operations and applications   (o)

Algebra (A) is divided into three strands:
- Patterns, relationships, sequences and generalisations   (p)
- Algebraic conventions and manipulations   (a)
- Functions, formulae, equations and inequalities   (f)

Shape, Space and Measures (SSM) is divided into three strands:
- Exploration of shape   (s)
- Position, movement and direction   (pmd)
- Measures   (m)

Handling Data (HD) is divided into three strands:
- Collect and record data   (c)
- Represent, analyse and interpret data   (r)
- Probability   (pr)

Therefore the code which appears in the following charts may be exemplified as follows:

N.o.(a)   **Attainment Target:** Number
               Strand: Number operations and applications
               Paragraph: (a)

Scottish Mathematics 5–14 and Northern Ireland curriculum matching chart

Abacus 7 Unit	Mathematics 5–14	NI Curriculum
N1 Place-value To round decimal numbers to the nearest whole number, tenth or hundredth To round decimal numbers to 1 or 2 decimal places To key in decimal numbers and read the calculator display	E rtn 3 E t 1 F rtn 3 F rn 1	N.n.(c) (d)
N2 Number facts To consolidate the rapid recall of addition pairs to 1 and 10, extending to decimals To derive quickly decimal complements to 1 and 10 To rehearse the doubles of 2-digit numbers including decimals, and corresponding halves To consolidate the rapid recall of doubles, and corresponding halves	E as 1 E t 1 F as 1 F md 1	N.o.(a) (f) N.n. (d)
N3 Multiplication/division To consolidate and extend mental methods of calculation To extend the use of factors for multiplying and dividing To extend the use of partitioning for multiplying and dividing To rehearse and extend the use of doubling for multiplying To multiply by doubling one number and halving the other To multiply by partitioning the multiplier into combinations of 1, 2, 4, 8, 16	F md 1 F rtn 6	N.o.(a) (b) (f) N.n.(d) (e)
N4 Fractions To find equivalent fractions by cancelling To compare and order sets of fractions by converting them to fractions with a common denominator To order fractions by positioning them on a number line	E rtn 2 F fpr 1	N.n.(f) N.o.(c)
N5 Addition/subtraction To rehearse strategies for adding mentally To add near doubles by doubling then adjusting To add by partitioning and dealing with the most significant digit first To add by adding too much then compensating To rehearse strategies for subtracting mentally To subtract by partitioning and dealing with the most significant digit first To subtract by subtracting too much then compensating	E as 1, 2 F as 1	N.n.(d) (e) N.o.(a) (b) (f)
N6 Factors and primes To rehearse tests for divisibility To recognise prime numbers, and to test by checking for divisibility To find the factors of a number by checking for divisibility by primes To find common factors of numbers To find the prime numbers up to 100	F rtn 6 E ps 3 F md 1	N.n.(a) N.o.(a) (b) (e) A.p.(a)
N7 Place-value To rehearse multiplying and dividing an integer by 10, 100 or 1000 To multiply and divide integers and decimals by 10, 100 or 1000 To multiply and divide by 0·1, 0·01 and 0·001 To recognise the equivalence of multiplying and dividing by 10/0·1, 100/0·01, 1000/0·001	E md 1, 2 F md 2, 4 F rn 1	N.o.(f) (g) N.n.(b) (d)
N8 Fractions To recognise equivalence between $\frac{1}{4}$ of 12, $\frac{1}{4}$ x 12, 12 x $\frac{1}{4}$ To multiply a fraction by a whole number or a whole number by a fraction To rehearse converting an improper fraction to a mixed number	E fpr 1, 2 F fpr 2	N.n.(d) (f) N.o.(c) (f)
N9 Division To rehearse division, giving the quotient as a fraction To divide giving the quotient as a decimal, correct to 1 or 2 decimal places To interpret calculator displays after division, including recurring decimals To recognise when to round up or down after division To divide, giving the remainder as a fraction and as a decimal To recognise recurring decimals	E md 3, 4 F md 2, 3 F rn 1 F rtn 7	N.n.(c) (d) (e) N.o.(b) (f)
N10 Decimals To rehearse and extend understanding of decimal notation To compare and order decimals in different contexts To locate decimals numbers lying between two others To add 0·1 or 0·01 to any number To subtract 0·1 or 0·01 from any number	F rtn 3 F as 2	N.n.(b) (c) (f) N.o.(b)
N11 Addition To use standard written methods to add decimal numbers with three places of decimals To add numbers with different numbers of digits To use standard written methods to add decimals with different numbers of digits and decimal places	F as 2, 3	N.n.(e) N.o.(b)
N12 Subtraction To use standard written methods to subtract decimal numbers with three decimals places To subtract decimal numbers with different numbers of digits To use standard written methods to subtract decimals with different numbers of digits/decimal places	F as 2, 3	N.n.(e) N.o.(b)
N13 Powers To introduce index notation to write powers of small numbers To write numbers as the product of prime numbers using index notation	F rtn 4, 5, 6, 7	N.n.(g) N.o.(e)

Scottish Mathematics 5-14 and Northern Ireland curriculum matching chart (cont.)

Abacus 7 Unit	Mathematics 5–14	NI Curriculum
N13 Powers (cont.) To recognise powers of 10 To interpret a million and a billion using powers of 10		
N14 Positive and negative numbers To rehearse the ordering of positive and negative numbers To add positive and negative whole numbers in context To add positive and negative decimal numbers To subtract positive and negative whole numbers in context	E rtn 1 F rtn 1, 2, 3 E as 5 F as 1, 2	N.o.(d) (f) N.n.(d)
N15 Multiplication To use informal written methods to multiply TU·t x U·t To use standard long multiplication to multiply TU·t x U·t To use standard long multiplication to multiply U·th x TU	F md 2, 3	N.n.(d) (e) N.o.(b) (f)
N16 Division To use standard written methods to divide HTU·t ÷ U To use standard written methods to divide TU·th ÷ TU To use standard written methods to divide HTU ÷ U·t To rehearse rounding decimals to 1 decimal place	F md 2, 3 E rn 1 F rn 1	N.n.(c) (d) (e) N.o.(b) (f)
N17 Percentages To calculate percentages of numbers and quantities without using a calculator To calculate percentages of numbers and quantities using a calculator	E fpr 1, 2, 3	N.n.(d) (f) N.o.(c) (f)
N18 Fractions, decimals, percentages To convert a fraction to a percentage with and without a calculator To convert a decimal to a percentage without a calculator To convert a percentage to a fraction and a decimal	F fpr 1	N.n.(f) N.o.(c)
N19 Ratio and proportion To consolidate links between ratio and proportion To use direct proportion in simple contexts To simplify ratios by cancelling	E fpr 4, 5 F fpr 1, 4	N.o.(c) (f) N.n.(d)
N20 Checking results To use rounding to approximate the size of the answer To check by doing the inverse operation To check using knowledge of the number system To check a calculation by doing an equivalent calculation	D rn 1 E as 4 F as 4 E md 5 F md 5	N.n.(d) (e) N.o.(b) (f)
N21 Squares, cubes, roots To rehearse recognition of square numbers up to 12 x 12, and to extend to squares of larger numbers To understand the concept of square roots To estimate a square root To use a calculator to find squares and square roots To recognise cubes and cube roots	F rtn 4 F md 3 E ps 1	N.o.(e) N.n.(g)
N22 Order of operations To know and use the order of operations, including brackets and powers	F as 4 F md 5	N.n.(e) N.o.(b)
A1 Algebra To use letters or symbols to represent unknowns To recognise algebraic conventions, e.g. 4n, 2x + 5, y^2 To begin to use simple expressions with brackets	F al 1	A.a.(a) (b) (c) A.f.(d)
A2 Algebra To use algebra to generalise patterns To simplify linear algebraic expressions by collecting like terms	F al 1, 2	A.p.(a) A.a.(a) (c)
A3 Algebra To substitute numbers in simple algebraic expressions To begin to multiply a single term over a bracket	F al 1, 2	A.a.(c)
A4 Algebra To use mathematical formulae To substitute numbers in simple formulae To derive a formula	F al 2, 4 E m 1	A.f.(e) A.a.(c) N.n.(d)
A5 Algebra To solve simple equations To construct simple equations	E fe 3 F al 2, 3, 4	A.a.(c)
A6 Algebra To find coordinate pairs that satisfy a rule, e.g. y = 3x, and plot them on a coordinate grid To recognise that a function such as y = 3x + 1 corresponds to a straight-line graph To construct a table of values for a given equation before drawing a straight-line graph To recognise patterns in parallel straight-line graphs	E pm 2 F al 4	A.f.(b) (c) (f)
A7 Algebra To recognise and interpret a distance-time graph To interpret and plot graphs of linear functions arising from everyday life	E d 1 F t 3 E i 1, 3 F al 4	A.f.(b) (c) (f) N.n.(d)

PLANNING

Scottish Mathematics 5-14 and Northern Ireland curriculum matching chart (cont.)

Abacus 7 Unit	Mathematics 5–14	NI Curriculum
A8 Algebra To explore simple function machines To express simple functions in words, then symbols To find outputs for given inputs and inputs for given outputs	E fe 1, 3	A.f.(b)
A9 Algebra To generate terms of a sequence given a rule To describe a rule for a given sequence	E fe 3, 4 F al 4	A.p.(a) A.a.(a)
A10 Algebra To describe the general term of a sequence using words, and using symbols To calculate a number in a sequence given the general term To generate a sequence given the general term	E fe 3, 4 F al 4	A.p.(a) A.a.(a)
M1 Measures To rehearse the units of capacity/weight To rehearse the relationship between metric and imperial units of capacity/weight To read and interpret scales To convert from one unit of capacity/weight to another To introduce the cubic centimetre, written cm^3	E me 1, 3, 4, 5, 6 D me 1, 2, 3, 5, 9	SSM.m.(a) (b) (c) (e) N.n.(d) N.o.(f)
M2 Area To rehearse the concept of surface area To derive and use a formula for finding the surface area of a cuboid To find the surface area of compound shapes made from cuboids	E pfs 1 F pfs 1	SSM.m.(j)
M3 Area To derive and use the formula for the area of a right-angled triangle To find the area and perimeter of compound shapes To introduce the hectare as a large unit of area	E me 2, 5 E pfs 1 F pfs 1	SSM.m.(i) (j) N.n.(d) N.o.(f)
S1 Lines and angles To recognise vertically opposite angles, adjacent angles, corresponding angles and alternate angles To understand and use notation for labelling parallel sides To recognise exterior angles of triangles and recognise them as the sum of two opposite interior angles	E a 1, 2, 3, 4 F a 1	SSM.s.(b) (c)
S2 Coordinates To rehearse recognition of coordinates in all four quadrants To find coordinates of points determined by geometric information To recognise congruent shapes on a coordinate grid	D pm 3 E pm 2, 3	SSM.pmd.(b) SSM.s.(g)
S3 Reflections To locate the image of an object which is reflected in different lines, including one side of the object To reflect a shape in a coordinate axis and extend to one coordinate axis, followed by another To reflect objects in mirror lines placed at different angles	D sy 1, 2 E sy 2	SSM.pmd.(c) (d)
S4 Rotations To rotate 2-d shapes about a given point, on or outside the shape To combine the transformations: rotation, reflection and translation	D pm 4 E sy 2	SSM.pmd.(a) (b) (c) (d)
S5 Rotational symmetry To recognise rotational symmetry and recognise the 'order' of rotational symmetry To construct shapes and patterns with rotational symmetry	D pm 4 E sy 1, 2	SSM.pmd.(c) (d)
S6 3-d shape To draw front views, side views and top views of 3-d shapes To construct a 3-d shape given drawings of its front, side, back and top views	E rs 4	SSM.s.(f)
S7 Triangles and quadrilaterals To recognise congruency in triangles and quadrilaterals To rehearse the names of types of triangles and quadrilaterals To recognise an isosceles trapezium To rehearse the properties of kites and arrowheads To recognise symmetry and congruency in kites and arrowheads	D sy 1 E a 4 E rs 1, 2	SSM.s.(b) (c) (g)
S8 Constructing shapes To construct a triangle, using a ruler and protractor, given two sides and the angle between To construct a triangle using a ruler and protractor, given one side and two angles To construct a quadrilateral, using a ruler and protractor	E rs 5 F rs 1	SSM.s.(a) (f)
D1 Graphs To collect data from surveys and experiments To construct and interpret compound bar charts to represent data To construct and interpret pie charts to represent data	E d 2 F c 1, 2 E i 1, 3 F o 1 E o 1, 2, 3 F d 3	HD.c.(b) N.o.(f) HD.r.(a) N.n.(d)
D2 Averages To rehearse the types of average: mean, median, mode To find the mean of a simple frequency distribution To compare two sets of data using the mean and the range	E i 4 F i 3	HD.c.(b) HD.r.(a) (c)
D3 Probability To list all the outcomes of an event To assign probabilities to an event	F pr 1, 2, 3, 4	HD.pr.(a) (b) (c)

PLANNING

9 Answers

Pupils' written work

Some of the pages in the Abacus 7 Textbook include the unique feature of providing clear guidance to pupils on how their work should be recorded. Pupils should be encouraged to follow this guidance where it appears, which will make marking their work substantially easier and clearly focused. Where pupils are left to choose their own method, check how they have laid out their work to ensure that they have recorded their work in an appropriate manner.

Marking the pupils' work

Clearly it is important that pupils' work is seen and checked by the teacher regularly, but it is not always necessary for all work to be marked by the teacher. Decisions about which work should be teacher-marked, and how it should be marked will be made alongside the need to maximise time available for teaching and guiding pupils through their activities.

A suggested approach within Abacus is to make these decisions Unit by Unit. Decide, for example, for each Unit, which parts you want to mark, and which parts the pupils can mark themselves.

Marking the 'Explores'

The 'Explores' should generally be marked by the teacher. The 'Explores' often require a systematic approach, and the answers give suggestions for these. These approaches can be communicated to the pupils, to help them develop systematic ways of working. Also, the pupils' responses to the 'Explores' may well vary because of the often open-ended nature of the activities.

For many 'Explores' you may want to ask the pupils to work in pairs or groups, possibly leading to a group display of the results of their 'exploration' or investigation.

Contents

Textbook

Photocopy Masters

Assessment

Textbook

page 3
Rounding

 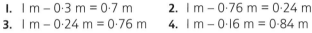

1. a $2·09 \rightarrow 2·1$ b $2·24 \rightarrow 2·2$
c $2·32 \rightarrow 2·3$ d $2·59 \rightarrow 2·6$
e $2·84 \rightarrow 2·8$ f $2·93 \rightarrow 2·9$

2. g $4·617 \rightarrow 4·62$ h $4·634 \rightarrow 4·63$
i $4·653 \rightarrow 4·65$ j $4·673 \rightarrow 4·67$
k $4·684 \rightarrow 4·68$ l $4·697 \rightarrow 4·70$

🌑 1. a 2   b 2
c 2   d 3
e 3   f 3

2. g 5   h 5
i 5   j 5
k 5   l 5

3. $4·8 \times 3·7 = 17·76$ $17·76 \rightarrow 17·8$
4. $6·4 \times 1·8 = 11·52$ $11·52 \rightarrow 11·5$
5. $5·3 \times 7·7 = 40·81$ $40·81 \rightarrow 40·8$
6. $14·2 \times 9·8 = 139·16$ $139·16 \rightarrow 139·2$
7. $15·6 \times 7·3 = 113·88$ $113·88 \rightarrow 113·9$
8. $11·2 \times 12·7 = 142·24$ $142·24 \rightarrow 142·2$
9. $15·31 \times 8·2 = 125·542$ $125·542 \rightarrow 125·5$
10. $17·25 \times 4·3 = 74·175$ $74·175 \rightarrow 74·2$
11. $9·63 \times 9·63 = 92·7369$ $92·7369 \rightarrow 92·7$
12. $4·15 \times 4·15 = 17·2225$ $17·2225 \rightarrow 17·2$
13. $11·59 \times 4·6 = 53·314$ $53·314 \rightarrow 53·3$
14. $6·8 \times 0·91 = 6·188$ $6·188 \rightarrow 6·2$

🌑 Answers will vary.
15. Darren $3·71 \text{ m} \rightarrow 3·7 \text{m}$
16. Sylvia $2·89 \text{ m} \rightarrow 2·9 \text{ m}$
17. Greg $3·51 \text{ m} \rightarrow 3·5 \text{ m}$
18. Tanya $3·44 \text{ m} \rightarrow 3·4 \text{ m}$
19. Michele $2·86 \text{ m} \rightarrow 2·9 \text{ m}$

page 4
Rounding

1. $1·476 \text{ m} \rightarrow 1·48 \text{m}$ 2. $2·352 \text{ m} \rightarrow 2·35 \text{ m}$
3. $3·176 \text{ m} \rightarrow 3·18 \text{ m}$ 4. $2·891 \text{ m} \rightarrow 2·89 \text{ m}$
5. $4·738 \text{ m} \rightarrow 4·74 \text{ m}$ 6. $0·986 \text{ m} \rightarrow 0·99 \text{ m}$
7. $4·078 \text{ m} \rightarrow 4·08 \text{ m}$ 8. $3·807 \text{ m} \rightarrow 3·81 \text{ m}$
9. $5·781 \rightarrow 5·78$ $5·781 \rightarrow 5·8$
🌑 $5·781 \rightarrow 6$
10. $6·293 \rightarrow 6·29$ $6·293 \rightarrow 6·3$
🌑 $6·293 \rightarrow 6$
11. $8·357 \rightarrow 8·36$ $8·357 \rightarrow 8·4$
🌑 $8·357 \rightarrow 8$
12. $4·569 \rightarrow 4·57$ $4·569 \rightarrow 4·6$
🌑 $4·569 \rightarrow 5$
13. $17·3816 \rightarrow 17·38$ $17·3816 \rightarrow 17·4$
🌑 $17·3816 \rightarrow 17$
14. $5·2739 \rightarrow 5·27$ $5·2739 \rightarrow 5·3$
🌑 $5·2739 \rightarrow 5$
15. $14·3546 \rightarrow 14·35$ $14·3546 \rightarrow 14·4$
🌑 $14·3546 \rightarrow 14$
16. $7·281 \rightarrow 7·28$ $7·281 \rightarrow 7·3$
🌑 $7·281 \rightarrow 7$
17. $12·0854 \rightarrow 12·09$ $12·0854 \rightarrow 12·1$ 🌑 $12·0854 \rightarrow 12$
18. $3·17265 \rightarrow 3·17$ $3·17265 \rightarrow 3·2$ 🌑 $3·17265 \rightarrow 3$

---

19. $4·27503 \rightarrow 4·28$ $4·27503 \rightarrow 4·3$ 🌑 $4·27503 \rightarrow 4$
20. $15·8610 \rightarrow 15·86$ $15·8610 \rightarrow 15·9$ 🌑 $15·8610 \rightarrow 16$
21. $33·7524 \rightarrow 33·75$ $33·7524 \rightarrow 33·8$ 🌑 $33·7524 \rightarrow 34$
22. $16·00831 \rightarrow 16·01$ $16·00831 \rightarrow 16·0$ 🌑 $16·00831 \rightarrow 16$
23. $27·2054 \rightarrow 27·21$ $27·2054 \rightarrow 27·2$ 🌑 $27·2054 \rightarrow 27$
24. $42·75126 \rightarrow 42·75$ $42·75126 \rightarrow 42·8$ 🌑 $42·75126 \rightarrow 43$
25. $22 \div 3 = 7·3333333 \rightarrow 7·33$ 26. $5 \div 8 = 1·875 \rightarrow 1·88$
27. $11 \div 6 = 1·8333333 \rightarrow 1·83$ 28. $44 \div 7 = 6·2857142 \rightarrow 6·29$
29. $2 \div 9 = 0·2222222 \rightarrow 0·22$ 30. $43 \div 11 = 3·9090909 \rightarrow 3·91$
31. $55 \div 8 = 6·875 \rightarrow 6·88$ 32. $217 \div 9 = 24·1111111 \rightarrow 24·11$
33. $158 \div 13 = 12·153846 \rightarrow 12·15$

page 5
Rounding

1. 6100 people   2. £30 each   3. 6 hours
4. about £50   5. about 2 kg   6. £30

Explore
Children could devise a table to record results clearly.
Check their averages and rounding.

page 6
Making 1 and 10

1. $1 \text{ m} - 0·3 \text{ m} = 0·7 \text{ m}$ 2. $1 \text{ m} - 0·76 \text{ m} = 0·24 \text{ m}$
3. $1 \text{ m} - 0·24 \text{ m} = 0·76 \text{ m}$ 4. $1 \text{ m} - 0·16 \text{ m} = 0·84 \text{ m}$
5. $1 \text{ m} - 0·40 \text{ m} = 0·60 \text{ m}$ 6. $1 \text{ m} - 0·38 \text{ m} = 0·62 \text{ m}$
7. $1 \text{ m} - 48 \text{ cm} = 0·52 \text{ m}$ 8. $1 \text{ m} - 27 \text{ cm} = 0·73 \text{ m}$
9. $1 \text{ m} - 370 \text{ mm} = 0·63 \text{ m}$ 10. $£10 - £7·36 = £2·64$
11. $£10 - £8·15 = £1·85$ 12. $£10 - £0·72 = £9·28$
13. $£10 - £5·50 = £4·50$ 14. $£10 - £4·63 = £5·37$
15. $£10 - £1·98 = £8·02$ 16. $£10 - £7·09 = £2·91$
17. $£10 - £6·27 = £3·73$ 18. $£10 - £2·03 = £7·97$
19. $£10 - £6·88 = £3·12$ 20. $£10 - £0·84 = £9·16$
21. $£10 - £9·21 = £0·79$

22. $1 \text{ l} - 0·735 \text{ l} = 0·265 \text{ l}$ 23. $1 \text{ l} - 0·526 \text{ l} = 0·474 \text{ l}$
24. $1 \text{ l} - 0·418 \text{ l} = 0·582 \text{ l}$ 25. $1 \text{ l} - 0·925 \text{ l} = 0·075 \text{ l}$
26. $1 \text{ l} - 275 \text{ ml} = 0·725$ 27. $1 \text{ l} - 38 \text{ cl} = 0·62 \text{ l}$
28. $1 \text{ l} - 158 \text{ ml} = 0·842 \text{ l}$ 29. $1 \text{ l} - 0·805 \text{ l} = 0·195 \text{ l}$
30. $1 \text{ l} - 0·075 \text{ l} = 0·925 \text{ l}$
🌑 Estimates will vary. using $1 \text{l} = 1\frac{3}{4}$ pints:
22. $0·265 \text{ l} \approx 0·5 \text{ pt}$ 23. $0·474 \text{ l} \approx 0·8 \text{ pt}$
24. $0·582 \text{ l} \approx 1 \text{ pt}$ 25. $0·075 \text{ l} \approx 0·1 \text{ pt}$
26. $0·725 \text{ l} \approx 1·3 \text{ pt}$ 27. $0·62 \text{ l} \approx 1·1 \text{ pt}$
28. $0·842 \text{ l} \approx 1·5 \text{ pt}$ 29. $0·195 \text{ l} \approx 0·3 \text{ pt}$
30. $0·925 \text{ l} \approx 1·6 \text{ pt}$

page 7
Doubling and halving

1. double $26 = 52$ 2. double $4·7 = 9·4$
3. double $0·35 = 0·7$ 4. double $2·8 = 5·6$
5. double $37 = 74$ 6. double $0·58 = 1·16$
7. double $7·7 = 15·4$ 8. double $59 = 118$
9. double $0·18 = 0·36$ 10. double $6·7 = 13·4$
11. double $74 = 148$ 12. double $0·29 = 0·58$
13. double $9·3 = 18·6$ 14. double $0·47 = 0·94$
15. double $0·86 = 1·72$ 16. double $0·76 \text{ m} = 1·52 \text{ m}$
17. double $0·39 \text{ m} = 0·78 \text{ m}$ 18. double $0·47 \text{ m} = 0·94 \text{ m}$
19. double $0·28 \text{ m} = 0·56 \text{ m}$ 20. double $0·93 \text{ m} = 1·86 \text{ m}$

21. double 0·67 m = 1·34 m   22. double 0·58 m = 1·16 m
23. double 0·37 m = 0·74 m

🅔

16. 3 years   17. 4 years   18. 4 years
19. 5 years   20. 3 years   21. 3 years
22. 4 years   23. 4 years
24. 7·6 km ÷ 2 = 3·8 km   25. 5·6 km ÷ 2 = 2·8 km
26. 15·8 km ÷ 2 = 7·9 km   27. 3·2 km ÷ 2 = 1·6 km
28. 17·0 km ÷ 2 = 8·5 km   29. 19·4 km ÷ 2 = 9·7 km
30. 13·8 km ÷ 2 = 6·9 km   31. 9·2 km ÷ 2 = 4·6 km
32. 11·4 km ÷ 2 = 5·7 km

🅔

24. 3·8 km ≈ 2·4 miles   25. 2·8 km ≈ 1·8 miles
26. 7·9 km ≈ 4·9 miles   27. 1·6 km ≈ 1 mile
28. 8·5 km ≈ 5·3 miles   29. 9·7 km ≈ 6·1 miles
30. 6·9 km ≈ 4·3 miles   31. 4·6 km ≈ 2·9 miles
32. 5·7 km ≈ 3·6 miles

33. half of £8·96 = £4·48   34. half of £13·78 = £6·89
35. half of £12·46 = £6·23   36. half of £15·48 = £7·74
37. half of £4·38 = £2·19   38. half of £5·78 = £2·89
39. half of £16·98 = £8·49   40. half of £11·38 = £5·69

🅔

33. double £8·96 = £17·92   34. double £13·78 = £27·56
35. double £12·46 = £24·92   36. double £15·48 = £30·96
37. double £4·38 = £8·76   38. double £5·78 = £11·56
39. double £16·98 = £33·96   40. double £11·38 = £22·76

---

page 8
Doubling and halving   Number facts **N2**

1. £6·45 × 2 = £12·90
2. £10 − £4·85 = £5·15
3. £20 − (£4·70 × 2) = £10·60
4. £11·60 ÷ 2 = £5·80   Hawaiian
5. £22·45 − £4·70 − (£6·45 × 2) = £4·85 Napoletana
6. £4·70 + (£4·70 ÷ 2) + £5·80 + (£5·80 ÷ 2) = £15·75

---

page 9
Multiplying and dividing   Multiplication/division **N3**

1. 4·5 m × 16 m = 72 m²   2. 5·3 m × 18 m = 95·4 m²
3. 6·1 m × 14 m = 85·4 m²   4. 8·3 m × 12 m = 99·6 m²
5. 3·25 m × 36 m = 117 m²   6. 9·25 m × 32 m = 296 m²

1a.- 6a. Check children reach the same answers
        using partitioning.

7. 138 m² ÷ 6 m = 23 m   8. 372 m² ÷ 12 m = 31 m
9. 345 m² ÷ 15 m = 23 m   10. 378 m² ÷ 18 m = 21 m
11. 432 m² ÷ 16 m = 27 m   12. 490 m² ÷ 14 m = 35 m
13. 176 ÷ 9 = 19 r 5   14. 126 ÷ 8 = 15 r 6

15. 234 ÷ 6 = 39   16. 184 ÷ 15 = 12 r 4
17. 223 ÷ 13 = 17 r 2   18. 312 ÷ 12 = 26
19. 516 ÷ 21 = 24 r 12   20. 231 ÷ 18 = 12 r 15
21. 335 ÷ 11 = 30 r 5

---

page 10
Multiplying and dividing   Multiplication/division **N3**

1. 43 cm × 16 cm = 688 cm²   2. 18 cm × 23 cm = 414 cm²
3. 33 cm × 14 cm = 462 cm²   4. 37·5 cm × 22 cm = 825 cm²
5. 46·5 cm × 12 cm = 558 cm² 6. 18 cm × 6·5 cm = 117 cm²

2·37	× 1	= 2·37
2·37	× 2	= 4·74
2·37	× 4	= 9·48
2·37	× 8	= 18·96
2·37	× 16	= 37·92

7. 2·37 × 9 = 21·33   8. 2·37 × 17 = 40·29
9. 2·37 × 12 = 28·44   10. 2·37 × 7 = 16·59
11. 2·37 × 14 = 33·18   12. 2·37 × 31 = 73·47

13. 3·24 kg × 7 = 22·68 kg   14. 3·24 kg × 15 = 48·6 kg
15. 3·24 kg × 13 = 42·12 kg 16. 5·32 kg × 5 = 26·6 kg
17. 5·32 kg × 18 = 95·76 kg 18. 5·32 kg × 25 = 133 kg

19. - 22. Check that the children arrive at the following
          answers using all four methods:

18 × 26 = 468   2·45 × 12 = 29·4   3·65 × 18 = 65·7

---

page 11
Multiplying and dividing   Multiplication/division **N3**
problems

1. 16 × 32 = 512   512 balls
2. £1·80 × (2350 ÷ 2) = £2115
3. 5200 ÷ 26 = 200   200 complete rows
4. £5167·50 ÷ £32·50 = 159   159 tickets
5. £15·50 − (£1·35 × 6) = £7·40
   £7·40 ÷ 4 = £1·85   Hot dogs cost £1·85.
6. 842 kg × 8 = 105·25 kg
   The average mass is 105·25 kg.
7. £558 − £294 = £264
   £264 ÷ 12 = £22 Shorts cost £22 a pair.
8. 231 ÷ 2·75 = 84   The average speed is 84 m.p.h.

---

page 12
Equivalent fractions   Fractions **N4**

1. $\frac{3}{4} = \frac{6}{8}$ 2. $\frac{4}{5} = \frac{16}{20}$ 3. $\frac{2}{3} = \frac{8}{12}$
4. $\frac{2}{6} = \frac{1}{3}$ 5. $\frac{6}{8} = \frac{3}{4}$ 6. $\frac{1}{4} = \frac{2}{8}$
7. $\frac{8}{10} = \frac{4}{5}$ 8. $\frac{5}{12} = \frac{25}{60}$ 9. $\frac{7}{15} = \frac{14}{30}$
10. $\frac{7}{9} = \frac{14}{18}$ 11. $\frac{17}{20} = \frac{85}{100}$ 12. $\frac{19}{25} = \frac{76}{100}$
13. $\frac{4}{6} = \frac{2}{3}$ 14. $\frac{8}{12} = \frac{2}{3}$ 15. $\frac{12}{18} = \frac{2}{3}$
16. $\frac{12}{16} = \frac{3}{4}$ 17. $\frac{20}{30} = \frac{2}{3}$ 18. $\frac{9}{15} = \frac{3}{5}$
19. $\frac{7}{21} = \frac{1}{3}$ 20. $\frac{8}{20} = \frac{2}{5}$ 21. $\frac{24}{30} = \frac{4}{5}$
22. $\frac{2}{18} = \frac{1}{9}$ 23. $\frac{16}{20} = \frac{4}{5}$ 24. $\frac{6}{18} = \frac{1}{3}$
25. $\frac{21}{28} = \frac{3}{4}$ 26. $\frac{12}{36} = \frac{1}{3}$ 27. $\frac{20}{25} = \frac{4}{5}$
28. $\frac{6}{15} = \frac{2}{5}$ 29. $\frac{35}{50} = \frac{7}{10}$ 30. $\frac{28}{36} = \frac{7}{9}$
31. $\frac{72}{81} = \frac{8}{9}$ 32. $\frac{85}{100} = \frac{17}{20}$

🅔

13.-17. $\frac{4}{6} = \frac{8}{12} = \frac{12}{18} = \frac{20}{30}, \frac{12}{16}$ 18.-22. $\frac{2}{18}, \frac{7}{21}, \frac{8}{20}, \frac{9}{15}, \frac{24}{30}$

23.-27. $\frac{6}{18} = \frac{12}{36}, \frac{21}{28}, \frac{16}{20} = \frac{20}{25}$ 28.-32. $\frac{6}{15}, \frac{35}{50}, \frac{28}{36}, \frac{85}{100}, \frac{72}{81}$

33. $\frac{2}{5} = \frac{4}{10}, \frac{3}{10} < \frac{4}{10}, \frac{3}{10} < \frac{2}{5}$
34. $\frac{2}{3} = \frac{4}{6}, \frac{4}{6} < \frac{5}{6}, \frac{2}{3} < \frac{5}{6}$
35. $\frac{3}{4} = \frac{6}{8}, \frac{5}{8} < \frac{6}{8}, \frac{5}{8} < \frac{3}{4}$
36. $\frac{1}{2} = \frac{3}{6}, \frac{3}{6} < \frac{5}{6}, \frac{1}{2} < \frac{5}{6}$
37. $\frac{2}{3} = \frac{6}{9}, \frac{6}{9} < \frac{7}{9}, \frac{2}{3} < \frac{7}{9}$

38. $\frac{5}{7} = \frac{10}{14}$, $\frac{10}{14} < \frac{11}{14}$, $\frac{5}{7} < \frac{11}{14}$

39. $\frac{3}{4} = \frac{9}{12}$, $\frac{2}{3} = \frac{8}{12}$, $\frac{8}{12} < \frac{9}{12}$, $\frac{2}{3} < \frac{3}{4}$

40. $\frac{1}{2} = \frac{5}{10}$, $\frac{3}{5} = \frac{6}{10}$, $\frac{5}{10} < \frac{6}{10}$, $\frac{1}{2} < \frac{3}{5}$

41. $\frac{1}{2} = \frac{3}{6}$, $\frac{2}{3} = \frac{4}{6}$, $\frac{3}{6} < \frac{4}{6}$, $\frac{1}{2} < \frac{2}{3}$

42. $\frac{3}{4} = \frac{15}{20}$, $\frac{4}{5} = \frac{16}{20}$, $\frac{15}{20} < \frac{16}{20}$, $\frac{3}{4} < \frac{4}{5}$

43. $\frac{2}{3} = \frac{20}{30}$, $\frac{7}{10} = \frac{21}{30}$, $\frac{20}{30} < \frac{21}{30}$, $\frac{2}{3} < \frac{7}{10}$

44. $\frac{31}{50} = \frac{62}{100}$, $\frac{62}{100} < \frac{63}{100}$, $\frac{31}{50} < \frac{63}{100}$

page 13

Fractions **N4**

Equivalent fractions

1. $\frac{2}{8}, \frac{4}{8}, \frac{3}{8}$
2. $\frac{2}{6}, \frac{3}{6}, \frac{5}{6}$
3. $\frac{6}{10}, \frac{5}{10}, \frac{7}{10}$
4. $\frac{4}{12}, \frac{3}{12}, \frac{5}{12}$
5. $\frac{10}{12}, \frac{11}{12}, \frac{9}{12}$
6. $\frac{8}{12}, \frac{6}{12}, \frac{7}{12}$
7. $\frac{9}{15}, \frac{10}{15}, \frac{11}{15}$
8. $\frac{8}{24}, \frac{9}{24}, \frac{6}{24}$
9. $\frac{8}{12}, \frac{10}{12}, \frac{3}{12}$
10. $\frac{9}{20}, \frac{8}{20}, \frac{5}{20}$
11. $\frac{40}{60}, \frac{45}{60}, \frac{48}{60}$
12. $\frac{20}{30}, \frac{15}{30}, \frac{25}{30}$
13. $\frac{10}{30}, \frac{12}{30}, \frac{25}{30}$
14. $\frac{55}{100}, \frac{60}{100}, \frac{76}{100}$
15. $\frac{32}{40}, \frac{35}{40}, \frac{34}{40}$

1. $\frac{4}{8} - \frac{2}{8} = \frac{2}{8} = \frac{1}{4}$
2. $\frac{5}{6} - \frac{2}{6} = \frac{3}{6} = \frac{1}{2}$
3. $\frac{7}{10} - \frac{5}{10} = \frac{2}{10} = \frac{1}{5}$
4. $\frac{5}{12} - \frac{3}{12} = \frac{2}{12} = \frac{1}{6}$
5. $\frac{11}{12} - \frac{9}{12} = \frac{2}{12} = \frac{1}{6}$
6. $\frac{8}{12} - \frac{6}{12} = \frac{2}{12} = \frac{1}{6}$
7. $\frac{11}{15} - \frac{9}{15} = \frac{2}{15}$
8. $\frac{9}{24} - \frac{6}{24} = \frac{3}{24} = \frac{1}{8}$
9. $\frac{10}{12} - \frac{3}{12} = \frac{7}{12}$
10. $\frac{9}{20} - \frac{5}{20} = \frac{4}{20} = \frac{1}{5}$
11. $\frac{48}{60} - \frac{40}{60} = \frac{8}{60} = \frac{2}{15}$
12. $\frac{25}{30} - \frac{15}{30} = \frac{10}{30} = \frac{1}{3}$
13. $\frac{25}{30} - \frac{10}{30} = \frac{15}{30} = \frac{1}{2}$
14. $\frac{76}{100} - \frac{55}{100} = \frac{21}{100}$
15. $\frac{35}{40} - \frac{32}{40} = \frac{3}{40}$
16. $1 - (\frac{1}{3} + \frac{1}{4}) = 1 - (\frac{4}{12} + \frac{3}{12}) = \frac{5}{12}$
17. $1 - (\frac{1}{3} + \frac{1}{6}) = 1 - (\frac{2}{6} + \frac{1}{6}) = \frac{3}{6} = \frac{1}{2}$
18. $1 - (\frac{3}{8} + \frac{1}{4}) = 1 - (\frac{3}{8} + \frac{2}{8}) = \frac{3}{8}$
19. $1 - (\frac{1}{2} + \frac{1}{3} + \frac{1}{8}) = 1 - (\frac{12}{24} + \frac{8}{24} + \frac{3}{24}) = \frac{1}{24}$

Explore
Answers will vary

page 14

Addition/subtraction **N5**

Adding

1. 4.6 kg + 4.8 kg = 9·4 kg
2. 6.7 kg + 6.4 kg = 13·1 kg
3. 8.7 kg + 8.9 kg = 17·6 kg
4. 5.36 kg + 5.38 kg = 10·74 kg
5. 6.69 kg + 6.72 kg = 13·41 kg
6. 8.54 kg + 8.51 kg = 17·05 kg
7. 4.9 l + 8.3 l = 13·2 l
8. 5.74 l + 2.6 l = 8·34 l
9. 7.57 l + 4.6 l = 12·17 l
10. 3.27 l + 1.46 l = 4·73 l
11. 5.83 l + 2.43 l = 8·26 l
12. 7.28 l + 2.83 l = 10·11 l
13. 7.3 km + 2.9 km = 10·2 km
14. 8.63 km + 4.8 km = 13·43 km
15. 6.29 km + 3.7 km = 9·99 km
16. 5.35 km + 1.95 km = 7·3 km
17. 4.28 km + 3.87 km = 8·15 km
18. 19.36 km + 2.78 km = 22·14 km

Check the children have used subtraction correctly.

page 15

Addition/subtraction **N5**

Subtracting

1. 8.3 s − 4.8 s = 3·5 s
2. 6.5 s + 2.7 s = 3·8 s
3. 6.52 s − 3.8 s = 2·72 s
4. 11.73 s − 5.3 s = 6·43 s
5. 6.59 s − 2.84 s = 3·75 s
6. 19.49 s − 13.96 s = 5·53 s
7. 9.4 m − 4.7 m = 4·7 m
8. 11.3 m − 6.6 m = 4·7 m
9. 14.35 m − 6.8 m = 7·55 m
10. 8.34 m − 2.8 m = 5·54 m
11. 4.78 m − 1.34 m = 3·44 m
12. 15.29 m − 6.77 m = 8·52 m

Check that children have checked three answers correctly.

7a - 12a Check the children's methods.

13. 9.7 − 3.8 = 5·9
14. 4.65 + 1.56 = 6·21
15. 7.45 − 0.15 = 7.3÷2 = 3·65
16. 7.81 − 2.9 = 4·91
17. 3.8 + 1.85 = 5·65
18. 12.66 − 9.82 = 2.84÷2 = 1·42

page 16

Addition/subtraction **N5**

Adding and subtracting

1. 3.45 m − 1.7 m = 1·75 m
2. 4.67 m + 0.82 m = 5·49 m
3. 5.4 m − 0.65 m = 4·75 m
4. 4.08 m − 3.9 m = 0·18 m
5. 3.97 m + 0.46 m = 4·43 m
6. 3.6 m + 1.99 m = 5·59 m
7. 2980 × 1p = 2980 p = £29·80
   a. £29·80 − £15·99 = £13·81
   b. £29·80 − £6·75 = £23·05
   c. £29·80 − £11.49 = £18·31
   d. £29·80 − £0·95 = £28·85
8. 845 × 2p = 1690p = £16·90
   a. £16·90 − £15·99 = £0·91
   b. £16·90 − £6·75 = £10·15
   c. £16·90 − £11.49 = £5·41
   d. £16·90 − £0·95 = £15·95
9. 434 ×5p = 2170p = £21·70
   a. £21·70 − £15·99 = £5·71
   b. £21·70 − £6·75 = £14·95
   c. £21·70 − £11.49 = £10·21
   d. £21·70 − £0·95 = £20·75

page 17

Factors and primes **N6**

Factors and primes

1. 23247, 23547 or 23847
2. 5256
3. 27560 or 27565
4. 15260, 15264 or 15268
5. 372 or 376
6. 532670, 532672, 532674, 532676 or 532678
7. 272196, 275196 or 278196
8. 7063
9. 232 or 272
10. 474

11. 1, 82   2, 41
12. 1, 75   3, 25   5, 15,
13. 1, 108   2, 54   3, 36   4, 27   6, 18   9, 12
14. 1, 145   5, 29
15. 1, 188   2, 94   4, 47
16. 1, 221   13, 17
17. 1, 103
18. 1, 94   2, 47
19. 2
20. 2, 4
21. 3, 5, 15
22. 2, 4, 8
23. 2
24. 2, 3, 4, 6, 8, 12, 24
25. 2, 5, 10
26. 3, 9
27. 7

Explore
Answers will vary. For example, for 12 the largest product possible is 36 (6 × 6) for the sum of two numbers, or 60 (3 × 4 × 5) for the sum of three numbers.
Check that the children have worked logically. The maximum product is created when the two multipliers are equal (even start numbers) or consecutive (odd start

ANSWERS

numbers). For three multipliers the maximum product is created with consecutive numbers.

page 18
Factors and primes

1. 23	**2.** 37	**3.** 11	**4.** 17
5. 11	**6.** 43	**7.** 19	**8.** 59
9. 41	**10.** 71	**11.** 97	**12.** 101

13. $270 = 2 \times 3 \times 3 \times 3 \times 5$
14. $1690 = 2 \times 5 \times 13 \times 13$
15. $976 = 2 \times 2 \times 2 \times 2 \times 61$
16. $837 = 3 \times 3 \times 3 \times 31$
17. $2500 = 2 \times 2 \times 5 \times 5 \times 5 \times 5$
18. $2662 = 2 \times 11 \times 11 \times 11$
19. $4332 = 2 \times 2 \times 3 \times 19 \times 19$
20. $30030 = 2 \times 3 \times 5 \times 7 \times 11 \times 13$

21. 4 or 16	**22.** 4	**23.** 15	**24.** 2
25. 6	**26.** 15	**27.** 16	**28.** 37
29. 23	**30.** 19		

Explore
Answers will vary. Pairs of consecutive odd numbers which are both prime numbers, up to 200 are:

3, 5	5, 7	11, 13	17, 19
29, 31	41, 43	59, 61	71, 73
101, 103	107, 109	137, 139	149, 151
179, 181	191, 193	197, 199	

page 19
Multiplying and dividing by 10, 100 and 1000

1. $10 \times 0.4 = 4$
2. $5.7 \div 10 = 0.57$
3. $0.8 \times 10 = 8$
4. $10 \times 4.6 = 46$
5. $100 \times 3.25 = 325$
6. $10 \times 7.68 = 76.8$
7. $4.32 \div 10 = 0.432$
8. $4.57 \times 1000 = 4570$
9. $28.6 \div 10 = 2.86$
10. $1.8 \div 100 = 0.018$
11. $6 \div 10 = 0.6$
12. $2.79 \times 10 = 27.9$
13. $39.4 \div 1000 = 0.0394$
14. $1000 \times 2.71 = 2710$
15. $18 \div 1000 = 0.018$
16. $10 \times 43.7 = 437$
17. $472 \div 100 = 4.72$
18. $39.4 \div 10 = 3.94$
19. $9.01 \times 10 = 90.1$
20. $4.17 \div 1000 = 0.00417$
21. $2.87 \times 100 = 287$
22. $31.6 \div 100 = 0.316$
23. $456 \div 1000 = 0.456$
24. $4.38 \times 10 = 43.8$
25. $7.65 \div 10 = 0.765$
26. $0.83 \times 1000 = 830$
27. $1.93 \times 100 = 193$
28. $71.5 \div 1000 = 0.0715$
29. $27.6 \div 10 = 2.76$
30. $8.72 \div 100 = 0.0872$
31. $0.35 \times 100 = 35$
32. $5.46 \times 1000 = 5460$

✐

21. $28.7 \div 10 = 28.7 \times 0.1 = 2.87$
22. $31.6 \div 10 = 31.6 \times 0.1 = 3.16$
23. $456 \div 100 = 456 \times 0.01 = 4.5$
24. $4.38 \times 1 = 4.38 \div 1 = 4.38$
25. $7.65 \times 1 = 7.65 \div 1 = 7.65$
26. $0.83 \times 10 = 0.83 \div 0.1 = 8.3$
27. $1.93 \times 1 = 1.93 \div 1 = 1.93$
28. $71.5 \div 10 = 71.5 \times 0.1 = 7.15$
29. $27.6 \div 10 = 27.6 \times 0.1 = 2.76$
30. $8.72 \times 1 = 8.72 \div 1 = 8.72$
31. $0.35 \times 10 = 0.35 \div 0.1 = 3.5$
32. $5.46 \times 1 = 5.46 \div 1 = 5.46$
33. $2.47 \text{ kg} \div 1000 = 0.00247 \text{ kg} = 2.47\text{g}$ each
34. £57.60 $\div 10$ = £5.76, £10 − £5.76 = £4.24, £4.24 change
35. $38.6 \text{ km} \div 100 = 0.386 \text{ km} = 386 \text{ m}$

page 20
Multiplying and dividing by 0·1 and 0·01

1. $5.2 \times 0.1 = 0.52$
2. $8.6 \div 0.1 = 86$
3. $2.3 \times 0.01 = 0.023$
4. $56.7 \times 0.01 = 0.567$
5. $2.3 \div 0.01 = 230$
6. $11 \div 0.1 = 110$
7. $72.3 \div 0.1 = 723$
8. $7 \times 0.1 = 0.7$
9. $15.7 \div 0.01 = 1570$
10. $138 \times 0.01 = 1.38$
11. $0.83 \div 0.01 = 83$
12. $8.35 \times 0.1 = 0.835$
13. $46.7 \times 0.1 = 4.67$
14. $432 \div 0.1 = 4320$
15. $9.62 \div 0.01 = 962$
16. $5.64 \div 0.1 = 56.4$
17. $4 \times 0.01 = 0.04$
18. $10 \div 0.01 = 1000$
19. $5.6 \times 0.1 = 0.56$
20. $7.83 \times 0.01 = 0.0783$
21. $8.3 \div 0.1 = 83$
22. $56.2 \times 0.01 = 0.562$
23. $42.8 \div 0.01 = 4280$
24. $2.7 \times 0.01 = 0.027$
25. $19.4 \div 0.1 = 194$
26. $143 \times 0.01 = 1.43$
27. $396 \div 0.01 = 39600$
28. $0.28 \div 0.01 = 28.0$

29. $0.4 \div 10 = 0.04$ $400 \times 0.01 = 4$ false
30. $1.7 \times 0.1 = 0.17$ $0.017 \div 0.1 = 0.17$ true
31. $5.62 \div 0.01 = 562$ $5620 \times 0.1 = 562$ true
32. $38.3 \times 0.01 = 0.383$ $3.83 \div 0.1 = 38.3$ false
33. $174 \div 0.1 = 1740$ $174000 \times 0.01 = 1740$ true
34. $14.71 \times 0.1 = 1.471$ $1.471 \times 10 = 14.71$ false
35. $96.8 \div 0.01 = 9680$ $9.68 \times 1000 = 9680$ true
36. $4030 \times 0.01 = 40.3$ $4.03 \times 100 = 403$ false
37. $127.51 \div 100 = 1.2751$ $0.12751 \div 0.1 = 1.2751$ true
38. $0.043 \times 1000 = 43$ $0.43 \div 0.01 = 43$ true

page 21
Multiplying fractions

1. $\frac{2}{3}$ of £24 = £16
2. $\frac{3}{4}$ of £24 = £18
3. $\frac{5}{6}$ of £24 = £20
4. $\frac{7}{8}$ of £24 = £21
5. $\frac{7}{10}$ of £20 = £14
6. $\frac{3}{5}$ of £20 = £12
7. $\frac{3}{4}$ of £20 = £15
8. $\frac{6}{5}$ of £20 = £24
9. $\frac{2}{3}$ of £36 = £24
10. $\frac{5}{6}$ of £36 = £30
11. $\frac{3}{4}$ of £36 = £27
12. $\frac{7}{12}$ of £36 = £21
13. $\frac{3}{5}$ of £30 = £18
14. $\frac{2}{3}$ of £30 = £20
15. $\frac{5}{6}$ of £30 = £25
16. $\frac{4}{15}$ of £30 = £8
17. $\frac{2}{3} \times 12 = 8$
18. $\frac{3}{4} \times 8 = 6$
19. $\frac{4}{5} \times 20 = 16$
20. $\frac{5}{6} \times 18 = 15$
21. $\frac{3}{7} \times 14 = 6$
22. $\frac{5}{8} \times 24 = 15$
23. $15 \times \frac{3}{5} = 9$
24. $16 \times \frac{3}{8} = 6$
25. $30 \times \frac{7}{10} = 21$
26. $18 \times \frac{7}{9} = 14$
27. $21 \times \frac{5}{7} = 15$
28. $9 \times \frac{1}{6} = \frac{3}{2} = 1\frac{1}{2}$
29. $\frac{1}{3} \times 24 = 8$
30. $\frac{1}{2} \times 40 = 20$

31. $\frac{1}{8} \times 32 = 4$ **32.** $\frac{1}{5} \times 15 = 3$

33. $\frac{2}{3} \times 9 = 6$ **34.** $\frac{3}{4} \times 12 = 9$

35. $10 \times \frac{4}{5} = 8$ **36.** $12 \times \frac{5}{6} = 10$

37. $15 \times \frac{2}{3} = 10$ **38.** $20 \times \frac{4}{5} = 16$

---

page 22
Multiplying fractions
Fractions **N8**

1.

×	9	15	8	12
$\frac{2}{3}$	6	10	$5\frac{1}{3}$	8
$\frac{1}{4}$	$2\frac{1}{4}$	$3\frac{3}{4}$	2	3
$\frac{3}{5}$	$5\frac{2}{5}$	9	$4\frac{4}{5}$	$7\frac{1}{5}$
$\frac{5}{6}$	$7\frac{1}{2}$	$12\frac{1}{2}$	$6\frac{2}{3}$	10

2.

×	$\frac{1}{6}$	$\frac{3}{4}$	$\frac{4}{5}$	$\frac{7}{10}$
20	$3\frac{1}{3}$	15	16	14
16	$2\frac{2}{3}$	12	$12\frac{4}{5}$	$11\frac{1}{5}$
6	1	$4\frac{1}{2}$	$4\frac{4}{5}$	$4\frac{1}{5}$
30	5	$22\frac{1}{2}$	24	21

3. ABC   A $\frac{3}{5} \times 10 = 6$ B $12 \times \frac{2}{3} = 8$ C $\frac{5}{8}$ of $16 = 10$

4. DFE   D $\frac{4}{9}$ of $18 = 8$ E $\frac{6}{7} \times 14 = 12$ F $15 \times \frac{3}{4} = 11\frac{1}{4}$

5. HIG   G $12 \times \frac{5}{6} = 10$ H $\frac{3}{8}$ of $16 = 6$ I $\frac{4}{7} \times 14 = 8$

6. JKL   J $\frac{3}{4}$ of $7 = 5\frac{1}{4}$ K $\frac{2}{3} \times 8 = 5\frac{1}{3}$ L $10 \times \frac{4}{5} = 8$

7. NOM   M $\frac{4}{5} \times 11 = 8\frac{4}{5}$ N $10 \times \frac{3}{4} = 7\frac{1}{2}$ O $\frac{1}{6}$ of $48 = 8$

Explore
Answers will vary.

---

page 23
Fractions problems
Fractions **N8**

1. $\frac{1}{3}$ of £12 = £4, £12 – £4 = £8, $\frac{3}{4}$ of £8 = £6, £8 – £6 = £2

David spends £2 on sweets.

2. 20 is $\frac{4}{5}$ of Class 6, $20 = \frac{4}{5} \times 25$, 25 – 20 = 5 children go home.

3. $20 = \frac{1}{4}$ of 80   There are 80 sweets in the bag.

4. 210 – (30 + 60) = 120, $\frac{120}{210} = \frac{4}{7}$, $\frac{4}{7}$ of the pupils walk.

5. £15 = $\frac{1}{3}$ of £45, £45 left after holiday and clothes

£45 = $\frac{3}{4}$ of £60, £60 left after holiday

£60 = $\frac{1}{2}$ of £120, Josh started with £120.

6. 3600 m – 450 m = 3150 m $\frac{3150}{3600} = \frac{7}{8}$ left to run.

7. $\frac{2}{5}$ of 30 = 12, $\frac{4}{15}$ of 30 = 8, $\frac{1}{3}$ of 30 = 10

The boat trip gets the most votes.

8. Carolyn is at school for 6 hours.

$6 - (\frac{1}{4} + \frac{5}{6} + \frac{1}{3}) = 6 - (\frac{3}{12} + \frac{10}{12} + \frac{4}{12}) = 4\frac{7}{12}$ hr = 4 hours 35 minutes

---

page 24
Dividing
Division **N9**

1. $30 \div 5 = 6$ **2.** $17 \div 5 = 3\frac{2}{5} = 3\cdot4$ **3.** $15 \div 5 = 3$

4. $41 \div 5 = 8\frac{1}{5} = 8\cdot2$ **5.** $29 \div 5 = 5\frac{4}{5} = 5\cdot8$

1. a. $30 \div 10 = 3$ b. $30 \div 2 = 15$
c. $30 \div 100 = \frac{3}{10} = 0\cdot3$ d. $30 \div 20 = 1\frac{1}{2} = 1\cdot5$
e. $30 \div 4 = 7\frac{1}{2} = 7\cdot5$

2. a. $17 \div 10 = 1\frac{7}{10} = 1\cdot7$ b. $17 \div 2 = 8\frac{1}{2} = 8\cdot5$
c. $17 \div 100 = \frac{17}{100} = 0\cdot17$ d. $17 \div 20 = \frac{17}{20} = 0\cdot85$
e. $17 \div 4 = 4\frac{1}{4} = 4\cdot25$

3. a. $15 \div 10 = 1\frac{1}{2} = 1\cdot5$ b. $15 \div 2 = 7\frac{1}{2} = 7\cdot5$
c. $15 \div 100 = \frac{3}{20} = 0\cdot15$ d. $15 \div 20 = \frac{3}{4} = 0\cdot75$
e. $15 \div 4 = 3\frac{3}{4} = 3\cdot75$

4. a. $41 \div 10 = 4\frac{1}{10} = 4\cdot1$ b. $41 \div 2 = 20\frac{1}{2} = 20\cdot5$
c. $41 \div 100 = \frac{41}{100} = 0\cdot41$ d. $41 \div 20 = 2\frac{1}{20} = 2\cdot05$
e. $41 \div 4 = 10\frac{1}{4} = 10\cdot25$

5. a. $29 \div 10 = 2\frac{9}{10} = 2\cdot9$ b. $29 \div 2 = 14\frac{1}{2} = 14\cdot5$
c. $29 \div 100 = \frac{29}{100} = 0\cdot29$ d. $29 \div 20 = 1\frac{9}{20} = 1\cdot45$
e. $29 \div 4 = 7\frac{1}{4} = 7\cdot25$

6. $17 \div 2 = 8\cdot5$ **7.** $193 \div 100 = 1\cdot93$

8. $81 \div 10 = 8\cdot1$ **9.** $151 \div 2 = 75\cdot5$

10. $23 \div 4 = 5\cdot75$ **11.** $41 \div 4 = 10\cdot25$

12. $117 \div 20 = 5\cdot85$ **13.** $\frac{33}{5} = 6\cdot6$

14. $\frac{47}{4} = 11\cdot75$ **15.** $\frac{63}{2} = 31\cdot5$

16. $\frac{51}{10} = 5\cdot1$ **17.** $\frac{73}{20} = 3\cdot65$

18. 0·125, 0·25, 0·375, 0·5, 0·625, 0·75, 0·875

19. $46 \div 8 = 5\cdot75$ **20.** $33 \div 8 = 4\cdot125$

21. $15 \div 8 = 1\cdot875$ **22.** $70 \div 8 = 8\cdot75$

23. $\frac{55}{8} = 6\cdot875$ **24.** $17 \div 8 = 2\cdot125$

25. $29 \div 8 = 3\cdot625$ **26.** $87 \div 8 = 10\cdot875$

27. $92 \div 13 = 7$ r 1   8 buses needed
28. $114 \div 12 = 9$ r 6   10 buses needed
29. $74 \div 14 = 5$ r 4   6 buses needed
30. $168 \div 15 = 11$ r 3   12 buses needed
31. $136 \div 11 = 12$ r 4   13 buses needed
32. $87 \div 9 = 9$ r 6   10 buses needed

27. $92 \div 16 = 5$ r 12   6 buses needed
28. $114 \div 16 = 7$ r 2   8 buses needed
29. $74 \div 16 = 4$ r 10   5 buses needed
30. $168 \div 16 = 10$ r 8   11 buses needed
31. $136 \div 16 = 8$ r 8   9 buses needed
32. $87 \div 16 = 5$ r 7   6 buses needed

---

page 25
Dividing
Division **N9**

Answers rounded to 2 d.p.

1. £137 ÷ 6 = £22·83   **2.** £128 ÷ 9 = £14·22
3. £209 ÷ 8 = £26·13   **4.** £189 ÷ 11 = £17·18
5. £146 ÷ 7 = £20·86   **6.** £393 ÷ 12 = £32·75

1. £23   **2.** £14   **3.** £26   **4.** £17   **5.** £21   **6.** £33

7. $84 ÷ 8 = 10\frac{1}{2}$ days

8. $94 ÷ 6 = 15\frac{2}{3}$ days

9. $102 ÷ 9 = 11\frac{1}{3}$ days

10. $105 ÷ 4 = 26\frac{1}{4}$ days

11. $66 ÷ 7 = 9\frac{3}{7}$ days

12. $206 ÷ 8 = 25\frac{3}{4}$ days

Explore

All possible answers are listed.

$\frac{1}{2} = 0.5$	$\frac{1}{4} = 0.25$	$\frac{1}{5} = 0.2$	$\frac{2}{4} = 0.5$
$\frac{2}{5} = 0.4$	$\frac{3}{2} = 1.5$	$\frac{3}{4} = 0.75$	$\frac{3}{5} = 0.6$
$\frac{3}{6} = 0.5$	$\frac{4}{5} = 0.8$	$\frac{4}{8} = 0.5$	$\frac{6}{4} = 1.5$
$\frac{6}{5} = 1.2$	$\frac{6}{8} = 0.75$	$\frac{7}{2} = 3.5$	$\frac{7}{5} = 1.4$
$\frac{8}{5} = 1.6$	$\frac{9}{2} = 4.5$	$\frac{9}{5} = 1.8$	$\frac{9}{6} = 1.5$
$\frac{13}{2} = 6.5$	$\frac{17}{2} = 8.5$	$\frac{10}{4} = 2.5$	$\frac{30}{4} = 7.5$
$\frac{38}{4} = 9.5$	$\frac{13}{5} = 2.6$	$\frac{14}{5} = 2.8$	$\frac{16}{5} = 3.2$
$\frac{17}{5} = 3.4$	$\frac{18}{5} = 3.6$	$\frac{19}{5} = 3.8$	$\frac{23}{5} = 4.6$
$\frac{31}{5} = 6.2$	$\frac{32}{5} = 6.4$	$\frac{34}{5} = 6.8$	$\frac{36}{5} = 7.2$
$\frac{37}{5} = 7.4$	$\frac{38}{5} = 7.6$	$\frac{39}{57} = 7.8$	$\frac{41}{5} = 8.2$
$\frac{43}{5} = 8.6$	$\frac{46}{5} = 9.2$	$\frac{48}{5} = 9.6$	$\frac{21}{6} = 3.5$
$\frac{27}{6} = 4.5$	$\frac{36}{8} = 4.5$	$\frac{60}{8} = 7.5$	$\frac{76}{8} = 9.5$

---

page 26
Dividing
Division **N9**

1. £150 ÷ £23 = 6 r 12
John needs to work for 7 weeks.

2. 320 ÷ 12 = 26 r 8   Ruth can sell 26 packs.
26 × £1·50 = £39
Ruth will earn £39 if she sells all the packs.

3. 85 ÷ 7 = 12 r 1
Gary must make 13 trips to move all the bricks.

4. 470 km ÷ 9 km = 52 r 2
53 people are needed to complete the walk.

5. 230 ÷ 9 = 25 r 5
230 passengers will take up 25 complete rows.

6. 258 ÷ 6 = 43
Sally needs to buy at least 43 packs of stickers.

7. 237 ÷ 12 = 19 r 8
The minibus needs to make 20 trips.

8. £16 ÷ 23p = 1600p ÷ 23p = 69 r 13
Pinda can buy 69 cans.

Explore

Answers will vary. Dividing any number which is not a multiple of 3 by a multiple of 3 will give an answer with a 1-digit recurring decimal. Dividing any number which is not a multiple of 11 by a multiple of 11 will give an answer with a 2-digit recurring decimal.

Decimal numbers

1. 3·2, 3·45, 3·6, 3·65, 3·7   **2.** 5·6, 5·61, 5·635, 5·645, 5·68

3. 3·24 < 3·25 < 3·26   **4.** 6·92 < 7·16 < 7·4

5. 4·27 < 4·5 < 5·4   **6.** 4·09 < 4·85 < 4·9

7. 23·451 < 23·54 < 24·351   **8.** 5·06 < 5·1 < 5·61

9. 3·236 < 3·24 < 3·62   **10.** 6·475 < 6·477 < 6·48

11. 34·45 cm, 34·454 cm, 34·5 cm, 34·54 cm, 35·4 cm

12. 1·4 kg, 1·415 kg, 1·45 kg, 1·5 kg, 1·54 kg

13. 28 cm, 28·45 cm, 28·591 cm, 28·6 cm, 29·1 cm

14. 6·455 cm, 6·5 cm, 6·504 cm, 6·545 cm, 6·55 cm

Explore

Answers will vary. Using cards 1 to 9 there are 504 numbers between 1 and 5.

---

page 28
Adding and subtracting decimals **N10**
Adding and subtracting decimals

1. 3·8, 3·9, 4·0, 4·1, 4·2, 4·3

2. 4·96, 4·97, 4·98, 4·99, 5·00, 5·01

3. 2·3, 2·2, 2·1, 2·0, 1·9, 1·8

4. 5·03, 5·02, 5·01, 5·00, 4·99, 4·98

5. 5·8 − 0·1 = 5·7   **6.** 3 − 0·1 = 2·9

7. 8·35 + 0·1 = 8·45   **8.** 4·26 + 0·01 = 4·27

9. 9·24 − 0·01 = 9·23   **10.** 4·63 − 0·1 = 4·53

11. 3·99 + 0·01 = 4   **12.** 7·96 + 0·1 = 8·06

13. 4·1 − 0·01 = 4·09   **14.** 5·8 + 0·01 = 5·81

15. 6 − 0·01 = 5·99   **16.** 6·325 + 0·01 = 6·335

17. 2·948 + 0·1 = 3·048   **18.** 5·736 − 0·1 = 5·636

19. 3·072 − 0·1 = 2·972

20. 16·57 + 0·1 = 16·67   **21.** 16·57 + 10 = 26·57

22. 16·57 + 0·43 = 17   **23.** 16·57 + 0·01 = 16·58

24. 16·57 + 1 = 17·57   **25.** 4·99 + 0·1 = 5·09

26. 4·99 + 0·01 = 5   **27.** 4·99 + 1 = 5·99

28. 4·99 + 10 = 14·99   **29.** 4·99 + 5·01 = 10

30. 3·22 − 1 = 2·22   **31.** 3·22 − 0·1 = 3·12

32. 3·22 − 0·01 = 3·21   **33.** 3·22 − 0·22 = 3

34. 3·22 − 0·3 = 2·92   **35.** 5·04 − 1 = 4·04

36. 5·04 − 0·04 = 5   **37.** 5·04 − 0·1 = 4·94

38. 5·04 − 0·01 = 5·03   **39.** 5·04 − 0·94 = 4·1

---

page 29
Decimals **N10**
Adding and subtracting decimals

1. 1·85 kg + 0·03 kg = 1·88 kg

2. 2·34 kg + 0·03 kg = 2·37 kg

3. 3·7 kg + 0·03 kg = 3·73 kg

4. 2·98 kg + 0·03 kg = 3·01 kg

5. 1·28 l − 0·07 l = 1·21 l

6. 1·34 l − 0·07 l = 1·27 l

7. 2·5 l − 0·07 l = 2·43 l

8. 2·435 l − 0·07 l = 2·365 l

9. 2·7 km + 0·087 km = 2·787 km

10. 3·41 km + 0·087 km = 3·497 km

11. 4·572 km + 0·087 km = 4·659 km

12. 5·64 km + 0·087 km = 5·727 km

13. 2·565 m − 0·045 m = 2·52 m

14. 1·67 m − 0·045 m = 1·625 m

15. 2·42 m − 0·045 m = 2·375 m

16. 3·2 m − 0·045 m = 3·155 m

page 30
Adding decimals

 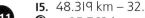

1. 5·723 + 2·869 = 8·592
2. 7·358 + 0·496 = 7·854
3. 6·379 + 5·284 = 11·663
4. 7·146 + 2·397 + 0·485 = 10·028
5. 8·716 + 9·485 + 1·397 = 19·598
6. 2·168 + 4·379 + 5·286 = 11·833
7. 1·762 kg + 3·546 kg = 5·308 kg
8. 0·356 kg + 4·73 kg = 5·086 kg
9. 2·540 kg + 0·48 kg = 3·02 kg
10. 1·762 kg + 0·356 kg + 2·540 kg = 4·658 kg
11. 3·546 kg + 0·356 kg + 4·73 kg = 8·632 kg
12. 2·540 kg + 3·546 kg + 0·356 kg + 1·762 kg = 8·204 kg
13. 31·8 + 2·746 = 34·546
14. 15·8 + 0·973 + 1·46 = 18·233
15. 2·794 + 13·86 + 143·7 = 160·354
16. 0·058 + 15·9 + 6·73 + 5·492 = 28·18
17. 13 + 7·654 + 2·8 = 23·454
18. 9·3 + 7·582 + 15·6 + 23 + 0·49 = 55·972

page 31
Adding decimals

1. 1·324 m + 0·763 m = 2·087 m
2. 1·582 m + 2·346 m = 3·928 m
3. 1·86 m + 1·39 m = 3·25 m
4. 0·46 m + 0·852 m + 1·7 m = 3·012 m
5. 0·658 m + 1·27 m + 0·69 m = 2·618 m
6. 1·356 m + 0·782 m + 0·552 m = 2·69 m
7. 2·356 l + 0·857 l + 1·6 l + 2·78 l = 7·593 l
   10 l − 7·593 l = 2·407 l
   Danny must drink 2·407 l on Friday.
8. (2 × 2·436 km) + (2 × 1·728 km) + (2 × 0·874) = 4·872 km + 3·456 km + 1·748 km = 10·076km
   Billie has cycled 10·076 km.

Explore

All possible answers are listed. There are 5 different totals.
   1·234 + 9·876 = 11·11
   4·321 + 8·765 = 13·086
   4·321 + 9·876 = 14·197
   4·321 + 6·789 = 11·11
   5·432 + 9·876 = 15·308
   5·432 + 6·789 = 12·221
   2·345 + 9·876 = 12·221

page 32
Subtracting decimals

1. 5·723 − 1·468 = 4·255
2. 6·947 −2·319 = 4·628
3. 4·735 − 2·596 = 2·139
4. 21·647 − 14·358 = 7·289
5. 19·741 − 8·394 = 11·347
6. 11·526 − 7·683 = 3·843
7. 4·392 − 0·168 = 4·224
8. 12·704 − 9·351 = 3·353
9. 8·006 − 1·278 = 6·728
10. 25·763 km − 13·275 km = 12·488 km
11. 11·751 km − 8·346 km = 3·405 km
12. 16·348 km − 5·271 km = 11·077 km
13. 12·562 km − 9·347 km = 3·215 km
14. 24·385 km − 9·471 km = 14·914 km

15. 48.319 km − 32.564 km = 15.755 km
10. 25·763 km + 13·275 km = 39·038 km
    39·038 km ÷ 2 = 19·519 km
11. 11·751 km + 8.346 km = 20·097 km
    20·097 km ÷ 2 = 10·0485 km
12. 16·348 km + 5·271 km = 21·619 km
    21·619 km ÷ 2 =10·8095 km
13. 12·562 km + 9.347 km = 21·909 km
    21·909 km ÷ 2 = 10·9545 km
14. 24·385 km + 9·471 km = 33·856 km
    33·856 km ÷ 2 = 16·928 km
15. 48·319 km + 32·564 km = 80·883 km
    80·883 km ÷ 2 = 40·4415 km

page 33
Subtracting decimals

1. 6·42 − 5·358 = 1·062
2. 7·16 − 3·472 = 3·688
3. 5·04 − 2·751 = 2·289
4. 11·8 − 1·653 = 10·147
5. 14·3 − 10·546 = 3·754
6. 9·7 − 4·308 = 5·392
7. 15·04 − 4·365 = 10·675
8. 10·03 − 4·549 = 5·481
9. 8·0 − 4·652 = 3·348

1. 1·06
2. 3·69
3. 2·29
4. 10·15
5. 3·75
6. 5·39
7. 10·68
8. 5·48
9. 3·35

10. 6·725 m − 5·63 m = 1·095 m
11. 5·237 m − 4·821 m = 0·416 m
12. 9·2 m − 7·436 m = 1·764 m
13. 13·46 m − 11·735 m = 1·725 m
14. 1·8 m − 1·524 m = 0·276 m
15. 7·59 m − 6·358 m = 1·232 m
16. 9·064 − 2·275 = 6·789
17. 13·598 − 3·92 = 9·678
18. 20·223 − 12·534 = 7·689
Answers will vary.

page 34
Decimals problems

1. 12·75 m + 10·25 m = 23 m
2. 200 m − (15·4 m + 22·73 m) = 161·87 m
3. 80 l − (42·7 l + 4·8 l) = 32·5 l
4. 5 m − 3·56 m = 1·44 m
5. 9·3 m − 4·68 m = 4·62 m
6. 0·8 m + 1·6 m + 0·95 m + 0·75 m = 4·1 m   4·1 m > 4 m
   The fittings will not fit along one wall.
7. 2·5 l + 2·85 l + 3·48 l = 8·83 l
8. 300 kg − 14·62 kg = 285·38 kg

page 35
Powers and prime factors

1. 3^2
2. 4^3
3. 2^5
4. 5^2
5. 6^4
6. 10^3
7. 1^4
8. 7^6
9. $2^3 \times 5^2$
10. $3^2 \times 7^4$
11. $2^2 \times 3^3 \times 11^2$
12. $2^2 \times 3^3$
13. $4^2 = 16$
14. $2^3 = 8$
15. $7^2 = 49$
16. $2^4 = 16$
17. $10^3 = 1000$
18. $2^6 = 64$
19. $3^3 = 27$
20. $2^5 = 32$
21. $60 = 2^2 \times 3 \times 5$
22. $33 = 3 \times 11$
23. $18 = 2 \times 3$
24. $42 = 2 \times 3 \times 7$
25. $56 = 2^3 \times 7$
26. $144 = 2^4 \times 3^2$

27. $500 = 2^2 \times 5^3$ **28.** $120 = 2^3 \times 3 \times 5$
29. $2464 = 2^5 \times 7 \times 11$

Explore

Power Number	1	2	3	4	5	6
2	2	4	8	16	32	64
3	3	9	27	81	243	729
4	4	16	64	256	1024	4096
5	5	25	125	625	3125	15 625
6	6	36	216	1296	7776	46 656

page 36
Powers   Powers   **N13**

I. $2^3 - 2 = 6$ 6   **2.** $2^2 + 3 = 7$ 7
3. $16 \times 2 = 32$ 32   **4.** $2^6 = 64$ 6
5. $3^2 + 5 = 14$ 2   **6.** $4^2 = 16 = 2^4$ 4
7. $10^2 + 25 = 125 = 5^3$ 5   **8.** $10^3 \div 2 = 500$ 500
9. $2^5 + 4 = 36 = 6^2$ 6   **10.** $10^6 = 1\,000\,000$ 6
II. 10^2 cm = 1 m   **12.** 10^3 g = 1 kg
13. 10^3 m = 1 km   **14.** 10^3 mm = 1 m
15. 10^5 cm = 1 km   **16.** 10^2 cl = 1 l
17. 10^6 mm = 1 km   **18.** 10^3 ml = 1 l
19. 10^2 mm^2 = 1 cm^2 **20.** 10^4 cm^2 = 1 m^2

Explore

Number	Units digit pattern
2	2, 4, 8, 6, 2, 4, 8, 6, …
3	3, 9, 7, 1, 3, 9, 7, 1, …
4	4, 6, 4, 6, 4, 6, …
5	5, 5, 5, 5, 5, 5, …
6	6, 6, 6, 6, 6, 6, …
7	7, 9, 3, 1, 7, 9, 3, 1, …
8	8, 4, 2, 6, 8, 4, 2, 6, …
9	9, 8, 7, 6, 5, 4, 3, 2, 1, 0, …

$2^{10} = 1024 \rightarrow$ units digit 4
$3^{12} = 53\,144 \rightarrow$ units digit 1
$4^7 = 16\,384 \rightarrow$ units digit 4
$6^{11} = 362\,797\,056 \rightarrow$ units digit 6

page 37
Positive and   Positive and negative numbers   **N14**
negative numbers

I. $^+£8$ add $^-£5 = {}^+£3$
2. $^+£9$ add $^-£4 = {}^+£5$
3. $^+£3 \cdot 50$ add $^-£2 = {}^+£1 \cdot 50$
4. $^+£1 \cdot 80$ add $^-£4 \cdot 50 = {}^-£2 \cdot 70$
5. $^-£13 \cdot 60$ add $^+£5 \cdot 50 = {}^-£8 \cdot 10$
6. $^-£1 \cdot 25$ add $^+£7 = {}^+£5 \cdot 75$
7. $^+£12$ add $^-£5 \cdot 80 = {}^+£6 \cdot 20$
8. $^-£4 \cdot 75$ add $^-£1 \cdot 50 = {}^-£6 \cdot 25$
9. $^+£9$ add $^+£13$ add $^-£18 = {}^+£4$
10. $^-£17$ add $^+£16$ add $^+£15 = {}^+£14$
II. $^-£3 \cdot 50$ add $^+£10$ add $^-£6 \cdot 80 = {}^-£0 \cdot 30$
12. $^+£25$ add $^-£4 \cdot 50$ add $^-£11 \cdot 75 = {}^+£8 \cdot 75$
13. $^+3$ add $^-2 = {}^+1$ **14.** $^+5$ add $^-4 = {}^+1$
15. $^-3$ add $^+6 = {}^+3$ **16.** $^+4$ add $^+3 = {}^+7$

17. $^-4$ add $^-5 = {}^-9$ **18.** $^-7$ add $^+12 = {}^+5$
19. $(^+3) + (^-4) = {}^-1$ **20.** $(^+5) + (^-6) = {}^-1$
21. $(^-7) + (^-1) = {}^-8$ **22.** $(^-5) + (^+2) = {}^-3$
23. $(^+3) + (^+4 \cdot 5) = {}^+7 \cdot 5$ **24.** $(^+1 \cdot 5) + (^-2 \cdot 6) = {}^-1 \cdot 1$
25. $(^+5) + (^+3) + (^-4) = {}^+4$ **26.** $(^-4) + (^-3) + (^-7) = {}^-14$
27. $(^+5) + (^-3) + (^-10) = {}^-8$ **28.** $(^+74) + (^-63) + (^-18) = {}^-7$
29. $(^-48) + (^+17) + (^+53) = {}^+22$
30. $(^+0 \cdot 3) + (^-0 \cdot 8) + (^-0 \cdot 5) = {}^-1 \cdot 0$

Explore
Answers will vary. E.g.
- $^-2$ add $^-1$
- $^+2$ add $^-5$
- $^+7$ add $^+4$ add $^-14$
- $^-8$ add $^-5$ add $^+10$

page 38
Adding and subtracting   Positive and negative numbers   **N14**
negative numbers

I. $^+5$ subtract $^+2 = {}^+3$ **2.** $^+2$ subtract $^+5 = {}^-3$
3. $^+3$ subtract $^-1 = {}^+4$ **4.** $^-2$ subtract $^+5 = {}^-7$
5. $^-4$ subtract $^-7 = {}^+3$ **6.** $^-3$ subtract $^-1 = {}^-2$
7. $(+8) - (^-3) = {}^+11$ **8.** $(^-6) + (^+4) = {}^-2$
9. $(^+1 \cdot 5) - (^-2) = {}^+3 \cdot 5$ **10.** $(^-3 \cdot 5) - (^+1) = {}^-4 \cdot 5$
II. $(^-3) - (^-1 \cdot 5) = {}^-1 \cdot 5$ **12.** $(^+\frac{1}{2}) - (^-2\frac{1}{4}) = {}^+2\frac{3}{4}$

13. add $^-3$

in	$^+3$	$^-4$	$^-1$	0	$^+5$	$^-3$	$^+1 \cdot 3$	$^-\frac{1}{2}$
out	0	$^-7$	$^-4$	$^-3$	$^+2$	$^-6$	$^-1 \cdot 7$	$^-3\frac{1}{2}$

14. subtract $^+5$

in	$^+1$	$^-2$	$^+6$	$^-7$	0	$^-5$	$^+1 \cdot 8$	$^-\frac{3}{4}$
out	$^-4$	$^-7$	$^+1$	$^-12$	$^-5$	$^-10$	$^-3 \cdot 2$	$^-5\frac{3}{4}$

15. subtract $^-3$

in	$^-4$	$^+2$	$^-1$	$^+7$	$^+1 \cdot 5$	$^-2 \cdot 5$	0	$^+\frac{1}{2}$
out	$^-1$	$^+5$	$^+2$	$^+10$	$^+4 \cdot 5$	$^+0 \cdot 5$	$^+3$	$^+3\frac{1}{2}$

16. addition

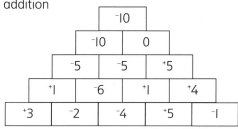

subtraction

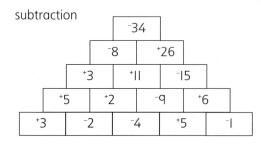

17. addition

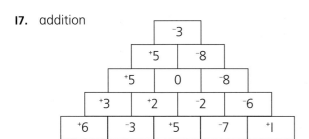

subtraction

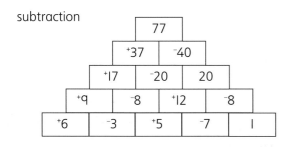

page 39
Multiplying decimals

Estimates will vary.

1. $4 \cdot 32 \times 5 \cdot 7 = 24 \cdot 624$
2. $36 \cdot 4 \times 4 \cdot 8 = 174 \cdot 72$
3. $19 \cdot 7 \times 3 \cdot 6 = 70 \cdot 92$
4. $26 \cdot 5 \times 1 \cdot 9 = 50 \cdot 35$
5. $58 \cdot 7 \times 9 \cdot 3 = 545 \cdot 91$
6. $61 \cdot 2 \times 4 \cdot 3 = 263 \cdot 16$

7. $35 \cdot 6 \text{ m} \times 4 \cdot 3 \text{ m} = 153 \cdot 08 \text{ m}^2$
8. $28 \cdot 7 \text{ m} \times 3 \cdot 9 \text{ m} = 111 \cdot 93 \text{ m}^2$
9. $23 \cdot 6 \text{ m} \times 4 \cdot 6 \text{ m} = 108 \cdot 56 \text{ m}^2$
10. $13 \cdot 4 \text{ m} \times 2 \cdot 9 \text{ m} = 38 \cdot 86 \text{ m}^2$
11. $15 \cdot 6 \text{ m} \times 7 \cdot 3 \text{ m} = 113 \cdot 88 \text{ m}^2$
12. $12 \cdot 8 \text{ m} \times 6 \cdot 4 \text{ m} = 81 \cdot 92 \text{ m}^2$

@

Total area = $608 \cdot 23 \text{ m}^2$ $608 \cdot 23 \div 15 = 40 \cdot 55$, 41 tins

13. $25 \cdot 7 \text{ cm} \times 4 \cdot 6 \text{ cm} = 118 \cdot 22 \text{ cm}^2$
$31 \cdot 2 \text{ cm} \times 3 \cdot 4 \text{ cm} = 106 \cdot 08 \text{ cm}^2$
$118 \cdot 22 \text{ cm}^2 - 106 \cdot 08 \text{ cm}^2 = 12 \cdot 14 \text{ cm}^2$

14. $31 \cdot 6 \text{ cm} \times 3 \cdot 9 \text{ cm} = 123 \cdot 24 \text{ cm}^2$
$42 \cdot 7 \text{ cm} \times 2 \cdot 8 \text{ cm} = 119 \cdot 56 \text{ cm}^2$
$123 \cdot 24 \text{ cm}^2 - 119 \cdot 56 \text{ cm}^2 = 3 \cdot 68 \text{ cm}^2$

15. $43 \cdot 8 \text{ cm} \times 2 \cdot 7 \text{ cm} = 118 \cdot 26 \text{ cm}^2$
$31 \cdot 7 \text{ cm} \times 3 \cdot 5 \text{ cm} = 110 \cdot 95 \text{ cm}^2$
$118 \cdot 26 \text{ cm}^2 - 110 \cdot 95 \text{ cm}^2 = 7 \cdot 31 \text{ cm}^2$

16. $28 \cdot 6 \text{ cm} \times 4 \cdot 9 \text{ cm} = 140 \cdot 14 \text{ cm}^2$
$26 \cdot 7 \text{ cm} \times 5 \cdot 3 \text{ cm} = 141 \cdot 51 \text{ cm}^2$
$141 \cdot 51 \text{ cm}^2 - 140 \cdot 14 \text{ cm}^2 = 1 \cdot 37 \text{ cm}^2$

page 40
Multiplying decimals

Estimates will vary.

1. £2·75 × 28 = £77
2. £4·45 × 53 = £235·85
3. £3·55 × 24 = £85·20
4. £4·85 × 32 = £155·20
5. £5·35 × 18 = £96·30
6. £6·65 × 44 = £292·60

7. $4 \cdot 35 \text{ m} \times 28 = 121 \cdot 8 \text{ m}$
8. $3 \cdot 72 \text{ m} \times 32 = 119 \cdot 04 \text{ m}$
9. $5 \cdot 46 \text{ m} \times 41 = 223 \cdot 86 \text{ m}$
10. $2 \cdot 86 \text{ m} \times 63 = 180 \cdot 18 \text{ m}$

11. $4 \cdot 19 \text{ m} \times 45 = 188 \cdot 55 \text{ m}$
12. $5 \cdot 08 \text{ m} \times 53 = 269 \cdot 24$

@

7. $121 \cdot 8 \text{ m} \approx 360 \text{ feet}$ 8. $119 \cdot 04 \text{ m} \approx 360 \text{ feet}$
9. $223 \cdot 86 \text{ m} \approx 660 \text{ feet}$ 10. $180 \cdot 18 \text{ m} \approx 540 \text{ feet}$
11. $188 \cdot 55 \text{ m} \approx 570 \text{ feet}$ 12. $269 \cdot 24 \text{ m} \approx 810 \text{ feet}$

Explore
All possible answers are listed.

$5 \cdot 46 \times 37 = 202 \cdot 02$ $3 \cdot 76 \times 54 = 203 \cdot 04$
$5 \cdot 74 \times 36 = 206 \cdot 64$ $3 \cdot 64 \times 57 = 207 \cdot 48$
$3 \cdot 74 \times 56 = 209 \cdot 44$ $6 \cdot 57 \times 34 = 223 \cdot 38$
$3 \cdot 47 \times 65 = 225 \cdot 55$ $6 \cdot 47 \times 35 = 226 \cdot 45$
$3 \cdot 57 \times 64 = 228 \cdot 48$ $3 \cdot 45 \times 67 = 231 \cdot 15$
$6 \cdot 74 \times 35 = 235 \cdot 9$ $3 \cdot 54 \times 67 = 237 \cdot 18$
$6 \cdot 45 \times 37 = 238 \cdot 65$ $3 \cdot 75 \times 64 = 240$
$6 \cdot 54 \times 37 = 241 \cdot 98$ $3 \cdot 74 \times 65 = 243 \cdot 1$
$5 \cdot 67 \times 43 = 243 \cdot 81$ $5 \cdot 37 \times 46 = 247 \cdot 02$
$4 \cdot 67 \times 53 = 247 \cdot 51$ $5 \cdot 76 \times 43 = 247 \cdot 68$

page 41
Dividing decimals

1. $252 \cdot 8 \div 8 = 31 \cdot 6$ hours per week
2. $200 \cdot 2 \div 7 = 28 \cdot 6$ hours per week
3. $147 \cdot 6 \div 9 = 16 \cdot 4$ hours per week
4. $142 \cdot 2 \div 6 = 23 \cdot 7$ hours per week
5. $213 \cdot 5 \div 5 = 42 \cdot 7$ hours per week
6. $268 \cdot 8 \div 7 = 38 \cdot 4$ hours per week
7. $106 \cdot 4 \div 4 = 26 \cdot 6$ hours per week
8. $149 \cdot 6 \div 8 = 18 \cdot 7$ hours per week

1a. $31 \cdot 6 \times 8 = 252 \cdot 8$ 2a. $28 \cdot 6 \times 7 = 200 \cdot 2$
3a. $16 \cdot 4 \times 9 = 147 \cdot 6$ 4a. $23 \cdot 7 \times 6 = 142 \cdot 2$
5a. $42 \cdot 7 \times 5 = 213 \cdot 5$ 6a. $38 \cdot 4 \times 7 = 268 \cdot 8$
7a. $26 \cdot 6 \times 4 = 106 \cdot 4$ 8a. $18 \cdot 7 \times 8 = 149 \cdot 6$

9. £85·44 ÷ 16 = £5·34   10. £80·64 ÷ 12 = £6·72
11. £84·78 ÷ 18 = £4·71   12. £84·89 ÷ 13 = £6·53
13. £78·54 ÷ 21 = £3·74   14. £92·14 ÷ 17 = £5·42

@

All answers to two decimal places.

9. (£85·44 + £8.54) ÷ 16 = £5·87
10. (£80·64 + £8.06) ÷ 12 = £7·39
11. (£84·78 + £8.48) ÷ 18 = £5·18
12. (£84·89 + £8.49) ÷ 13 = £7·18
13. (£78·54 + £7.85) ÷ 21 = £4·11
14. (£92·14 + £9.21) ÷ 17 = £5·96

Estimates will vary.

15. $98 \cdot 4 \div 8 = 12 \cdot 3$ 16. $88 \cdot 2 \div 6 = 14 \cdot 7$
17. $90 \cdot 3 \div 7 = 12 \cdot 9$ 18. $77 \cdot 04 \div 12 = 6 \cdot 42$
19. $75 \cdot 53 \div 13 = 5 \cdot 81$ 20. $28 \cdot 64 \div 16 = 1 \cdot 79$
15a. $12 \cdot 3 \times 8 = 98 \cdot 4$ 16a. $14 \cdot 7 \times 6 = 88 \cdot 2$
17a. $12 \cdot 9 \times 7 = 90 \cdot 3$ 18a. $6 \cdot 42 \times 12 = 77 \cdot 04$
19a. $5 \cdot 81 \times 13 = 75 \cdot 53$ 20a. $1 \cdot 79 \times 16 = 28 \cdot 64$

page 42
Dividing decimals

1. $426 \div 2 \cdot 7 = 4260 \div 27 = 157 \frac{7}{9}$
2. $38 \cdot 6 \div 1 \cdot 7 = 386 \div 17 = 22 \frac{12}{17}$

3. $625 ÷ 0.6 = 6250 ÷ 6 = 1041\frac{2}{3}$

4. $5430 ÷ 6.8 = 54300 ÷ 68 = 798\frac{9}{17}$

5. $21.3 ÷ 0.42 = 2130 ÷ 42 = 50\frac{5}{7}$

6. $4.76 ÷ 2.4 = 476 ÷ 240 = 1\frac{59}{60}$

7. $362 ÷ 2.8 = 129\frac{2}{7}$ Need 130 boxes.

   $\frac{5}{7}$ of $2.8 = 2.0$ Need 2.0 kg more to fill the last box.

8. $184 ÷ 3.5 = 52\frac{4}{7}$ Need 53 boxes.

   $\frac{3}{7}$ of $3.5 = 1.5$ Need 1.5 kg more to fill the last box.

9. $237 ÷ 4.6 = 51\frac{12}{23}$ Need 52 boxes.

   $\frac{11}{23}$ of $4.6 = 2.2$ Need 2.2 kg to fill the last box.

10. $423 ÷ 1.9 = 222\frac{12}{19}$ Need 223 boxes .

    $\frac{7}{19}$ of $1.9 = 0.7$ Need 0.7 kg to fill the last box.

11. $516 ÷ 2.6 = 198\frac{6}{13}$ Need 199 boxes.

    $\frac{7}{13}$ of $2.6 = 1.4$ Need 1.4 kg to fill the last box.

12. $258 ÷ 3.2 = 80\frac{5}{8}$ Need 81 boxes.

    $\frac{3}{8}$ of $3.2 = 1.2$ Need 1.2 kg to fill the last box.

$452 ÷ 1.6 = 282.5$ $452 ÷ 2.7 = 167.4$ $452 ÷ 3.4 = 132.9$

$326 ÷ 1.6 = 203.8$ $326 ÷ 2.7 = 120.7$ $326 ÷ 3.4 = 95.9$

$187 ÷ 1.6 = 116.9$ $187 ÷ 2.7 = 69.3$ $187 ÷ 3.4 = 55$

page 43
Decimal problems
Division **N15** **N16**

Children's methods will vary.

1. $3 × 1.5 l = 4.5 l$
   $4.5 l ÷ 0.3 ml = 4500 ÷ 0.3 = 45 000 ÷ 3 = 15 000$
   15 000 glasses can be filled.

2. $4 × 0.35 kg = 1.4 kg$
   Riley needs 1.4 kg of flour to make 48 cakes.

3. $250 ÷ 5 = 50$
   Each slice weighs 50 g.
   $1.5 kg ÷ 50 g = 1.5 ÷ 0.05 = 30$
   30 slices in the pack.

4. $16 × 0.018 kg = 0.288 kg$
   0.288 kg of chocolate is eaten altogether.

5. $£3.96 ÷ £1.32 = 3$ $3 × 1 kg = 3 kg$
   $3 kg ÷ 0.125 kg = 24$
   Carly can buy 24 apples.

6. $0.6 l ÷ 0.15 l = 4$ $0.375 l × 4 = 1.5 l$
   Marlon needs 1.5 l of boiling water.

7. $(12 × 0.375 l) + (3 × 1.5 l) + (7 × 0.75 l) = 14.25 l$
   14.25 l of liquid is drunk altogether.

8. $0.017 kg × 36 = 0.612 kg$
   Chris uses 0.612 kg of bread.

page 44
Calculating percentages
Percentages **N17**

1. 11% of 3500 m = 385 m
2. 53% of 1600 km = 848 km

3. 14% of 4300 km = 602 km
4. 44% of 2800 m = 1232 m
5. 89% of 3700 km = 3293 km
6. 119% of 8400 m = 9996 m
7. 21% of £600 = £126
8. 26% of £1400 = £364
9. 52% of £1100 = £572
10. 49% of £6.50 = £3.185 (rounds to £3.19)
11. 18% of £25000 = £4500
12. 121% of £800 = £968

13. Pink 31% of 15 000 = 4650
    Yellow 43% of 15 000 = 6450
    Purple 26% of 15 000 = 3900
14. Pink 72% of 18 000 = 12 960
    Yellow 9% of 18 000 = 1620
    Purple 19% of 18 000 = 3420
15. Pink 18% of 24 000 = 4320
    Yellow 63% of 24 000 = 15 120
    Purple 19% of 24 000 = 4560
16. Pink 46% of 32 000 = 14 720
    Yellow 22% of 32 000 = 7040
    Purple 32% of 32 000 = 10 240

Pink	36 650
Yellow	30 230
Purple	22 120

page 45
Calculating percentages
Percentages **N17**

1. 26% of £4300 = £1118   0.26 $\frac{13}{50}$
2. 18% of £700 = £126   0.18 $\frac{9}{50}$
3. 29% of £1800 = £522   0.29 $\frac{29}{100}$
4. 43% of £4700 = £2021   0.43 $\frac{43}{100}$
5. 17% of £3600 = £612   0.17 $\frac{17}{100}$
6. 89% of £800 = £712   0.89 $\frac{89}{100}$
7. 50% off £87.50 = £43.75 new price £43.75
8. 15% off £28 = £4.20   new price £23.80
9. 35% off £19 = £6.65   new price £12.35
10. 12% off £34.50 = £4.14   new price £30.36
11. $\frac{1}{3}$ off £76.20 = £25.40   new price £50.80
12. 45% off £48 = £21.60   new price £26.40
13. new price £12 320 $0.88 × 14000 = 12320$
14. population 20 160 $1.12 × 18000 = 20160$
15. season ticket £464 $1.16 × 400 = 464$
16. target weight 80.36 kg $0.82 × 98 = 80.36$
17. 4 CDs with £9.96 change $0.77 × 13 = 10.01$
    $50 ÷ 10.01 = 4 r 9.96$
18. change £36.75 $1.15 × 55 = 63.25$
    $100 - 63.25 = 36.75$

page 46
Calculating percentages
Percentages **N17**

1. 17.5% of £300 = £52.50   total cost £352.50
2. 17.5% of £500 = £87.50   total cost £587.50
3. 17.5% of £900 = £157.50   total cost £1057.50

4. 17·5% of £250 = £43·75   total cost £293·75
5. 17·5% of £840 = £147   total cost £987
6. 17·5% of £190 = £33·25   total cost £223·25
7. 17·5% of £398 = £69·65   total cost £467·65
8. 17·5% of £688 = £120·40   total cost £808·40
9. 17·5% of £424= £74·20   total cost £498·20

e

1. £300 = ¥60 000   105% of ¥60 000 = ¥63 000
2. £500 = ¥100 000   105% of ¥100 000 = ¥105 000
3. £900 = ¥180 000   105% of ¥180 000 = ¥189 000
4. £250 = ¥50 000   105% of ¥50 000 = ¥52 500
5. £840 = ¥168 000   105% of ¥168 000 = ¥176 400
6. £190 = ¥38 000   105% of ¥38 000 = ¥39 900
7. £398 = ¥79 600   105% of ¥79 600 = ¥83 580
8. £688 = ¥137 600   105% of ¥137 600 = ¥144 480
9. £424 = ¥84 800   105% of ¥84 800 = ¥89 040

Explore

Children may find this concept difficult. They should be encouraged to check their answers carefully.

£3000 is 75% of value 1 year ago.

£3000 ÷ 0·75 = £4000

a) £8100 ÷ 0·75 = £10 800
b) £2400 ÷ 0·75 = £3200
c) £1200 ÷ 0·75 = £1600
d) £990 ÷ 0·75 = £1320

---

page 47

Fractions and percentages

1. $\frac{7}{10}$ = 70%
2. $\frac{1}{4}$ = 25%
3. $1\frac{3}{4}$ = 175%
4. $2\frac{1}{2}$ = 250%
5. $\frac{13}{100}$ = 13%
6. $\frac{3}{8}$ = 37·5%
7. 75% = $\frac{3}{4}$
8. 60% = $\frac{3}{5}$
9. 150% = $1\frac{1}{2}$
10. 225% = $2\frac{1}{4}$
11. 87% = $\frac{87}{100}$
12. 12·5% = $\frac{1}{8}$
13. $\frac{3}{5}$ = $\frac{60}{100}$ = 60%
14. $\frac{7}{20}$ = $\frac{35}{100}$ = 35%
15. $\frac{13}{50}$ = $\frac{26}{100}$ = 26%
16. $\frac{27}{50}$ = $\frac{54}{100}$ = 54%
17. $\frac{17}{25}$ = $\frac{68}{100}$ = 68%
18. $\frac{34}{25}$ = $\frac{136}{100}$ = 136%
19. $\frac{3}{5}$ = 60%, $\frac{4}{10}$ = 40%, $\frac{11}{20}$ = 55%, $\frac{1}{2}$ = 50%, $\frac{3}{4}$ = 75%
    B, D, C, A, E
20. $\frac{17}{25}$ = 68%, $\frac{35}{100}$ = 35%, $\frac{1}{4}$ = 25%, $\frac{3}{2}$ = 150%, $\frac{7}{10}$ = 70%
    H, G, F, J, I
21. $\frac{68}{200}$ = 34%, $\frac{7}{10}$ = 70%, $\frac{37}{50}$ = 74%, $\frac{13}{20}$ = 65%, $\frac{3}{5}$ = 60%
    K, O, N, L, M
22. $\frac{6}{25}$ = 24%, $\frac{5}{2}$ = 250%, $\frac{3}{10}$ = 30%, $\frac{7}{20}$ = 35%, $\frac{69}{300}$ = 23%
    T, P, R, S, Q
23. 10% = $\frac{1}{10}$
24. 25% = $\frac{1}{4}$
25. 60% = $\frac{3}{5}$
26. 5% = $\frac{1}{20}$
27. 65% = $\frac{13}{20}$
28. 80% = $\frac{4}{5}$
29. 4% = $\frac{1}{25}$
30. 120% = $1\frac{1}{5}$
31. 135% = $1\frac{7}{20}$
32. 72% = $\frac{18}{25}$

---

33. 86% = $\frac{43}{50}$
34. 64% = $\frac{16}{25}$
35. 35% = $\frac{7}{20}$
36. 18% = $\frac{9}{50}$
37. 7% = $\frac{7}{100}$
38. 12·5% = $\frac{1}{8}$

---

page 48

Fractions, decimals and percentages

1. $\frac{5}{6}$ = 83·3%
2. $\frac{4}{7}$ = 57·1%
3. $\frac{7}{9}$ = 77%
4. $\frac{3}{11}$ = 27·3%
5. $\frac{4}{3}$ = 133·3%
6. $\frac{8}{15}$ = 53·3%
7. $\frac{5}{12}$ = 41·7%
8. $\frac{7}{8}$ = 87·5%
9. $\frac{11}{18}$ = 61·1%
10. $\frac{6}{13}$ = 46·2%
11. 37·5%
12. 62·5%
13. 25%
14. 25%
15. 12·5%
16. 50%
17. 62·5%
18. 62·5%
19. 16·7%
20. 16·7%
21. 33·3%
22. 83·3%
23. 0%
24. 50%
25. 41·7%
26. 58·3%
27. 25%
28. 25%
29. 58·3%
30. 25%
31. $\frac{3}{4}$ > 0·72
32. 0·81 > $\frac{4}{5}$
33. $\frac{7}{20}$ > 34%
34. 45% > $\frac{11}{25}$
35. $\frac{3}{7}$ < 43%
36. 45% > $\frac{5}{12}$
37. $\frac{5}{6}$ > 0·8
38. $\frac{7}{8}$ > 0·82
39. $\frac{4}{7}$ < $\frac{6}{9}$
40. 57·1% (1 d.p.) $\frac{4}{7}$ failed
41. $\frac{7}{25}$ 100% − 72% = 28% $\frac{28}{100}$ = $\frac{7}{25}$
42. 7·5% (1 d.p.)   1 − ($\frac{5}{12}$ + $\frac{2}{7}$ + $\frac{2}{9}$) = $\frac{19}{252}$ = 7·5%
43. 12% $\frac{1}{5}$ of 60% = 12%

---

page 49

Proportion

1. $\frac{75}{450}$ = $\frac{1}{6}$
2. $\frac{150}{450}$ = $\frac{1}{3}$
3. $\frac{225}{450}$ = $\frac{1}{2}$
4. 75:150 = 2:1
5. 225:75 = 2:1
6. 150:225 = 2:3
7. 75:225 = 1:3
8. $\frac{50}{300}$ = $\frac{1}{6}$
9. $\frac{75}{300}$ = $\frac{1}{4}$
10. $\frac{100}{300}$ = $\frac{1}{3}$
11. $\frac{75}{300}$ = $\frac{1}{4}$
12. 75:100 = 3:4
13. 50:75 = 2:3
14. 75:100 = 3:4
15. 75:75 = 1:1
16. $\frac{450}{700}$ = $\frac{9}{14}$
17. $\frac{100}{700}$ = $\frac{1}{7}$
18. $\frac{100}{700}$ = $\frac{1}{7}$
19. $\frac{50}{700}$ = $\frac{1}{14}$
20. 100:450 = 2:9
21. 50:100 = 1:2
22. 100:450 = 2:9
23. 450:50 = 9:1
24. 150 g   12 ÷ 6 = 2, 75 g × 2 = 150 g
25. 50 g   75 g ÷ 12 = 6·25 g, 6·25 g × 8 = 50 g
26. 150 g   100 g ÷ 4 = 25 g, 25 g × 6 = 150 g
27. 200g : 300 g
28. 150 g : 250 g
29. 280 g : 360 g
30. 80 g : 120 g : 280 g
31. 100 g : 400 g : 700 g
32. 0·6 kg : 1 kg: 1·6 kg

---

page 50

Ratio

1. 8:12 = 2:3
2. 4:6 = 2:3
3. 12:6 = 2:1
4. 5:6 will not simplify
5. 7:21 = 1:3
6. 28:21 = 4:3
7. 12:9 = 4:3
8. 8:6 = 4:3
9. 15:21 = 5:7
10. 14:35 = 2:5
11. 18:24 = 3:4
12. 35:45 = 7:9

13. 6:18:36 = 1:3:6   **14.** 9:45:72 = 1:5:8
15. 15:25:65 = 3:5:13   **16.** 8:20:44 = 2:5:11
17. 2:3 = 1: 1·5   **18.** 5:8 = 1:1·6
19. 10:14 = 1:1·4   **20.** 4:7 = 1:1·75
21. 8:12 = 1:1·5   **22.** 9:30 = 1:3
23. 8:10 = 1:1·25   **24.** 4:21 = 1:5·25
25. 8:60 = 1:7·5   **26.** 4:58 = 1:14·5
27. 8:19 = 1:2·375   **28.** 5:27 = 1:5·4

29. 18:1 ratio pupils: teachers = 450:25 = 18:1

30. $\frac{1}{4}$ ratio Janice:Jason = 3:1 → proportions are $\frac{3}{4}$ and $\frac{1}{4}$

31. 15 girls 27 ÷ 9 parts = 3, 3 × 5 = 15

32. 9 hours playing 24 ÷ (3 + 1 + 4) = 3, 3 × 3 = 9

33. Richard £12, Karen £18, Lizzy £30
60 ÷ (2 + 3 + 5) = 6, 6 × 2 = 12, 6 × 3 = 18, 6 × 5 =30

34. a. $\frac{1}{3}$ **b.** $\frac{1}{6}$ **c.** $\frac{1}{2}$
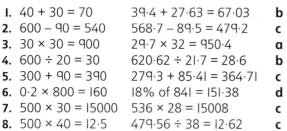
6 parts so $\frac{1}{6}$: $\frac{2}{6}$: $\frac{3}{6}$ of cement:sand:gravel
cement: 3 m³ $\frac{1}{6}$ of 18 = 3
sand: 6 m³ $\frac{1}{3}$ of 18 = 6
gravel: 9 m³ $\frac{1}{2}$ of 18 = 9

page 51
Checking calculations   Checking results   **N20**

1. 40 + 30 = 70   39·4 + 27·63 = 67·03   **b**
2. 600 − 90 = 540   568·7 − 89·5 = 479·2   **c**
3. 30 × 30 = 900   29·7 × 32 = 950·4   **a**
4. 600 ÷ 20 = 30   620·62 ÷ 21·7 = 28·6   **b**
5. 300 + 90 = 390   279·3 + 85·41 = 364·71   **c**
6. 0·2 × 800 = 160   18% of 841 = 151·38   **d**
7. 500 × 30 = 15000   536 × 28 = 15008   **c**
8. 500 × 40 = 12.5   479·56 ÷ 38 = 12·62   **c**

9. correct   230·06 − 156·2 = 73·86
                 or 230·06 − 73·86 = 156·2
10. correct   17·105 + 9·735 = 26·84
11. correct   43·13 − 0·96 = 42·17
                 or 43·13 − 42·17 = 0·96
12. correct   3·116 + 2·714 = 5·83
13. correct   6339·6 ÷ 27 = 234·8
                 or 6339·6 ÷ 234·8 = 27
14. correct   3·107 ÷ 0·65 = 4·78
                 or 3·107 ÷ 4·78 = 0·65
15. correct   23·5 × 4·74 = 111·39
16. correct   15·5 × 68 = 1054

page 52
Checking calculations   Checking results   **N20**

1. 37 149→9 **2.** 41 905→5 **3.** 44 196→6 **4.** 17·63→3
5. 14·12→2 **6.** 30·2→2 **7.** 0.537→7 **8.** 65·57→7
9. 208·78→8
10. correct   1562 − 398 = 1164
11. correct   274·6 + 5·83 = 280·43
12. incorrect   47·2 − 29·3 = 17·9
13. incorrect   82 × 76 = 6232
14. incorrect   3·7 × 1·4 = 5·18
15. correct   5·62 × 28 = 157·36
16. 65p × 21 = 1365p = £13·65
    or £13·65 ÷ 21 = 65p

17. 19p × 476 = 9044p = £90·44
or £90·44 ÷ 476 = £0·19 = 19p
18. 78p × 22 = 1716p = £17·16
or £17·96 ÷ 22 = £0·78 = 78p
19. 1222 ÷ 4700 = 0·26 = 26%
or 26% of 4700 = 1222
20. 99 cm × 43 cm = 4257 cm²
or (43 cm × 100) − 43 cm = 4257 cm³
21. 4·7 cm × 32 = 150·4 cm = 1·504 m
or 1·504 ÷ 32 = 0·047 m = 4·7 cm

page 53
Square numbers and cube numbers   Squares, cubes, roots **N21**

1. 9² = 81   **2.** 14² = 196
3. 21² = 441   **4.** 35² = 1225
5. 20² = 400   **6.** 50² = 2500
7. 40² = 1600   **8.** 80² = 6400
9. 300² = 90 000   **10.** 0·2² = 0·04
11. 1·2² = 1·44   **12.** 4³ = 64
13. 1³ = 1   **14.** 10³ = 1000
15. 20³ = 8000   **16.** (0·2)³ = 0·008
17. (0·5)² = 0·25   **18.** (0·4)³ = 0·064
19. (0·7)² = 0·49   **20.** (1·3)² = 1·69

Children's estimations will vary.

21. 28² ≈ 30² = 900   28²= 784
22. 17² ≈ 20² = 400   17²= 289
23. 21² ≈ 20² = 400   21²= 441
24. 32² ≈ 30² = 900   32²= 1024
25. (4·8)² ≈ 5² = 25   (4·8)² = 23·04
26. (7·2)² ≈ 7² = 49   (7·2)² = 51·84
27. (9·1)² ≈ 9² = 81   (9·1)² = 82·81
28. (1·9)² ≈ 2² = 4   (1·9)² = 3·61
29. (6·3)² ≈ 6² = 36   (6·3)² = 39·69
30. (10·5)² ≈ 10² =100   (10·5)² = 110·25
31. (9·9)² ≈ 10² =100   (9·9)² = 98·01
32. (12·7)² ≈ 13² =169   (12·7)² = 161·29

Explore
Children will notice all powers given end in 25.
They may notice a pattern that the 100 and 1000 digits can
be made from the 10 digit (t) of the original number
by t × (t + 1).

65²: 6 × 7 = 42   65² = 4225
95²: 9 × 10 = 90   95² = 9025
55²: 5 × 6 = 30   55² = 3025
85²: 8 × 9 = 72   85² = 7225

Alternatively they may notice a pattern in the 100s and
1000s units with a geometric progression and use that to
predict.

2_ _, 6_ _, 12_ _, 20_ _ , 30_ _, 42_ _, etc

page 54
Square roots and cube roots   Squares, cubes, roots **N21**

positive roots only
1. √81 = 9 (or −9)   **2.** √1 = 1
3. √36 = 6   **4.** √49 = 7

+	1	4	9	16	25	36	49
1	2	5	10	17	16	37	50
4		8	13	20	29	40	
9			18	25	34	45	
16				32	41		
25							
36							

5. $\sqrt{400} = 20$

6. $\sqrt{144} = 12$

7. $\sqrt{2500} = 50$

8. $\sqrt{1600} = 40$

9. $\sqrt{900} = 3$

10. $\sqrt{6400} = 80$

11. $\sqrt{40\,000} = 200$

12. $\sqrt[3]{8} = 2$

13. $\sqrt[3]{1000} = 10$

14. $\sqrt[3]{1} = 1$

15. $\sqrt[3]{125} = 5$

16. $\sqrt[3]{64} = 4$

17. $\sqrt{62500} = 250$

18. $\sqrt[3]{216} = 6$

19. $\sqrt{14400} = 120$

20. $\sqrt[3]{8000} = 20$

21. $\sqrt{150} \approx \sqrt{144} = 12$ | $\sqrt{150} = 12\cdot25$ (2 d.p.)

22. $\sqrt{31} \approx \sqrt{36} = 6$ | $\sqrt{31} = 5\cdot57$

23. $\sqrt{96} \approx \sqrt{100} = 10$ | $\sqrt{96} = 9\cdot80$

24. $\sqrt{8} \approx \sqrt{9} = 3$ | $\sqrt{8} = 2\cdot83$

25. $\sqrt{300} \approx \sqrt{289} = 17$ | $\sqrt{300} = 17\cdot32$

26. $\sqrt{240} \approx \sqrt{225} = 15$ | $\sqrt{240} = 15\cdot49$

27. $\sqrt{1000} \approx \sqrt{900} = 30$ | $\sqrt{1000} = 31\cdot62$

28. $\sqrt{3900} \approx \sqrt{3600} = 60$ | $\sqrt{3900} = 62\cdot45$

29. $\sqrt{15\,000} \approx \sqrt{14400} = 120$ | $\sqrt{15\,000} = 122\cdot47$

30. $\sqrt{8000} \approx \sqrt{8100} = 90$ | $\sqrt{8000} = 89\cdot44$

31. $\sqrt{630} \approx \sqrt{625} = 25$ | $\sqrt{630} = 25\cdot10$

32. $\sqrt{299} \approx \sqrt{289} = 17$ | $\sqrt{299} = 17\cdot29$

Explore

Children may need some help with this exercise. They should be 'encouraged' to find 12,21 and then to see the pattern 102,201 ,1002,2001...

This should then lead to number patterns such as 103,301 1003, 3001 and 10202, 20201.

There may be students who notice that writing 2 as 02 generates other pairs 02,20 03,30 which could be discussed.

The following can be made from the sum of 2 square numbers: 2, 5, 8, 10, 13, 16, 17, 18, 20, 25, 29, 32, 34, 37, 40, 41, 45, 50

---

page 55
Squares, cubes and roots
Squares, cubes, roots **N21**

1. 1 | $\sqrt{25} = 5$ | $5 - 4 = 1$

2. 1 | $1^2 = 1^3 = 1$

3. 1 or 64 | $4^3 = 8^2 = 64$

4. 8 | $\sqrt[3]{8} = 2 = \frac{1}{4}$ of 8

5. 2 | $2^2 \times 2 = 4 \times 2 = 8 = 2^3$

6. 36 | $3 + 6 = 9$ | $6 - 3 = 3$

7. 64 | $4^3 = 64$

8. 27 | $\sqrt[3]{27} = 3 = \sqrt{9}$

9. 25 | $\sqrt[3]{125} = 5 = \sqrt{25}$

10. 2 and 6 | $2^2 = 4$, $6^2 = 36$ | $36 - 4 = 32$

11. 7 | $7^2 = 49$ $49 + 1 = 50$ $50 \div 2 = 25 = 5^2$

12. 10 | $10^2 \times 10 = 10^3$

13. 729 | $729 = 9^3$

14. 7 | $10^2 = 100$ $100 \div 2 = 50$
$50 - 1 = 49$ $\sqrt{49} = 7$

15. 7

Explore

Children need some strategy to investigate all possibilities, for example an addition table. They should also see from their method that some numbers can be made in more than one way.

---

page 56
Using brackets
Order of operations

1. $12 \times 2 + 4 = 28$

2. $43 + 40 \div 5 = 51$

3. $6 \times 8 + 46 = 94$

4. $140 \div 7 + 351 = 371$

5. $287 + 42 \times 6 = 539$

6. $29 + 126 \div 6 = 50$

7. $4 \times 3 + 5 \times 4 = 32$

8. $6 \times 2 + 5 \times 3 = 27$

9. $10 \div 5 - 6 \div 3 = 0$

10. $60 \div 5 + 8 \times 3 = 36$

11. $120 \div 10 - 24 \div 8 = 9$

12. $40 - 60 \div 4 + 7 = 32$

13. $70 + 5 \times 11 - 12 = 113$

14. $15 + 9 \times 8 - 7 = 80$

15. $2150 \div 5 + 5416 \div 8 = 1107$

16. true | $(6 \times 5) \times 3 = 6 \times (5 \times 3) = 90$

17. false | $(8 - 2) \times 3 = 18$ | $8 - (2 \times 3) = 2$

18. true | $(6 + 5) + 3 = 6 + (5 + 3) = 14$

19. false | $(15 - 6) - 3 = 6$ | $15 - (6 - 3) = 12$

20. false | $(60 \div 6) \div 2 = 5$ | $60 \div (6 \div 2) = 20$

21. false | $(4 + 8) \times 2 = 24$ | $4 + (8 \times 2) = 20$

22. false | $(14 - 5) \times 2 = 18$ | $14 - (5 \times 2) = 4$

23. false | $(12 - 9) \div 3 = 1$ | $12 - (9 \div 3) = 9$

24. false | $(12 \div 3) \times 2 = 8$ | $12 \div (3 \times 2) = 2$

25. true | $(5 \times 6) \div 3 = 5 \times (6 \div 3) = 10$

26. $4 \times (3 + 6) = 36$

27. $(4 \times 2) + 7 = 15$

28. $6 \times (8 - 2) = 36$

29. $(7 \times 3) - 4 = 17$

30. $(40 \div 4) \times 5 = 50$

31. $40 \div (4 \times 5) = 2$

32. $20 \div (4 + 1) = 4$

33. $(20 \div 4) + 1 = 6$

34. $8 + (12 \div 3) + 4 = 16$

35. $42 - (5 \times 3) - 16 = 11$

---

page 57
Calculations with brackets
Order of operations **N22**

1. $(26 + 7) \times 4 = 132$

2. $5 \times (18 - 7) = 55$

3. $(15 + 9) \times 7 = 168$

4. $(42 \times 10) \div 20 = 21$

5. $(75 \times 4) \div 3 = 100$

6. $(165 \div 3) \times 2 = 110$

7. $48 - (27 + 3) \div 3 = 38$

8. $15 + 8 \times (22 - 19) = 39$

9. $(16 - 7) \times 7 + 17 = 80$

10. $17 + (27 + 6) \div 3 = 28$

11. $(16 - 9) \times 4 - 25 = 3$

12. $100 - 8 \times (6 + 4) = 20$

13. $(61 + 29) \div 9 + 13 = 23$

14. $(3 + 4 \times 3) - (3 \times 2 - 4) = 13$

15. $(17 - 6 \times 2) + (2 \times 2 + 3) = 12$

16. $2 \times (5 + 3)^2 = 128$

17. $18 - (16 - 14)^2 = 14$

18. $(7 - 5)^3 + 4 = 12$

19. $4^2 + (7 - 6)^4 = 17$

20. $3^3 - (3 + 2)^2 = 2$

21. $(2^2 + 3^2)^2 = 169$

22. $(7^2 - 6^2)^2 = 169$

23. $\dfrac{4^3}{(3 + 5)^2} = 1$

24. $\dfrac{(4^2 - 1)}{(2^3 - 3)} = 3$

Explore

There are many different ways to make the numbers e.g.

$(4 + 3)^2 - (1 \times 5) = 44$
$(1 + 3 + 4)^2 - 5 = 59$
$2^3 + (5 \times 4) + 1 = 29$

It is possible to make all the numbers up to 20. Check the children have worked logically, e.g. by drawing up a table. They could make a list of powers to help them, e.g. $2^1 = 2$, $2^3 = 8$, $2^4 = 16$, $2^5 = 32$, etc.

page 58
Algebra **A1**
Using letters

1. $a + 1$
2. $2x$
3. $3p$
4. $2q + 3$
5. $y + 3$
6. $4z + 2$
7. $4p$
8. $3b$
9. $5n$
10. $6w$
11. $2p + 2q$
12. $a + b + c$
13. $2t + 6$
14. $2x + 2y$
15. $2f + g$
16. x^2
17. 25
18. ab
19. $3q$
20. $4(a + 1) = 4a + 4$
21. $(p + 1)^2 = (p + 1)(p + 1) = p^2 + 2p + 1$

page 59
Algebra **A1**
Using letters

1. $6 + z$
2. $4 - p$
3. $2q$
4. $y + 8$
5. $c - 9$
6. $f + g$
7. $t - 3$
8. $z + 5 - y$
9. $5a$
10. $3b$
11. $4g$
12. $6p$
13. $\frac{5}{x}$
14. $\frac{y}{4}$
15. $\frac{1}{2}$
16. $\frac{p}{q}$
17. $2h$
18. $3w$
19. z^2
20. d^2
21. $x + 3 - p$
22. $y - 6 + z$
23. $2a + 3$
24. $3m - 5$
25. $10p + q$
26. $2d + 5$
27. $\frac{c}{2} + 4$
28. $8 + 2z$
29. $3t - 15$
30. $2z + 3$
31. $h^2 + 10$
32. $q^2 - 3$
33. $a \rightarrow 3a$
$2 \rightarrow 6$
$x + 1 \rightarrow 3x + 3$
$a + b \rightarrow 3a + 3b$
$2a \rightarrow 6a$
34. $4 \rightarrow 14$
$\frac{1}{2} \rightarrow 3\frac{1}{2}$

$f \rightarrow 3f + 2$
$c + 1 \rightarrow 3c + 5$
$2 + q \rightarrow 8 + 3q$

page 60
Algebra **A1**
Using letters

1. $t + 12$ cm
2. $x - 3$ people

3. $h - 4$ years old
4. $6g$ kg
5. $\frac{x}{5}$ biscuits
6. $£(p + q - 4)$
7. $2k + 3$ people
8. $\frac{n}{3}$ cm
9. perimeter $= 4z + 8$ cm
area $= z^2 + 4z$ cm^2
10. $f^2 - g^2$ cm^2
11.– 16. Check children have used letters in an appropriate way.

page 61
Algebra **A2**
Using letters

1. 20
2. 11
3. 12
4. $x + 1$
5. $x + 7$
6. $x + 2$
7. $x + 14$
8. $x + 8$
9. $x + 15$
10. $x + 16$
11. $x - 8$
12. $x + 6$
13. $5x + 2x = 7x$
14. $7a + 2a = 9a$
15. $7c - 3c = 4c$
16. $6b - 4b = 2b$
17. $5d + d = 6d$
18. $e + 7e = 8e$
19. $4f - f = 3f$
20. $15q + 3q = 18q$
21. $2g + 7g = 9g$
22. $9y - 3y = 6y$
23. $8a + 3a + a = 12a$
24. $4x + 7x - x = 10x$
25. $2z - z + 3z = 4z$
26. $5p - 2p + 3p = 6p$
27. $19w - 15w + 9w = 13w$

page 62
Algebra **A2**
Combining terms

1. $y + 1 + y + 7 = 2y + 8$
2. $y + 1 + y + 15 = 2y + 16$
3. $y + 1 + y + 8 = 2y + 9$
4. $y + 13 + y + 15 = 2y + 28$
5. $y + 6 + y + 7 = 2y + 13$
6. $y + 7 + y + 8 = 2y + 15$
7. $y + 8 + y + 9 = 2y + 17$
8. $y + 8 + y + 16 = 2y + 24$
9. $p + 1 + p + 11 = 2p + 12$
10. $p + 1 + p + 2 = 2p + 3$
11. $p + 20 + p + 21 = 2p + 41$
12. $p + 11 + p + 12 = 2p + 23$
13. $p + 2 + p + 20 = 2p + 22$
14. $p + 11 + p + 22 = 2p + 33$
15. $p + 9 + p + 21 = 2p + 30$
16. $5c + 3c + 2c = 10c$
17. $4x + 3x + 2 = 7x + 2$
18. $5y - 2y - 4 = 3y - 4$
19. $3y + 3 + 4y = 7y + 3$
20. $2a + 5a - 6 = 7a - 6$
21. $7b - 3 + 2b = 9b - 3$
22. $9 + 3y - y = 9 + 2y$
23. $10 + 5x - 2x = 10 + 3x$
24. $3q + 5q + 1 = 8q + 1$
25. $7t - t - 1 = 6t - 1$
26. $8m - 5m - m = 2m$
27. $3z - z - 2 = 2z - 2$

page 63
Algebra **A2**
Combining terms

1. $3a + c$
2. $b + 2c$
3. $2a + 2c$
4. $4a + 2b$
5. $2b + 2c$
6. $3a + b + c$
7. $5a + c$
8. $2a + 2c$
9. $2a + 2c$
10. $3a + b + c$
11. $3a + b + c$
12. $2a + 3b$
13. $3a + 4 + 5a + 2 = 8a + 6$
14. $6b + 7 + 3b + 1 = 9b + 8$
15. $4y + 2 + 3y - 1 = 7y + 1$
16. $7z + 3 + 4z - 2 = 11z + 1$
17. $3p + 5p + 7 - 2p = 6p + 7$
18. $5q - 3 + 2q - q = 6q - 3$
19. $10c + 3 - 2c - 1 = 8c + 2$
20. $4t - t + 7 - 2t = t + 7$
21. $5 + 4m - m - 3 = 2 + 3m$
22. $7 + 8h - 2 - 3h = 5 + 5h$
23. $6g + 3 + 2g + 7 = 8g + 10$
24. $5z + 4 + 2y - 1 = 5z + 2y + 3$
25. $3a + b - a + 4 = 2a + b + 4$
26. $4w - 3y + 6y - 2 = 4w + 3y - 2$

Explore
Answers will vary.

page 64
Algebra **A3**
Substituting

1. $3a = 9$
2. $5a = 15$
3. $a + 1 = 4$
4. $3a + 2 = 11$
5. $4a - 1 = 11$
6. $6 - a = 3$

7. $8 + 2a = 14$ **8.** $9 - 2a = 3$ **9.** $\frac{a}{3} = 1$

10. $\frac{a}{2} + 1\frac{1}{2} = 3$ **11.** $a^2 = 9$ **12.** $a^2 - 4a = -3$

ⓔ 1. $3a = 15$ **2.** $5a = 25$ **3.** $a + 1 = 6$

4. $3a + 2 = 17$ **5.** $4a - 1 = 19$ **6.** $6 - a = 1$

7. $8 + 2a = 18$ **8.** $9 - 2a = -1$ **9.** $\frac{a}{3} = \frac{5}{3} = 1\frac{2}{3}$

10. $\frac{a}{2} + 1\frac{1}{2} = 4$ **11.** $a^2 = 25$ **12.** $a^2 - 4a = 5$

	$6x$	$x + 7$	$x - 2$	$4x + 1$	$5x - 3$	$x^2 - 1$
$x = 4$	24	11	2	17	17	15
$x = 1$	6	8	−1	5	2	0
$x = 10$	60	17	8	41	47	99
$x = 2$	12	9	0	9	7	3
$x = 7$	42	14	5	29	32	48
$x = 0$	0	7	−2	1	−3	−1

Explore

Answers will vary. Check children have used a variety of operations, brackets and powers.

---

page 65

Brackets   Algebra **A3**

1. $4(c + 3) = 4c + 12$ **2.** $3(x + 5) = 3x + 15$

3. $6(y + 4) = 6y + 24$ **4.** $2(p + 2) = 2p + 4$

5. $q(q + 7) = q^2 + 7q$ **6.** $3(a - 2) = 3a - 6$

7. $4(c - 1) = 4c - 4$ **8.** $2(d + 7) = 2d + 14$

9. $5(4 - x) = 20 - 5x$ **10.** $6(3 + y) = 18 + 6y$

11. $a(b + c) = ab + ac$ **12.** $2(x + y) = 2x + 2y$

13. $3(b - d) = 3b - 3d$ **14.** $2(z + \frac{1}{2}) = 2z + 1$

15. $4(2x + 1) = 8x + 4$ **16.** $3(5a - 3) = 15a - 9$

17. $6(2b - 9) = 12b - 54$ **18.** $5x + 10 = 5(x + 2)$

19. $2x - 4 = 2(x - 2)$ **20.** $4a + 8 = 4(a + 2)$

21. $3p - 6 = 3(p - 2)$ **22.** $6q + 42 = 6(q + 7)$

23. $7h - 56 = 7(h - 8)$ **24.** $4g - 4 = 4(g - 1)$

25. $5p + 5q = 5(p + q)$ **26.** $2a + 2 = 2(a + 1)$

27. $6 + 3d = 3(2 + d)$ **28.** $8 + 2f = 2(4 + f)$

29. $4a + 6 = 2(2a + 3)$

---

page 66

Substituting   Algebra **A3**

1. $p + q = 4 + 3 = 7$ **2.** $p - q = 4 - 3 = 1$

3. $2p - q = 8 - 3 = 5$ **4.** $3q + p = 9 + 4 = 13$

5. $pq = 4 \times 3 = 12$ **6.** $5p - 1 = 20 - 1 = 19$

7. $3 + 4q = 3 + 12 = 15$ **8.** $4pq = 4 \times 4 \times 3 = 48$

9. $3(p + q) = 3(4 + 3) = 21$ **10.** $5(p - 2) = 5(4 - 2) = 10$

11. $4(6 - q) = 4(6 - 3) = 12$ **12.** $2(3p - q) = 2(12 - 3) = 18$

13. $p^2 + 2q = 4^2 + 6 = 22$ **14.** $q^2 - p = 3^2 - 4 = 5$

15. $3p - 2q = 12 - 6 = 6$ **16.** $5q - 3p = 15 - 12 = 3$

17. $\frac{p}{2} = \frac{4}{2} = 2$ **18.** $\frac{q}{3} = \frac{3}{3} = 1$

19. $\frac{5p}{2} = \frac{20}{2} = 10$ **20.** $\frac{4q}{6} = \frac{12}{6} = 2$

ⓔ

1. $p + q = 0 + 1 = 1$ **2.** $p - q = 0 - 1 = -1$

3. $2p - q = 0 - 1 = -1$ **4.** $3q + p = 3 + 0 = 3$

5. $pq = 0 \times 1 = 0$ **6.** $5p - 1 = 0 - 1 = -1$

7. $3 + 4q = 3 + 4 = 7$ **8.** $4pq = 4 \times 0 \times 1 = 0$

---

9. $3(p + q) = 3(0 + 1) = 3$ **10.** $5(p - 2) = 5(0 - 2) = -10$

11. $4(6 - q) = 4(6 - 1) = 20$ **12.** $2(3p - q) = 2(0 - 1) = -2$

13. $p^2 + 2q = 0 + 2 = 2$ **14.** $q^2 - p = 1 - 0 = 1$

15. $3p - 2q = 0 - 2 = -2$ **16.** $5q - 3p = 5 - 0 = 5$

17. $\frac{p}{2} = \frac{0}{2} = 0$ **18.** $\frac{q}{3} = \frac{1}{3} = \frac{1}{3}$

19. $\frac{5p}{2} = \frac{0}{2} = 0$ **20.** $\frac{4q}{6} = \frac{4}{6} = \frac{2}{3}$

21. $C = (12 \times 5) + 2 = 62$ **22.** $A = 12 - (5 \times 2) = 2$

23. $G = 12 - 5 - 2 = 5$ **24.** $R = 12 + 5 + 4 = 21$

25. $L = \frac{12}{(5 - 2)} = 4$ **26.** $I = (12 \times 5) \div 2 = 30$

27. $A = 25 + 4 = 29$ **28.** $E = 5 + \frac{12}{2} = 11$

29. $B = 12^2 - (25 \times 5) = 19$

The letters spell the word ALGEBRAIC.

Explore

Answers will vary. Check children have used a variety of operations, brackets and powers.

---

page 67

Formulae   Algebra **A4**

1. $A = 8 \text{ cm} \times 4\cdot5 \text{ cm} = 36 \text{ cm}^2$

2. $l = 18 \text{ cm}^2 \div 8 \text{ cm} = 2\cdot25 \text{ cm}$

3. $w = 36 \text{ m}^2 \div 12 \text{ m} = 3 \text{ m}$

4. $P = 2(9 \text{ cm} + 3\cdot5 \text{ cm}) = 25 \text{ cm}$

5. $l = (56 \text{ cm} \div 2) - 11 \text{ cm} = 17 \text{ cm}$

6. $w = (34 \text{ m} \div 2) - 10\cdot5 \text{ m} = 6\cdot5 \text{ m}$

7. $(28 \text{ cm} \div 2) - 9 \text{ cm} = 5 \text{ cm}$ $A = 5 \text{ cm} \times 9 \text{ cm} = 45 \text{ cm}^2$

8. $48 \text{ m}^2 \div 6 \text{ m} = 8 \text{ m}$ $P = 2(8 \text{ m} + 6 \text{ m}) = 28 \text{ m}$

9. $A = 5 \text{ cm} \times 4 \text{ cm} \div 2 = 10 \text{ cm}^2$

10. $21 \text{ cm}^2 \times 2 = 42 \text{ cm}^2$ $b = 42 \text{ cm}^2 \div 7 \text{ cm} = 6 \text{ cm}$

11. $27 \text{ m}^2 \times 2 = 54 \text{ m}^2$ $h = 54 \text{ m}^2 \div 6 \text{ m} = 9 \text{ m}$

12. $40\cdot5 \text{ cm}^2 \times 2 = 81 \text{ cm}^2$ $h = b = \sqrt{81} \text{ cm}^2 = 9 \text{ cm}$

13. $hb = 9 \text{ cm}^2 \times 2 = 18 \text{ cm}^2$
$b{:}h = 2{:}1$ so $h = 2b$
$2b^2 = 18 \text{ cm}^2$
$b^2 = 9 \text{ cm}^2$
$b = 3 \text{ cm}$
$h = 2b = 6 \text{ cm}$

---

page 68

Formulae   Algebra **A4**

1. $K = (2 \times 3) - (6 \times 1) = 0$ **2.** $K = (2 \times 4) - (6 \times 2) = -4$

3. $K = (2 \times 6) - (6 \times 1) = 6$ **4.** $D = (7 \times 2) + (3 \times 1) = 17$

5. $D = (7 \times 3) + (3 \times 6) = 39$ **6.** $D = (7 \times 0\cdot5) + (3 \times 1\cdot5) = 8$

7. $P = 100 \div (4 \times 5) = 5$ **8.** $P = 100 \div (5 \times 10) = 2$

9. $P = 100 \div (3 \times 20) = 1\frac{2}{3}$ **10.** $Z = \frac{(11 + 7)}{2} = 9$

11. $Z = \frac{(4 + 9)}{2} = 6\frac{1}{2}$ **12.** $Z = \frac{(1\cdot2 + 0\cdot6)}{2} = 0\cdot9$

13. $T = \frac{7(7 + 1)}{2} = 28$ **14.** $T = \frac{10(10 + 1)}{2} = 55$

15. $T = \frac{1(1 + 1)}{2} = 1$ **16.** $G = \frac{4}{2} + (7 \times 3) = 23$

17. $G = \frac{18}{2} + (7 \times 2) = 23$ **18.** $G = \frac{13}{2} + (7 \times 0\cdot5) = 10$

ⓔ Various correct answers are possible except for T, where only $n = 1$ or $n = -2$ gives $T = 1$.

19. $10 \times 2\frac{1}{2} = 25$ A\$25   **20.** $14 \times 2\frac{1}{2} = 35$ A\$35

21. $9 \times 2\frac{1}{2} = 22\frac{1}{2}$ A\$22·50   **22.** $(20 \times 2) \div 5 = 8$ £8

23. $(15 \times 2) \div 5 = 6$ £6   **24.** $(30 \times 2) \div 5 = 12$ £12

25. $(9 \times 15) \div 5 + 32 = 59$ 59 °F

26. $(9 \times 20) \div 5 + 32 = 68$ 68 °F

27. $(9 \times 5) \div 5 + 32 = 41$ 41 °F

27. $2c + 15 = 29$ $c = \frac{14}{2} = 7$

28. $18 - 4d = 10$ $d = \frac{(18-10)}{4} = 2$

29. $5 + 11e = 49$ $e = \frac{(49-5)}{11} = 4$

30. $8f - 8 = 24$ $f = \frac{32}{8} = 4$

---

page 69
Finding formulae

I. $m = \frac{y}{12}$
2. $w = \frac{d}{7}$
3. $h = 24d$

4. $h = \frac{m}{60}$
5. $c = 100m$
6. $g = 1000k$

7. $v = 6h + 4s$
8. $w = 3t + 2b$
9. $l = 4c + 3s$

10. $w = b + 4$
II. $w = 2b + 6$
12. $w = 2b - 12$

page 70
Equations

I. $x = 6$
2. $y = 8$
3. $z = 11$

4. $p = 7$
5. $q = 8$
6. $p = 8$

7. $a = 12$
8. $b = 19$
9. $d = 6$

10. $f = 9$
II. $g = 22$
12. $f = 18$

13. $y = 9$
14. $x = 2$
15. $m = 30$

16. $m = 36 - 21 = 15$

17. $p = 48 - 19 = 29$ **18.** $q = 15 - 12 = 3$

19. $s = 47 - 36 = 11$ **20.** $t = 32 - 11 = 21$

21. $a + 6 = 13$ $a = 13 - 6 = 7$

22. $b - 14 = 9$ $b = 14 + 9 = 23$

23. $c + 7 = 21$ $c = 21 - 7 = 14$

24. $16 - d = 9$ $d = 16 - 9 = 7$

25. $e + 19 = 47$ $e = 47 - 19 = 28$

26. $f - 19 = 36$ $f = 36 + 19 = 55$

27. $15 + g = 71$ $g = 71 - 15 = 56$

28. $100 - h = 83$ $h = 100 - 83 = 17$

Ⓔ Answers will vary.

Explore

Answers will vary. Encourage children to spot patterns in their equations and use those patterns to predict other correct solutions.

e.g. $y + 1 = 6 \rightarrow 2y + 1 = 11 \rightarrow 3y + 1 = 16$ **or**

$y - 1 = 4 \rightarrow y - 2 = 3 \rightarrow y - 3 = 2$ etc.

---

page 71
Equations

I. $y = 6$
2. $z = 6$

3. $p = 7$
4. $q = 16$

5. $z = 8$
6. $h = 18$

7. $p = 9$
8. $g = 9$

9. $m = 8$
10. $y = 8$

II. $t = 12$
12. $n = 12$

13. $x = \frac{8}{2} = 4$
14. $a = \frac{8}{2} = 4$

15. $z = \frac{9}{3} = 3$
16. $h = \frac{20}{4} = 5$

17. $y = \frac{35}{5} = 7$
18. $g = \frac{24}{6} = 4$

19. $p = \frac{45}{9} = 5$
20. $q = \frac{24}{2} = 12$

21. $t = \frac{63}{7} = 9$
22. $d = \frac{40}{8} = 5$

23. $p = \frac{32}{4} = 8$
24. $b = \frac{27}{3} = 9$

25. $4a - 7 = 1$ $a = \frac{8}{4} = 2$

26. $3b + 1 = 13$ $b = \frac{12}{3} = 4$

---

page 72
Arithmogons

I.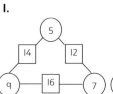
2.
3.

4.

$15 = 12 - x + 11 - x$
$\quad = 23 - 2x$
$2x = 8$
$x = 4$

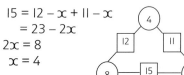

5.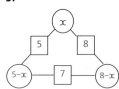

$7 = 5 - x + 8 - x$
$\quad = 13 - 2x$
$2x = 6$
$x = 3$

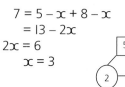

6.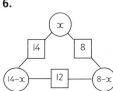

$12 = 14 - x + 8 - x$
$\quad = 22 - 2x$
$2x = 10$
$x = 5$

7.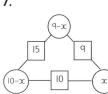

$15 = 10 - x + 9 - x$
$\quad = 19 - 2x$
$2x = 4$
$x = 2$

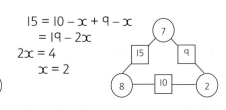

8.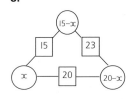

$23 = 15 - x + 20 - x$
$\quad = 35 - 2x$
$2x = 12$
$x = 6$

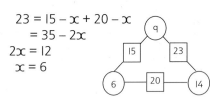

9.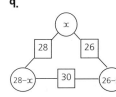

$30 = 28 - x + 26 - x$
$\quad = 54 - 2x$
$2x = 24$
$x = 12$

IO.

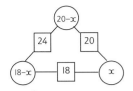

$24 = 20 - x + 18 - x$
$= 38 - 2x$
$2x = 14$
$x = 7$

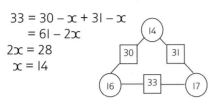

II.

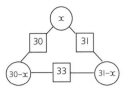

$33 = 30 - x + 31 - x$
$= 61 - 2x$
$2x = 28$
$x = 14$

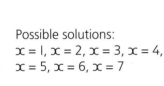

Explore

Letting one circle number be x (a positive number):

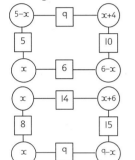

Possible solutions:
$x = 1, x = 2, x = 3, x = 4$

Possible solutions:
$x = 1, x = 2, x = 3, x = 4,$
$x = 5, x = 6, x = 7$

---

page 73
Straight-line graphs Algebra **A6**

Check children's graphs are correct.

I. $y = 3$	**2.** $x = 4$	**3.** $y = x$
4. $y = x + 1$	**5.** $y = x - 2$	**6.** $y = 2x$

Check children's graphs are correct.

7. $y = ^-2$	**8.** $x = ^-4$	**9.** $y = x - 1$
IO. $y = x + 3$	**II.** $y = x + 1$	**I2.** $y = 3x$

---

page 74
Straight-line graphs Algebra **A6**

I. $y = 2$: H, M	**2.** $y = ^-1$: J, D
3. $x = 4$: F, L	**4.** $y = 3$: N, A
5. $x = ^-3$: C, E	**6.** $x = 1$: A, K, I
7. $y = ^-5$: G, L	**8.** $x = 0$: M, B
9. $x = ^-4$: N, G	**IO.** $y = ^-4$: I

II.	(0,2)	(1,3)	(2,4)	(5,7)
I2.	(3,0)	(5,2)	(1,$^-$2)	(9,6)
I3.	(2,5)	(1,2)	(4,11)	(0,$^-$1)
I4.	(3,7)	(2,6)	($^-$3,1)	($^-$1,3)
I5.	(2,1)	(5,7)	(3,3)	(0,$^-$3)
I6.	(2,12)	(5,30)	(4,24)	(0,0)
I7.	(4,2)	(8,4)	(12,6)	(2,1)

I8. Many correct answers e.g. (0,1) (1,3) (2,5) (3,7)
I9. Many correct answers e.g. (0,0) (1,3) (2,6)(3,9)
20. Many correct answers e.g. (0,$^-$6) (1,$^-$5) (2,$^-$4) (3,$^-$3)
2I. Many correct answers e.g. (0,$^-$2) (1,3) (2,8) (3,13)
22. Many correct answers e.g. (0,0) (1,1) (2,2) (3,3)
23. Many correct answers e.g. (0,$^-$4) (1,$^-$1) (2,2) (3,5)

---

page 75
Straight-line graphs Algebra **A6**

I. $x = ^-1$
2. $y = ^-3$
3. $y = x$
4. $y = x + 2$

5.–8. Check children's graphs are correct. All lines start from (0,0) and get progressively steeper.
9.–13. Check children's graphs are correct. All lines are parallel to $y = x$.

Explore

Children should draw up tables of values for each equation. E.g. for x + y = 6:

x	0	I	2	3	4	5	6
y	6	5	4	3	2	I	0

All lines with equations of this type are parallel.

---

page 76
Graphs Algebra **A7**

I. IO minutes	**2.** 400 m
3. 4 minutes	**4.** 6 minutes
5. quicker coming back	**6.** 400 km
7. 6 hours	**8.** I stop
9. $133\frac{1}{3}$ km	**IO.** 16:00 to 18:00
II. 66·67 km/h	**I2.** 1000 m = I km
I3. 30 minutes	**I4.** 15 minutes

I5. The last part was slowest. It took 7·5 minutes.
I6. 15 minutes

---

page 77
Graphs

Look for suitable explanations, e.g. bath starts to fill (maybe only the hot tap is turned on), then rate of filling slows at 2 minutes (the tap may be turned down), the rate speeds up at 4 minutes (maybe both taps are turned on). The amount of water stays constant from 5 to 8 minutes (while someone is in the bath), then empties at a steady rate (when the plug is pulled out). All the water has drained away after IO minutes.

I. 4 hours	**2.** 20 km, 40 km	**3.** $4\frac{3}{4}$ hours
4. 20 km, 45 km	**5.** 12:00	**6.** 11:30
7. Anna 20 km, Tom 30 km		**8.** 12:30 **9.** I hour
IO. Tom	**II.** $\frac{3}{4}$ hour	**I2.** Anna 12:10, Tom 11:45

---

page 78
Graphs Algebra **A7**

I.

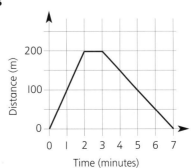

2.

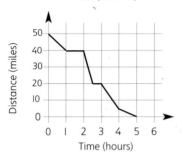

3.

Distance (miles) vs Time (hours) graph

4. £75   **5.** £125   **6.** £112·50
7. £90   **8.** 200 miles   **9.** 100 miles
10. 400 miles   **11.** 270 miles

4. 100 miles = 160 km   **5.** 300 miles = 480 km
6. 250 miles = 400 km   **7.** 180 miles = 288 km
8. 200 miles = 320 km   **9.** 150 miles = 240 km
10. 400 miles = 640 km   **11.** 270 miles = 432 km

Explore
Children's graphs and stories should discuss and be aware of sensible speeds for walking/cycling/driving/flying etc.

page 79
Function machines   Algebra **A8**

1. $x = 4 \to 11$ $x = 7 \to 20$ $x = 10 \to 29$
2. $x = 4 \to 10$ $x = 7 \to 16$ $x = 10 \to 22$
3. $x = 4 \to 37$ $x = 7 \to 67$ $x = 10 \to 97$
4. $x = 4 \to 23$ $x = 7 \to 35$ $x = 10 \to 47$
5. $x = 4 \to 18$ $x = 7 \to 51$ $x = 10 \to 102$
6. $x = 4 \to 27$ $x = 7 \to 42$ $x = 10 \to 57$
7. $2x + 1$

in	1	2	3	4	5
out	3	5	7	9	11

8. $3x - 1$

in	1	2	3	4	5
out	2	5	8	11	14

9. $4x - 3$

in	1	2	3	4	5
out	1	5	9	13	17

10. $2x + 3$

in	1	2	3	4	5
out	5	7	9	11	13

11. $3(x + 1)$

in	1	2	3	4	5
out	6	9	12	15	18

12. $x^2 - 1$

in	1	2	3	4	5
out	0	3	8	15	24

13. $5(x - 1)$

in	1	2	3	4	5
out	0	5	10	15	20

14. $(x + 6) - 3 = x + 3$

in	1	2	3	4	5
out	4	5	6	7	8

See equation above each table.

page 80
Function machines   Algebra **A8**

1. $2(x + 3) = 14$ $x = 4$ **2.** $3(x + 4) = 30$ $x = 6$
3. $3(x - 4) = 9$ $x = 7$ **4.** $2x - 1 = 5$ $x = 3$
5. $3x - 5 = 10$ $x = 5$ **6.** $5x - 3 = 42$ $x = 9$
7. $x^2 + 3 = 7$ $x = 2$ **8.** $10x - 7 = 73$ $x = 8$
9. $(x + 1)^2 = 49$ $x = 6$ **10.** $x^3 - 5 = 22$ $x = 3$
11. $2x + 3 = 17$ $x = 7$ **12.** $3x - 4 = 11$ $x = 5$
13. $5(x + 6) = 45$ $x = 3$ **14.** $4(x - 3) = 20$ $x = 8$
15. $x^2 - 7 = 9$ $x = 4$ **16.** $(x - 2)^2 = 25$ $x = 7$

page 81
Function machines   Algebra **A8**

1. $x \to 2x + 5$

in	1	2	3	4	5	6	7	8
out	7	9	11	13	15	17	19	21

2. $x \to 3x - 1$

in	1	2	3	4	5	6	7	8
out	2	5	18	11	14	17	20	23

3. $x \to 8 - x$

in	1	2	3	4	5	6	7	8
out	7	6	5	4	3	2	1	0

4. $x \to 4 + 3x$

in	1	2	3	4	5	6	7	8
out	7	10	13	16	19	22	25	28

5. $x \to 100 - 9x$

in	1	2	3	4	5	6	7	8
out	91	82	73	64	55	46	37	28

6. $x \rightarrow x^2 + 1$

in	1	2	3	4	5	6	7	8
out	2	5	10	17	26	37	50	65

7. $x \rightarrow \frac{x}{2} + 3$

in	1	2	3	4	5	6	7	8
out	3·5	4	4·5	5	5·5	6	6·5	7

8. $x \rightarrow x^2 + \frac{x}{2}$

in	1	2	3	4	5	6	7	8
out	1·5	5	10·5	18	27·5	39	52·5	68

9. $x \rightarrow 2x + 1$

in	2	5	4	7	3	6	8	10
out	5	11	9	15	7	13	17	21

10. $x \rightarrow 3x - 1$

in	4	8	2	6	3	7	1	5
out	11	23	5	17	8	20	2	14

11. $x \rightarrow 5x - 7$

in	10	5	7	8	4	9	6	3
out	43	18	28	33	13	38	23	8

12. $x \rightarrow x^2 + 1$

in	9	6	5	7	10	3	8	2
out	82	37	26	50	101	10	65	5

13. $x \rightarrow 20 - 2x$

in	4	7	3	5	2	9	6	8
out	12	6	14	10	16	2	8	4

14. $x \rightarrow (x - 1)^2$

in	1	3	5	7	4	8	2	6
out	0	4	16	36	9	49	1	25

page 82
Sequences
Algebra **A9**

1. 2, 4, 8, 16, 32, 64, 128
2. 73, 68, 63, 58, 53, 48, 43
3. 3, 4, 6, 9, 13, 18, 24
4. 8, 4, 2, 1, $\frac{1}{2}$, $\frac{1}{4}$, $\frac{1}{8}$
5. 1, 4, 9 16, 25, 36, 49
6. 3, 6, 12, 24, 48, 96, 192
7. 2, 5, 8, 11, 14, 17, 20
8. 1, 2, 4, 8, 16, 32, 64
9. 74, 69, 64, 59, 54, 49

10. 64, 32, 16, 8, 4, 2
11. 1, 3, 9, 27, 81, 243
12. 2, 20, 200, 2000, 20 000, 200 000
13. 1·2, 1·1, 1·0, 0·9, 0·8, 0·7
14. $1\frac{1}{4}$, $1\frac{1}{2}$, $1\frac{3}{4}$, 2, $2\frac{1}{4}$, $2\frac{1}{2}$

page 83
Sequences
Algebra **A9**

1. 2, 4, 6, 8, 10, 12	℮	add 2
2. 5, 9, 13, 17, 21, 25	℮	add 4
3. 56, 51, 46, 41, 36, 31	℮	subtract 5
4. 0·3, 0·55, 0·8, 1·05, 1·3, 1·55	℮	add 0·25
5. 7, 13, 19, 25, 31, 37	℮	add 6
6. 90, 77, 64, 51, 38, 25	℮	subtract 13

7. 4, 8, 12, 16, 20, 24, 28   add 4
8. 5, 9, 13, 17, 21, 25, 29   add 4
9. 4, 7, 10, 13, 16, 19, 22   add 3
10. 4, 6, 8, 10, 12, 14, 16   add 2
11. 3, 5, 7, 9, 11, 13, 15   add 2

page 84
Sequences
Algebra **A9**

1. 4, 12, 28, 60, 124, 252
2. 3, 4, 6, 10, 18, 34
3. 2, 3, 5, 9, 17, 33
4. 156, 76, 36, 16, 6, 1
5. 4, 12, 36, 108, 324, 972
6. $\frac{1}{4}$, 1, $2\frac{1}{2}$, $5\frac{1}{2}$, $11\frac{1}{2}$, $23\frac{1}{2}$
7. 0·14, 0·4, 3, 29, 289, 2889
8. 2, 7, 22, 67, 202, 607
9. 2, 4·2, 8·6, 17·4, 35, 70·2
10. 1, 1·4, 2·2, 3·8, 7, 13·4

Explore
6, 3, 10, 5, 16, 8, 4, 2, 1, 4, 2, 1, 4, ... the chain then repeats as 4, 2, 1, 4, 2, 1, ...

Check that children have used a logical approach, e.g. considering start numbers 1, 2, 3, ...

1, 4, 2, 1, 4, 2, 1, ...
2, 1, 4, 2, 1, ...
3, 10, 5, 16, 8, 4, 2, 1, ...
4, 2, 1, ...
5, 16, 8, 4, 2, 1, ...
7, 22, 11, 34, 17, 52, 26, 13, 40, 20, 10, 5, 16, 8, 4, 2, 1, ...
8, 4, 2, 1, ...
9, 28, 14, 7, 22, 11, 34, 17, 52, 26, 13, 40, 20, 10, 5, 16, 8, 4, 2, 1, ...
10, 5, 16, 8, 4, 2, 1, ...

Using this rule all numbers eventually follow the pattern 4, 2, 1, 4, 2, 1, ...

page 85
The nth term
Algebra **A10**

1. 6n
2. 2n + 1
3. 3n – 2
4. 10n + 1
5. 5n – 6
6. $\frac{n}{2} + 3$
7. $n^2 - 3$
8. 40

9. 30	**10.** 21
11. 30	**12.** 40
13. 32	**14.** 51
15. 52	**16.** 42

page 86
The nth term Algebra **A10**

1. $3 \times 4 + 7 = 19$ $3 \times 15 + 7 = 52$ $3 \times 21 + 7 = 70$
2. $4 \times 3 - 1 = 11$ $4 \times 11 - 1 = 43$ $4 \times 18 - 1 = 71$
3. $10 \times 6 - 3 = 57$ $10 \times 10 - 3 = 97$ $10 \times 50 - 3 = 497$
4. $6 \times 4 + 4 = 28$ $6 \times 8 + 4 = 52$ $6 \times 15 + 4 = 94$
5. $4^2 + 4 = 20$ $6^2 + 4 = 40$ $10^2 + 4 = 104$
6. $\frac{4}{2} + 5 = 7$ $\frac{18}{2} + 5 = 14$ $\frac{23}{2} + 5 = 16\frac{1}{2}$

7. double term number	2n
8. 10 × term number	10n
9. double term number add 1	2n + 1
10. 3 × term number add 1	3n + 1
11. 10 × term number add 3	10n + 3
12. 4 × term number	4n
13. 3 × term number subtract 1	3n − 1
14. 5 × term number subtract 2	5n − 2

page 87
The nth term Algebra **A10**

1a. 3, 5, 7, 9...	2n +1	**1b.** 3, 4, 5, 6...	n + 2
2a. 3, 6, 9, 12...	3n	**2b.** 3, 5, 7, 9...	2n + 1
3a. 3, 7, 11, 15...	4n − 1	**3b.** 3, 6, 9, 12...	3n
4a. 12, 19, 26, 33...	7n + 5	**4b.** 7, 10, 13, 16...	3n + 4
5a. 9, 14, 19, 24...	5n + 4	**5b.** 7, 10, 13, 16...	3n + 4

Explore

Check the children have drawn a table to help them find the nth term correctly.

$1 + 2 + 3 + 4 + 5 + 6 + 7 + 8 + 9 + 10 = 55$

Using the rule with n = 10 gives $\frac{1}{2}(10 \times 11) = 55$.

Using the rule with n = 100 gives $= \frac{1}{2}(100 \times 101) = 5050$.

page 88
Weight and capacity Measures **M1**

1. 3000 ml = 3 l	**2.** 4·6 l = 4600 ml	**3.** 430 cl = 4·3 l
4. 650 ml = 65 cl	**5.** 75 cl = 0·75 l	**6.** 0·56 l = 560 ml

7. 1·23 l = 123 cl   **8.** 2 l = 2000 cm³
9. 325 cm³ = 32·5 cl   **10.** 180 cm³ = 180 ml
11. 0·8 l = 800 cm³   **12.** 3·5 gallons = 28 pints
13. 20 pints = 2·5 gallons   **14.** 100 pints ≈ 57 l
15. 35 cl = 350 cm³

16. 46 cl = 0·46 l   460 cm³
  0·53 l   530 cm³
  650 ml = 0·65 l   650 cm³
  $1\frac{1}{2}$ pt ≈ 0·9 l   900 cm³
  $\frac{1}{4}$ gallon ≈ 1·1 l   1100 cm³
  1·6 l   1600 cm³

---

17. $\frac{1}{2}$ gall ≈ 2·2 l   2200 cm³
  2·3 l   2300 cm³
  2400 ml = 2·4 l   2400 cm³
  250 cl = 2·5 l   2500 cm³
  300 cl = 3 l   3000 cm³
  6 pt ≈ 3·4 l   3400 cm³

18. g or kg	**19.** tonnes
20. litres	**21.** g
22. ml or cl or cm³	**23.** kg
24. litres	**25.** 50 g
26. 350 ml	**27.** 30 g

page 89
Weight and capacity Measures **M1**

1. 426 g = 0·426 kg	**2.** 0·47 kg = 470 g
3. 700 g = 0·7 kg	**4.** 3500 kg = 3·5 tonnes
5. 2·6 tonnes = 2600 kg	**6.** 70 g = 0·07 kg
7. 9 g = 0·009 kg	**8.** 3 lb = 48 oz
9. 0·5 lb = 8 oz	**10.** 40 oz = 2·5 lb
11. 100 lb ≈ 45·5 kg	**12.** 2·5 kg ≈ 5·5 lb

13. 20 oz ≈ 0·6 kg   600 g
  650 g = 0·65 kg   650 g
  0·75 kg   750 g
  3·3 lb ≈ 1·5 kg   1500 g
  0·006 tonnes = 6 kg   6000 g

14. 100 oz ≈ 2·8 kg   2800 g
  3·7 kg   3700 g
  3900 g = 3·9 kg   3900 g
  0·004 tonnes = 4 kg   4000 g
  4700 g = 4·7 kg   4700 g
  11 lb ≈ 5 kg   5000 g

Explore
This task is best done by rough drawing.

  100 cubes are needed to fill one 10 × 10 tray.
  1000 cubes are needed for 10 trays.
  1000 cm³ = 1 litre.

page 90
Weight and capacity problems Measures **M1**

1. 5·5 kg − 0·65 kg = 4·85 kg
2. 425 g × 5 = 2125 g = 2·125 kg
3. 1 oz ≈ 28 g → 24p for 28 g ≈ 86p for 100g
  Supermarket is better value.
4. 1 kg ≈ 2·2 lb → £1.50/lb ≈ £3·30/kg
  Supermarket is cheaper.
5. 375 g + 500 g + 150 g = 1025 g = 1·025 kg
6. 1 litre ≈ 1·75 pt
  £2·10 for 6 pt ≈ 61p per litre
  £1·80 for 3 litre = 60p per litre
  Second shop is cheaper.
7. 1406p ÷ 76 p = 18·5
  Simon buys 18·5 litres
8. 5 lb ≈ 2·3 kg

6000g = 6 kg   100 oz ≈ 2·8 kg
She should choose 6000 g bar as it is the largest.

page 91
Surface area   Area

1. 2(4 cm × 5 cm) + 2(3 cm × 5 cm) +2(3 cm × 4 cm) = 94 cm²
2. 2(2 cm × 3 cm) + 2(2 cm × 8 cm) +2(3 cm × 8 cm) = 92 cm²
3. 2(4 cm × 8 cm) + 2(4 cm × 9 cm) +2(8 cm × 9 cm) = 280 cm²
4. 2(10 cm × 7 cm) + 2(10 cm × 3 cm) +2(7 cm × 3 cm) = 242 cm²
5. 2(5 cm × 15 cm) + 2(5 cm × 6 cm) +2(15 cm × 6 cm) = 390 cm²
6. 2(5 cm × 7 cm) + 2(5 cm × 7 cm) +2(7 cm × 7 cm) = 238 cm²
7. 18 cm²   8. 22 cm²
9. 26 cm²   10. 14 cm²
11. 18 cm²   12. 22 cm²

Explore
Children should be encouraged to show their results clearly in a table and look for patterns. E.g.

no cubes	no of different models	smallest surface area cm³
2	1	10
3	2	14 (both the same)
4	3	16

page 92
Surface area   Area

1. 2(30 + 60 + 18) + 2 (30 + 30 + 9) − 2(30) = 216 + 138 − 60 = 294 cm²
2. 2(35 + 65 + 91) + 2(20 + 28 + 35) − 2(35) = 382 + 166 − 70 = 478 cm²
3. 2(80 + 72 + 90) + 2(24 + 12 + 32) − 2(32) = 484 + 136 − 64 = 556 cm²
4. 2(84 + 24 + 14) + 2(35 + 35 + 49) − 2(35) = 244 + 238 − 70 = 412 cm²
5. 2(24 + 27 + 72) + 2(12 + 12 + 16) − 2(16) = 246 + 80 − 32 = 294 cm²
6. 2(120 + 40 + 48) + 2(30 + 40 + 12) − 2(40) + 2(30 + 40 + 12) − 2(40) = 416 + 164 − 80 + 164 − 80 = 584 cm²

7. √(96 ÷ 6) = √16 = 4   4cm
8. √(216 ÷ 6) = √36 = 6   6 cm
9. √(54 ÷ 6) = √9 = 3   3 cm
10. √(24 ÷ 6) = √4 = 2   2 cm
11. √(384 ÷ 6) = √64 = 8   8 cm
12. √(600 ÷ 6) = √100 =10   10 cm
13. √(294 ÷ 6) = √49 = 7   7 cm
14. √(150 ÷ 6) = √25 = 5   5 cm
15. √(486 ÷ 6) = √81 = 9   9 cm
16. √(60000 ÷ 6) = √10000 =100   100 cm

Explore
Children should be encouraged to tabulate their results clearly and note that, e.g. 16 × 2 × 1 is a different orientation of 1 × 2 × 16.

---

e.g. 32 cubes

length	width	height	S.A.(cm²)
32	1	1	130
16	1	2	100
8	1	4	88
8	2	2	72
4	4	2	64

4 × 4 × 2 gives smallest surface area

36 cubes

length	width	height	S.A.(cm²)
36	1	1	146
18	1	2	112
9	1	4	98
9	2	2	80
12	1	3	102
6	6	1	96
6	3	2	72
4	3	3	66

4 × 3 × 3 gives smallest surface area

page 93
Surface area   Area

whole cuboid
2(60 × 30) + 2(60 × 20) + 2(20 × 30) = 7200 cm²
small cuboid
2(10 × 30) + 2(10 × 20) + 2(20 × 30) = 2200 cm²
large cuboid
2(50 × 30) + 2(50 × 20) + 2(20 × 30) = 6200 cm²

red area = 7200 cm²
yellow area = 2 × 600 cm² = 1200 cm²
ratio yellow:red = 1200:7200 = 1:6
1. 2(100 + 280 + 280) = 1320 cm²
2. 2(112 + 154 + 352) = 1236 cm²
3. 2(280 + 680 + 476) = 2872 cm²
🌐1. lengths × 2 5280 cm²   lengths × 3 11 880 cm²
2. lengths × 2 4944 cm²   lengths × 3 11 124 cm²
3. lengths × 2 11 488 cm²   lengths × 3   25 848 cm²

Explore
6 faces each l × l = l²
Surface area = 6 l²

page 94
Area   Area

1. ½ (4 cm × 6 cm) = 12 cm²
2. ½ (3·6 cm × 8 cm) = 14·4 cm²
3. ½ (5 cm × 9 cm) = 22·5 cm²
4. ½ (4·8 cm × 6 cm) = 14·4 cm²
5. ½ (6·8 cm × 10 cm) = 34 cm²

6. $\frac{1}{2}$(12 cm × 11·8 cm) = 70·8 cm²

7. $\frac{1}{2}$(4 cm × 3·4 cm) = 6·8 cm²

8. $\frac{1}{2}$(13·2 cm × 8 cm) = 52·8 cm²

9. $\frac{1}{2}$(5 cm × 6 cm) = 15 cm²

10. h = 2 × 300 cm² × 20 cm = 30 cm
11. b = 2 × 14 cm² × 4 cm = 7 cm
12. h = 2 × 16·8 cm² × 8 cm = 4·2 cm
13. b = 2 × 70 cm² × 10 cm = 14 cm
14. h = 2 × 15·5 cm² × 6·2 cm = 5 cm
15. h = b = $\sqrt{(2 × 72 \text{ cm}^2)}$ = 12 cm
16. h = b = $\sqrt{(2 × 32 \text{ cm}^2)}$ = 8 cm

17. $\frac{1}{2}$(5 cm + 10 cm) × 4 cm = 30 cm²

18. $\frac{1}{2}$(5 cm + 8 cm) × 6 cm = 39 cm²

19. $\frac{1}{2}$(8 cm + 6 cm) × 7 cm = 49 cm²

20. (3 cm × 10 cm) + (3 cm × 5 cm) = 45 cm²

21. (8 cm × 9 cm) + (5 cm × 5 cm) = 97 cm²

22. (16 cm × 11 cm) + $\frac{1}{2}$(10 cm × 10 cm) = 226 cm²

page 95
Area   Area **M3**

1. (1000 m × 800 m) − (300 m × 600 m) = 620 000 m²
   = 6·2 hectares
2. (420 m × 350 m) − (200 m × 240 m) = 99 000 m²
   = 9·9 hectares
3. (650 m × 450 m) − (250 m × 150 m) = 255 000 m²
   = 25·5 hectares
4. (145 m × 310 m) − (85 m × 220 m) = 26 250 m²
   = 26·25 hectares
5. $\frac{1}{2}$(2 × 2) = 2 cm²
6. $\frac{1}{2}$(3 × 5) = 7·5 cm²
7. 2 × 3 = 6 cm²
8. $\frac{1}{2}$(2 + 4) × 4 = 12 cm²
9. $\frac{1}{2}$(3 + 5) × 3 = 12 cm²

Explore

Area (units ²)	No. of quadrilaterals
0·5	0
1	5
1·5	3
2	5
2·5	1
3	1
3·5	0
4	1

page 96
Area Problems   Area **M3**

1. 45·7 m × 38·2 m = 1745·74 m²
2. 851 m² ÷ 37 m = 23 m
3. (22 m × 18·5 m) − $\frac{1}{2}$(13·2 m × 7·5 m) = 357·5 m²
4. (650 m × 375 m) − (75 m × 60 m) = 239 250 m²
5. (52 m × 47 m) − 133 m² = 2311 m²

6. 14·5 m × 11·8 m = 171·1 m²
   172 × 23·5 = £4042
7. (13·8 m × 11·7 m) − 9·6 m2 = 151·86 m²
8. (66 m × 27 m) − (5 m × 8 m) = 1742 m²

page 97
Lines and angles   Lines and angles **S1**

1-4

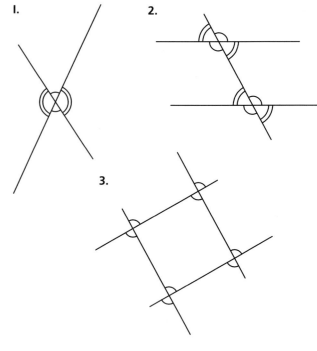

1.
2.
3.
4.

5. a = 35° b = 145° c = 145°
6. a = 50° b = 130° c = 130°
7. a = 65° b = 65° c = 115°
8. a = 108° b = 72° c = 108°
9. a = 66° b = 114° c = 114°
10. a = 95° b = 125° c = 55°
11. a = 68° b = 81° c = 99°
12. a = 64° b = 64° c = 64°
13. a = 70° b = 110° c = 70°
14. a = 116° b = 64° c = 64°
15. a = 90° b = 90° c = 75°

page 98
Angles of a triangle   Lines and angles **S1**

1. a = 54°
2. b = 43°
3. c = 140°
4. d = 125°
5. e = 50°
6. f = 122°
7. g = 52°
8. h = 68°
9. i = 142°

Explore
Check that children's explanations use knowledge of alternate angles, the sum of angles in a triangle and on a straight line, and that they recognise that the exterior angle equals the sum of two opposite interior angles.

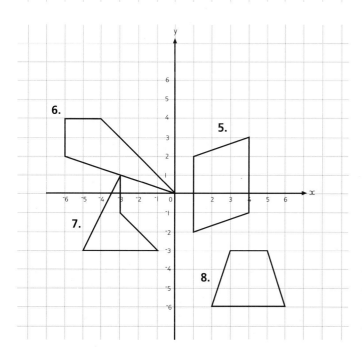

1. (⁻1,1)
2. (5,⁻6)
3. (⁻1,⁻3)
4. (1,2)
5. Children's answers will vary, probably (⁻1,⁻2) or (⁻5,⁻4)
   (or any points on lines y = 2x + 8 or y = 2x ⁻2)
6. Children's answers will vary, probably (4,1) or (1,5)
   or any point on line 8y + 2x = 29
7. Children's answers will vary, probably a
   point on line y = (3 or (6,⁻1) or (⁻2,⁻1)
8. Children's answers will vary, probably (0,1)
   or (⁻3,4) or (3,1) or (0,⁻2) or...
9. C (⁻2,4)
10. A (⁻1,⁻2)
11. E (1,2)
12. F (⁻3,2)
13. B (4,⁻4)
14. H (4,3)
15. D (⁻5,1)
16. G (1,⁻3)

These triangles are congruent:
    A and **J**
    B and **G**
    H and **I**
    D and **F**

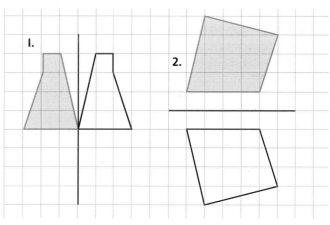

1. triangle (right-angled)
2. triangle
3. square
4. rectangle
5. parallelogram
6. kite
7. arrowhead
8. trapezium
9. (⁻3,4)
10. (4,2)
11. (⁻4,⁻1)
12. (⁻1,2)
13. (0,⁻2·5)
14. (⁻4·5,⁻3)
15. (⁻3,2)
16. (4,2)
17. (5,3)
18. (2,3)
19. (3,⁻3·5)
20. (1,0)
21. (⁻2,⁻1)
22. (⁻5,2)
23. (4,0)
24. (⁻3·5,⁻3)
25. (3,⁻2·5)
26. (0,⁻3·5)

27–32 Children's answers will vary.

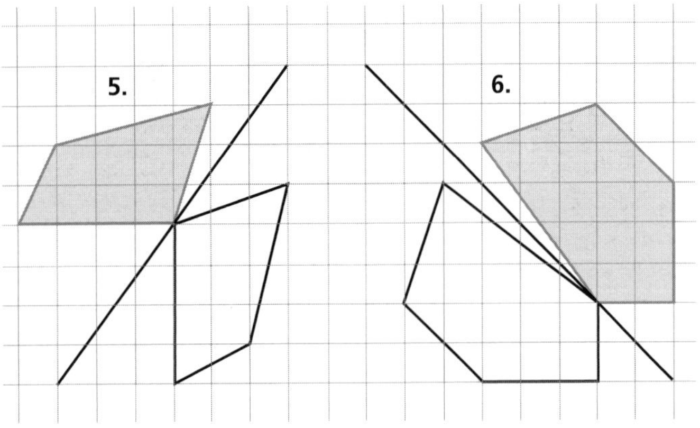
5.
6.

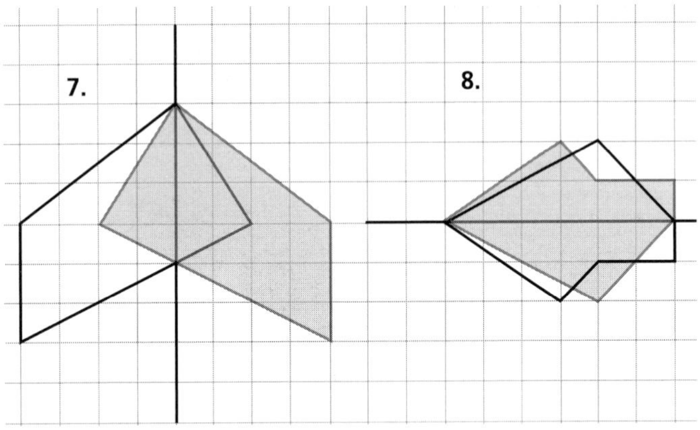
7.
8.

9-14 Children's own drawings

page 102
Drawing reflections

Reflections S3

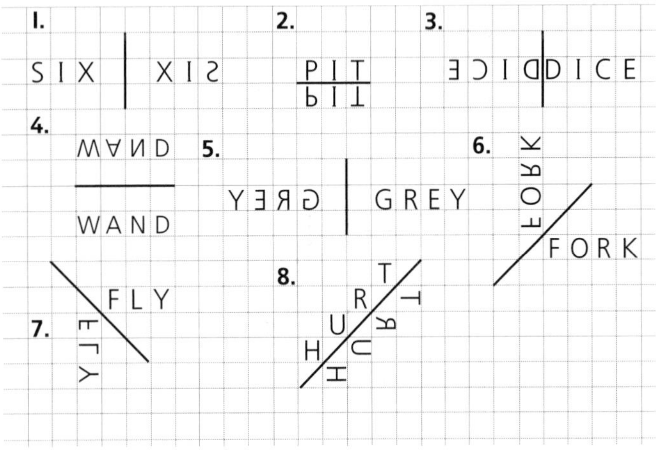
1.
SIX
2.
PIT
3.
DICE
4.
WAND
5.
GREY
6.
FORK
7.
FLY
8.
HURT

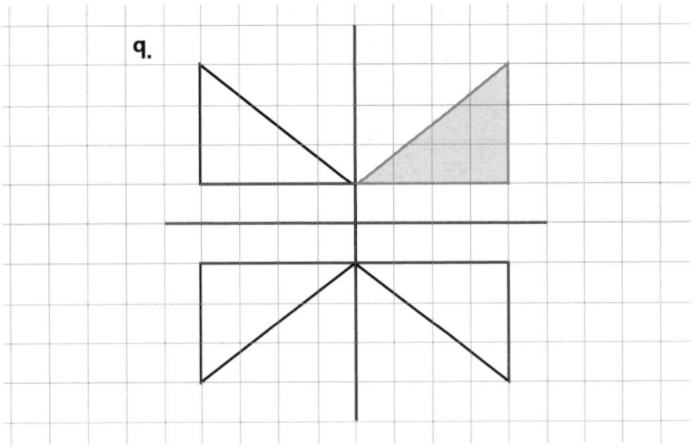
9.

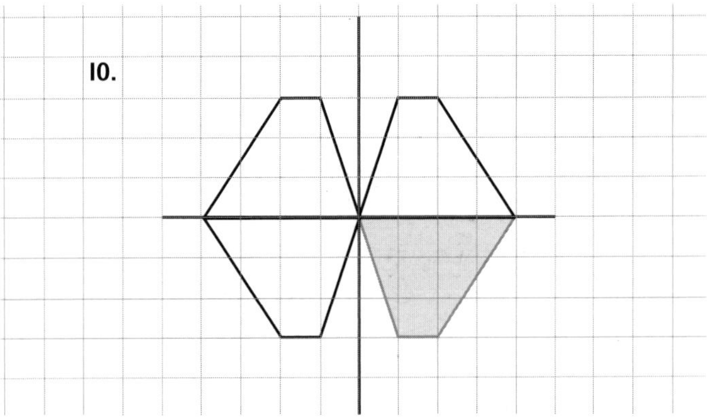
10.

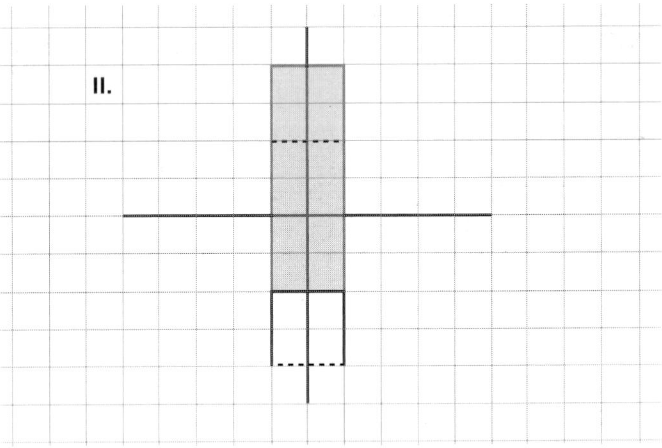
11.

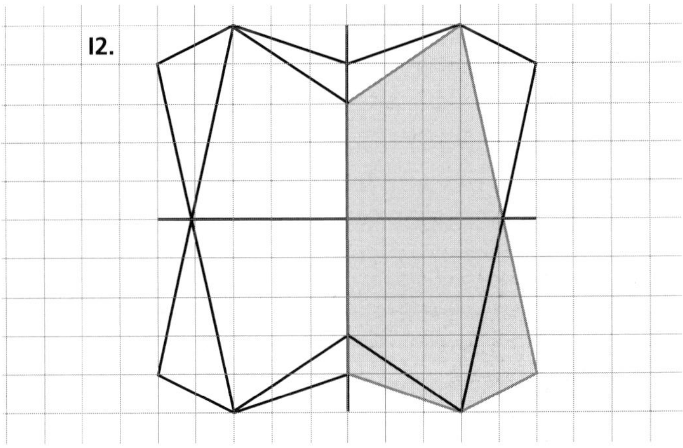
12.

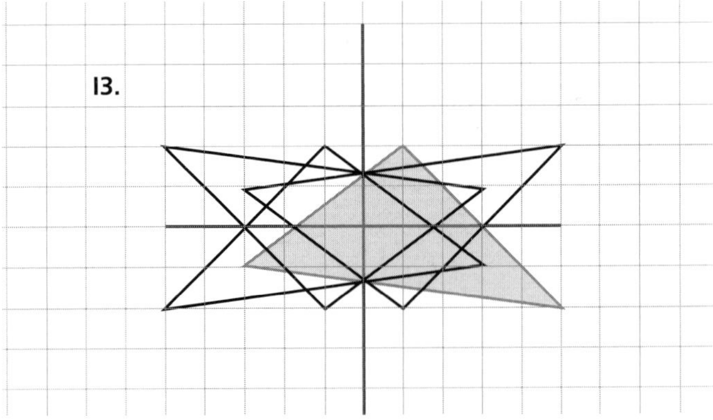
13.

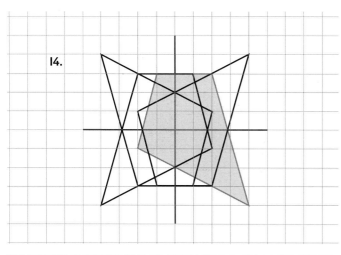

14.

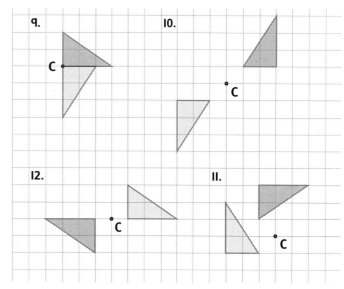

9. 10. 12. 11.

page 103
Rotating shapes

Rotations **S4**

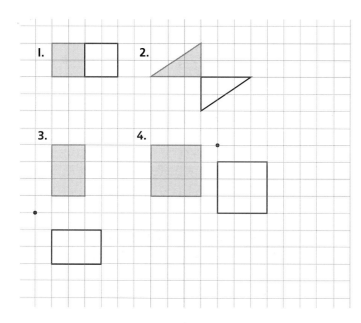

1. 2.

3. 4.

13.

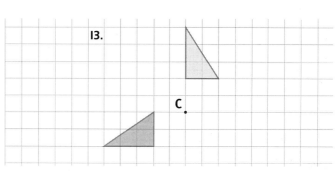

9. 90° anticlockwise or 270° clockwise
10. 180°
11. 90° clockwise or 270° anticlockwise
12. 180°
13. 90° anticlockwise or 270° clockwise

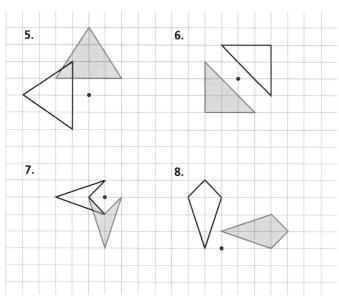

5. 6.

7. 8.

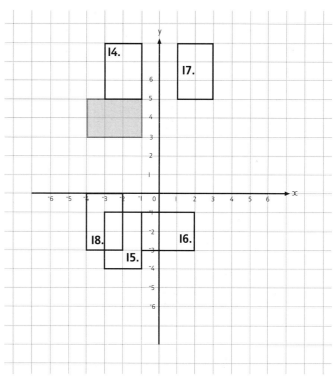

14. 17.
18. 16.
15.

page 104
Rotations, reflections, transformations

  I. rotation 180° centre (0,0)
  2. rotation 90° clockwise, centre (I,I)
  3. reflection in y axis
  4. reflection in $x = {}^-I$
  5. translation I left, 3 up
  6. reflection in x axis
  7. translation 3 right, 3 down
  8. rotation 180° centre (0,0)
  9. reflection in x axis
  10. rotation 180° centre (0·5, ⁻I·5)
  IIa. (5,I)   **b.** (I,⁻I) c. (⁻I, 5)
  I2a. (⁻6,⁻2) **b.** (⁻5,⁻7) c. (⁻I, 3)
  I3a. (I,⁻4) **b.** (⁻5,⁻2) c. (I, 0)

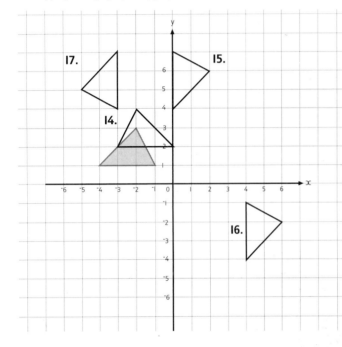

page 105
Order of rotational symmetry

  I. 6   **2.** 4   **3.** 4   **4.** 3   **5.** 5
  6. 2 **7.** 5   **8.** 3   **9.** 8   **I0.** 2

Letters
order 2   H,I,N,O,S,X,Z

Explore
Answers will vary.

page 106
Line symmetry and rotational symmetry

  I. A,E,H,J
  2. B,D,F,K,
  3. C,G,I,L

Explores
Answers will vary.

page 107
Views of 3-d shapes

	Front	Right	Left	Top

Explore
Answers will vary

page 108
Views of 3-d shapes

	Front	Right	Left	Top

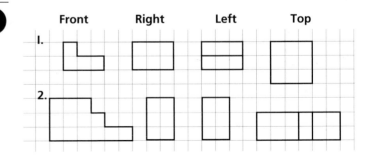

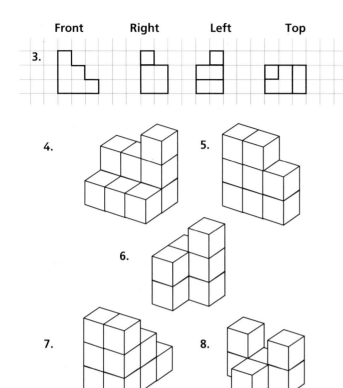

Front	Right	Left	Top

3.

4.

5.

6.

7.

8.

---

page 109
Congruent shapes
Triangles and quadrilaterals **S7**

I.-9. Answers will vary
10. any correct right-angled trapezium
II. any correct (concave) quadrilateral
12. any correct arrowhead
13. any correct isosceles trapezium
14. any correct hexagon
15. regular hexagon only

Explore
Answers will vary.

---

page 110
2-d shapes
Triangles and quadrilaterals **S7**

1. isosceles triangle
2. equilateral triangle
3. rhombus
4. regular
5. square or rectangle (or isosceles trapezium)
6. isosceles triangle
7. rectangle or parallelogram
8. square
9. right-angled isosceles triangle
10. rectangle
II. regular pentagon
12. isosceles trapezium
13. kite
14. scalene triangle
15. arrowhead kite
16. isosceles trapezium

Explore

quadrilateral	diagonals equal in length	diagonals meet at their mid-points	diagonals meet at right angles
square	✓	✓	✓
rectangle	✓	✓	✗
parallelogram	✗	✓	✗
rhombus	✗	✓	✓
kite	✗	✗	✓
arrowhead	✗	✗	✗
trapezium	?	?	✗

---

page 111
Constructing triangles
Constructing shapes **S8**

I. a = 7·2 cm   angles 74°, 46°
2. b = 10·5 cm   angles 42°, 53°
3. c = 54°   side 7·6 cm
4. d = 27°   side 11·3 cm
5. e = 7·6 cm   angles 29°, 103°
6. f = 9·7 cm   angles 31°, 87°
7. g = 3·9 cm h = 5·3 cm   angle 80°
8. i = 14·1 cm j = 14·6 cm   angle 20°
9. k = 8 cm l = 12·3 cm   angle 40°
10. m = 6·4 cm n = 7·2 cm   angle 56°
II. p = 9·6 cm o = 14·9 cm   angle 23°
12. q = 8·1 cm r = 4·9 cm   angle 45°

Explore
3 cm, 4 cm, 5 cm
6 cm, 8 cm, 10 cm
9 cm, 12 cm, 15 cm

Children should notice that each has a right angle. The three triangles are similar and so have the same angles.

---

page 112
Constructing triangles and quadrilaterals
Constructing shapes **S8**

I.–8. Check shapes constructed accurately.
9. **a** = 6·9 cm   **b** = 9·0 cm
10. **c** = 11·8 cm   **d** = 11·3 cm
II. **e** = 5·9 cm   **f** = 8·3 cm
   g = 8·1 cm

Explore
Check children have constructed shapes accurately.

---

page 113
Representing data
Graphs **D1**

Top of page
Check children have constructed an appropriate graph.
Middle of page
Check that children's bar graphs show these frequencies:

	BBC1,2	ITV,Ch4,5
29 May	2	3
30 May	I	5
31 May	I	3
I June	3	6

Check pie chart shows sectors of appropriate sizes, e.g.

decade of release	frequency	angle °
1990	9	135
1980	0	0
1970	3	45
1960	5	75
1950	3	45
1940	3	45
1930	1	15
total	24	360

Explore
Answers will vary.

page 114
Representing data
Graphs

1. bar chart or similar to show:

	Girls				Boys			
	1	2	3	4	1	2	3	4
No. words	6	7	5	8	7	4	7	8

2. bar chart or similar to show:

	Girls				Boys			
	1	2	3	4	1	2	3	4
no. 3-letter words remembered	3	3	2	4	4	3	4	4
no. 5-letter words remembered	3	4	3	4	3	1	3	4

3. bar chart or similar to show:

	Girls				Boys			
	1	2	3	4	1	2	3	4
no. red words remembered	4	5	1	4	3	2	5	3
no. green words remembered	2	2	4	4	4	2	2	5

Answers will vary.

page 115
Interpreting graphs
Graphs

1. about $\frac{1}{4}$ of 300 = 75
2. $\frac{1}{2}$ of 300 = 150 driven to infant school
   $\frac{1}{6}$ of 480 = 80 driven to junior school
   difference = 150 − 80 = 70 children
3. junior school $\frac{1}{4}$ of 480 = 120,
   infant school $\frac{1}{8}$ of 300 ≈ 38, $\frac{158}{780}$ ≈ 20%
4. $\frac{1}{4}$ of 480 = 120 take bus to junior school
   $\frac{1}{8}$ of 300 ≈ 38 take bus to infant school
   difference = 120 − 38 = 82 children
   This could be because infants are too young to travel on the bus on their own, or other acceptable answer.
5. 9 children
6. 55 children
7. $\frac{33}{55} = \frac{3}{5}$

8. Minimum £585.00
   (£0 × 6) + (£5 × 12) + (£10 × 15) + (£15 × 13) + (£20 × 9) = £585
   Maximum £859·45
   (£4·99 × 6) + (£9·99 × 12) + (£14·99 × 15) + (£19·99 × 13) + (£24·99 × 9) = £859·45

page 116
Mean, median, mode
Averages

1. mean 3·8°C   median 3°C   mode 2°C
2. mean 8·8°C   median 9°C   mode 9°C
3. mean 5·2°C   median 5°C   bimodal 5°C, 7°C
4. mean 0·5°C   median 0°C   mode ⁻1°C
5.

age	children	age × frequency
8	4	32
9	3	27
10	6	60
11	3	33
12	4	48
total	20	200

mean = 200 ÷ 20 = 10   10 years

6.

age	children	age × frequency
9	7	63
10	6	60
11	5	55
12	6	72
13	4	52
14	2	28
total	30	330

mean = 330 ÷ 30 = 11   11 years

7.

age	children	age × frequency
5	2	20
6	4	24
7	4	28
8	8	64
9	3	27
10	6	60
11	9	99
12	4	48
total	20	200

mean = 360 ÷ 40 = 9   9 years

8. 15 years old   7 + 13 + 8 + 12 = 40; (5 × 11) − 40 = 15)
9. 54 runs   2 + 69 = 141; (65 × 3) − 141 = 54)
10. 11 years   (23 + (9 × 6) = 77; 77 ÷ 7 = 11)
11. 9   (10 × 5 = 50 so 8,9,10,11,12; (8 + 9 + 10) ÷ 3 = 9) or other method.
12. 19 years   (9·1 × 10 = 91; 91 − (8 × 9) = 19)
13. 11   (9·5 × 4 = 38; so 8,9,10,11) or other method

page 117
Averages and spread

1. Boys: mean 5·0 range 8
   Girls: mean 6·5 range 3
2. Boys: mean 6·0 range 2
   Girls: mean 6·0 range 8
3. Boys: mean 15·5 range 8
   Girls: mean 15·7 range 8

Children should be encouraged to work these out without calculation.

4. $(1 + 2 + 3 + 4 + 5 + 6) \div 6 = 3\cdot5$
5. $(1 + 2 + 3 + 4 + 5 + 6 + 7 + 8 + 9) \div 9 = 5$
6. $(2 + 4 + 6 + 8 + 10 + 12) \div 6 = 7$
7. $(1 + 3 + 5 + 7 + 9 + 11 + 13) \div 7 = 7$
8. 16·5
9. $(1 + 4 + 9 + 16 + 25 + 36) \div 6 = 15\frac{1}{6}$
10. $(1 + 8 + 27 + 64 + 125) \div 5 = 45$
11. $(1 + 3 + 6 + 10 + 15 + 21) \div 6 = 9\frac{1}{3}$
12. $(2 + 3 + 5 + 7 + 11 + 13 + 17 + 19 + 23 + 29) \div 10 = 12\cdot9$

Explore
Answers will vary.

page 118
Averages problems

1. $(26 + 34 + 56 + 0) \div 4 = 29$ 29 runs
2. $(4 \times 5) - (3 + 4 + 1 + 5) = 7$ goals
3. $(150 \times 6) - (140 + 160 + 145 + 155 + 157) = 143$ 143 cm
4. Sam: mean 13, median 14, range 8
   Jamie: mean 12, median 12, range 2
   Sam has a higher mean, which suggests he is better, but Jamie has a lower range so he is more consistent.
5. $162 - 37 = 125$ 125 cm
6. mode 14 median 14 mean 16
   Median or mode best - the mean is affected by one older person (the driver).

page 119
Probability

Football strips: 8 kits

shirt	shorts	socks
red	black	red
red	black	yellow
red	yellow	red
red	yellow	yellow
blue	black	red
blue	black	yellow
blue	yellow	red
blue	yellow	yellow

Sandwiches: 6 options
brown cheese   white cheese
brown chicken   white chicken
brown egg   white egg

Cubes:
2 colours
Towers of 2   4 ways
Towers of 3   8 ways

3 colours
Towers of 3   27 ways

Explore
4 teams: 6 matches
5 teams: 10 matches
6 teams: 15 matches
7 teams: 21 matches
The number of matches is the triangular number series. Children should look for a logical way of tabulating the combinations, in order not to miss any.

page 120
Probability

1.

	1	2	3	4	5	6
1	2	3	4	5	6	7
2	3	4	5	6	7	8
3	4	5	6	7	8	9
4	5	6	7	8	9	10
5	6	7	8	9	10	11
6	7	8	9	10	11	12

2.

event	chance	probability
total is 2	1 in 36	$\frac{1}{4}$
total is 3	2 in 36	$\frac{2}{36} = \frac{1}{8}$
total is 4	3 in 36	$\frac{3}{36} = \frac{1}{2}$
total is 5	4 in 36	$\frac{4}{36} = \frac{1}{9}$
total is 6	5 in 36	$\frac{5}{36}$
total is 7	6 in 36	$\frac{6}{36} = \frac{1}{6}$
total is 8	5 in 36	$\frac{5}{36}$
total is 9	4 in 36	$\frac{4}{36} = \frac{1}{9}$
total is 10	3 in 36	$\frac{3}{36} = \frac{1}{2}$
total is 11	2 in 36	$\frac{2}{36} = \frac{1}{8}$
total is 12	1 in 36	$\frac{1}{36}$

3. Children's own answers.

4.

		coin 1	
coin 2		HH	HT
		TH	TT

5.

Event	chance	probability
both heads	1 in 4	$\frac{1}{4}$
both tails	1 in 4	$\frac{1}{4}$
1 head, 1 tail	2 in 4	$\frac{2}{4} = \frac{1}{2}$

6. Children's own answers

1. **a.** $\frac{1}{8}$ **b.** $\frac{4}{8} = \frac{1}{2}$ **c.** $\frac{2}{8} = \frac{1}{4}$

2. **a.** $\frac{1}{6}$ **b.** $\frac{3}{6} = \frac{1}{2}$ **c.** $\frac{2}{6} = \frac{1}{3}$

3. **a.** $\frac{2}{10} = \frac{1}{5}$ **b.** $\frac{7}{10}$ **c.** $\frac{7}{10}$

4. **a.** $\frac{4}{5}$ **b.** $\frac{2}{5}$ **c.** $\frac{3}{5}$

5. **a.** 10   **b.** 30   **c.** 36

6. **a.** 3   **b.** 9   **c.** 15

page 122
Mixed problems

1. 54 cm²
   27 = 3 × 3 × 3 so 6 faces each 3cm × 3cm
2. 1 hr 54 min = 114 min 114 − (1·5 × 8) = 102
   102 min ÷ 17 = 6 min
3. hot dog 95p cola 35p
4. (5 × 65p) + (8 × 34p) = 597p = £5·97
5. 600 ÷ 120 = 5
   75 g × 5 = 375 g
6. 4:30 + 8:40 = 01:10 01:10 − 5:00 = 8:10 p.m.
7. 2·5 kg = 2500 g
   2500 ÷ 20 × 13 = 16251·625 kg
8. 400 ÷ (10 × 5) = 8 cubes wide

page 123
Mixed problems

1. £180 × 1·05 = £189
   £189 × 1·05 = £198·45
2. £17·50 × 0·8 = £14
   £18·40 × $\frac{3}{40}$ = £13·80   2nd shop cheaper
3. 2 hr 40 min ÷ 20 min = 8
   30p × 8 = 240p = £2·40
4. (2·60 + 0·75 + 0·95) × 0·9 = 3·87   £3·87
5. £13·60 + £15·99 + £12·49 = £42·08
6. 5·55 ÷ 3 × 2 = 3·7   £3·70
7. 1053 − (27 × 9) = 810
   810 ÷ (27 − 9) = 45   other stamps cost 45p
8. 4500 g ÷ 12 = 375 g

page 124
Mixed problems

1. 36   2. 77   3. 6   4. 18
5. 512   6. 420   7. 2500
8. 1008   9. 17   10. 5

page 125
Mixed problems

1. 132 ÷ 1·1 = 120   £120
2. 3 m × 4·5 m = 13·5 m²
   £17 × 13·5 = £229·50
   or children may consider number of 'whole' m²
   3 m × 5 m = 15 m² £17 × 15 = £255
3. 180g ÷ 4 × 10 = 450 g

4. 75 + (80 × 4) = 395   395 min = 6 hr 35 min
5. 1200 − (400 + 80 + 120 + 35 + 25) = 540
   $\frac{540}{1200}$ = 0·45 = 45%
6. need 2 pieces of wood and 3 brackets
   (£7·35 × 2) + (£2·69 × 6) = £30·84
7. 37p for a pint to be delivered
   2j + p = 275 j + p = 156 → j = 119 and p = 37
8. 66 ÷ 12 = 5·5   needs 6 tins of paint

page 126
Mixed problems

1. 25 min (to train) + 25 min (train late) + 40min (train
   journey) = 90 min 07:20 + 90 min = 08:50
2. £256·80 ÷ 48 = £5·35 £5·35 + £6·45 = £11·80
3. 1500 ÷ 240 = 6·25 tanks of petrol   7 fills of tank
   £32 × 7 = £224
4. 6738 miles ÷ 12·75 hr = 529 m.p.h. (3 s.f.)
5. £239 × 8 = £1918
   £1918 × 0·85 = £1625·20
6. (£6·80 × 8) − £50 = £4·40 saving
7. £42 ÷ 3 = £14
   £42 ÷ 4 = £10·50
   £14 − £10·50 = £3·50 saving each
8. 423 ÷ 9 = 47
   Paris to London cheaper £47

page 127
Mixed problems

1. 47 × 48 = 2256
2. (a + 7) × 13 = 169
   a = 6
3. 3456 ÷ 6 = 576
   $\sqrt{576}$ = 24
   cube edge 24 cm
4. 5   8   13   20   29   40   53
   difference increasing by 2 each time
   nth term = n² + 4
5. sequence adds 0·3 so 8th number = 0·9 + (0·3 × 7) =
   3, a whole number.
   Then every tenth number will be (0·3 × 10), 3·0 more.
6. probability of scoring 7 = $\frac{1}{6}$
   probability of scoring 10 = $\frac{1}{2}$
   so more likely to score 7.
7. correct   (37 × 15) + 25 = 580
   incorrect   243 ÷ 9 − 6 = 21   243 ÷ (9 − 6) = 81
   incorrect   1057 + (18 × 43) = 1831
8. 1247 ÷ 43 = 29 or 1247 ÷ 29 = 43

page 128
Mixed problems

1. 1,6,8   2,3,8   2,4,6   3,4,4
2. 52 ÷ 4 × 3 = 39 white sandwiches
   so 39 × 2 = 78 slices white bread
3. 127 as 127 ÷ 3 = 42 r 1 127 = 5³ + 2 127 = 11² + 6
4. (5p × 100) + (3p × 200) + (2p × 156) = 4220p = £42·20
5. 2 × 3⁴ = 162   2 × 3⁵ = 486
   2² × 3³ = 108   2² × 3⁴ = 324   2² × 3⁵ = 972
   2³ × 3³ = 216   2³ × 3⁴ = 648
   2⁴ × 3² = 144   2⁴ × 3³ = 432

$2^5 \times 3^2 = 288$ $2^5 \times 3^3 = 864$
$2^6 \times 3 = 192$ $2^6 \times 3^2 = 576$

6. $4 = 2 + 2$
$9 = 2 + 7$
$16 = 3 + 13 = 5 + 11$
$25 = 2 + 23$
$36 = 5 + 31 = 7 + 29 = 13 + 23 = 17 + 19$
$49 = 2 + 47$
$64 = 3 + 61 = 5 + 59 = 11 + 53 = 17 + 47 = 23 + 41$
$81 = 2 + 79$
$100 = 3 + 97 = 11 + 89 = 17 + 83 = 29 + 71 = 47 + 53$

7. $2 \cdot 8 - 0 \cdot 4 = 2 \cdot 4$ cm $2 \cdot 4 \div 480 = 0 \cdot 005$ cm
$0 \cdot 005$ cm or ($0 \cdot 5$ mm) thick

8. $\frac{4}{9}$ of £279 = £124
$\frac{3}{8}$ of £300 = £112·50
So best is $\frac{4}{9}$ of £279

Photocopy Masters

page 4
Russian multiplication   Multiplication/division N3

The method works because doubling one number and halving the other in a multiplication gives the same product as the original calculation. When halves are ignored the product is less than the original, but this is compensated for at the end when the numbers in the right-hand column are added up. If there were no halves (i.e. if the number being halved is a power of two) all the rows apart from I x a would be crossed out and the answer found directly.

1. $57 \times 34 = 1938$
2. $27 \times 76 = 2052$
3. $34 \times 26 = 884$
4. $19 \times 31 = 589$
5. $43 \times 47 = 2021$
6. $92 \times 33 = 3036$

page 5
Fraction number lines   Fractions N4

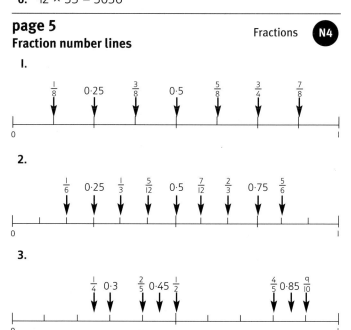

4.

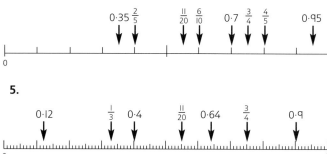

5.

6.

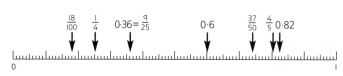

page 6
Pick your pair   Addition/subtraction N5

1. $4 \cdot 8 + 7 \cdot 9 = 12 \cdot 7$ $7 \cdot 9 - 4 \cdot 8 = 3 \cdot 1$
2. $6 \cdot 3 + 5 \cdot 8 = 12 \cdot 1$ $6 \cdot 3 - 5 \cdot 8 = 0 \cdot 5$
3. $12 \cdot 2 + 9 \cdot 3 = 21 \cdot 5$ $12 \cdot 2 - 9 \cdot 3 = 2 \cdot 9$
4. $14 \cdot 72 + 8 \cdot 5 = 23 \cdot 22$ $14 \cdot 72 - 8 \cdot 5 = 6 \cdot 22$
5. $15 \cdot 3 + 6 \cdot 94 = 22 \cdot 24$ $15 \cdot 3 - 6 \cdot 94 = 8 \cdot 36$
6. $7 \cdot 61 + 2 \cdot 34 = 9 \cdot 95$ $7 \cdot 61 - 2 \cdot 34 = 5 \cdot 27$
7. $5 \cdot 48 + 1 \cdot 96 = 7 \cdot 44$ $5 \cdot 48 - 1 \cdot 96 = 3 \cdot 52$
8. $6 \cdot 75 + 6 \cdot 75 = 13 \cdot 5$ $6 \cdot 75 - 6 \cdot 75 = 0$
9. $46 \cdot 5 + 9 \cdot 9 = 56 \cdot 4$ $46 \cdot 5 - 9 \cdot 9 = 36 \cdot 6$
10. $7 \cdot 9 + 12 \cdot 6 = 20 \cdot 5$ $12 \cdot 6 - 7 \cdot 9 = 4 \cdot 7$
11. $0 \cdot 35 + 0 \cdot 84 = 1 \cdot 19$ $0 \cdot 84 - 0 \cdot 35 = 0 \cdot 49$
12. $1 \cdot 95 + 0 \cdot 8 = 2 \cdot 75$ $1 \cdot 95 - 0 \cdot 8 = 1 \cdot 15$
13. $3 \cdot 7 + 4 \cdot 62 = 8 \cdot 32$ $4 \cdot 62 - 3 \cdot 7 = 0 \cdot 92$
14. $2 \cdot 9 + 10 \cdot 31 = 13 \cdot 21$ $10 \cdot 31 - 2 \cdot 9 = 7 \cdot 41$
15. $15 \cdot 8 + 23 \cdot 7 = 39 \cdot 5$ $23 \cdot 7 - 15 \cdot 8 = 7 \cdot 9$

page 8
Ten calculations   Division N7

$0 \cdot 572 \times 10 = 5 \cdot 72$ $572 \div 100 = 5 \cdot 72$
$0 \cdot 00572 \times 1000 = 5 \cdot 72$ $0 \cdot 572 \div 0 \cdot 1 = 5 \cdot 72$
$57 \cdot 2 \times 0 \cdot 1 = 5 \cdot 72$ $57 \cdot 2 \div 10 = 5 \cdot 72$
$572 \times 0 \cdot 01 = 5 \cdot 72$ $0 \cdot 0572 \div 0 \cdot 01 = 5 \cdot 72$
$0 \cdot 0572 \times 100 = 5 \cdot 72$ $5720 \div 1000 = 5 \cdot 72$

$1 \cdot 73 \div 0 \cdot 1 = 17 \cdot 3$ $0 \cdot 173 \times 100 = 17 \cdot 3$
$1730 \div 100 = 17 \cdot 3$ $0 \cdot 173 \div 0 \cdot 01 = 17 \cdot 3$
$1730 \times 0 \cdot 01 = 17 \cdot 3$ $0 \cdot 0173 \times 1000 = 17 \cdot 3$
$173 \div 10 = 17 \cdot 3$ $1 \cdot 73 \times 10 = 17 \cdot 3$
$17\,300 \div 1000 = 17 \cdot 3$ $173 \times 0 \cdot 1 = 17 \cdot 3$

$0 \cdot 468 \times 1000 = 468$ $4 \cdot 68 \div 0 \cdot 01 = 468$
$468\,000 \div 1000 = 468$ $4 \cdot 68 \times 100 = 468$
$46\,800 \times 0 \cdot 01 = 468$ $46 \cdot 8 \times 10 = 468$
$4680 \div 10 = 468$ $46 \cdot 8 \div 0 \cdot 1 = 468$
$4680 \times 0 \cdot 1 = 468$ $46\,800 \div 100 = 468$

page 9
Dice numerators
Fractions **N8**

The following answers are possible:

1. $\frac{1}{6} \times 12 = 2$ $\frac{2}{6} \times 12 = 4$ $\frac{3}{6} \times 12 = 6$
   $\frac{4}{6} \times 12 = 8$ $\frac{5}{6} \times 12 = 10$ $\frac{6}{6} \times 12 = 12$
2. $15 \times \frac{1}{5} = 3$ $15 \times \frac{2}{5} = 6$ $15 \times \frac{3}{5} = 9$
   $15 \times \frac{4}{5} = 12$ $15 \times \frac{5}{5} = 15$ $15 \times \frac{6}{5} = 18$
3. $\frac{1}{4} \times 16 = 4$ $\frac{2}{4} \times 16 = 8$ $\frac{3}{4} \times 16 = 12$
   $\frac{4}{4} \times 16 = 16$ $\frac{5}{4} \times 16 = 20$ $\frac{6}{4} \times 16 = 24$
4. $21 \times \frac{1}{3} = 7$ $21 \times \frac{2}{3} = 14$ $21 \times \frac{3}{3} = 21$
   $21 \times \frac{4}{3} = 28$ $21 \times \frac{5}{3} = 35$ $21 \times \frac{6}{3} = 42$
5. $\frac{1}{7} \times 28 = 4$ $\frac{2}{7} \times 28 = 8$ $\frac{3}{7} \times 28 = 12$
   $\frac{4}{7} \times 28 = 16$ $\frac{5}{7} \times 28 = 20$ $\frac{6}{7} \times 28 = 24$
6. $40 \times \frac{1}{8} = 5$ $40 \times \frac{2}{8} = 10$ $40 \times \frac{3}{8} = 15$
   $40 \times \frac{4}{8} = 20$ $40 \times \frac{5}{8} = 25$ $40 \times \frac{6}{8} = 30$
7. $63 \times \frac{1}{7} = 9$ $63 \times \frac{2}{7} = 18$ $63 \times \frac{3}{7} = 27$
   $63 \times \frac{4}{7} = 36$ $63 \times \frac{5}{7} = 45$ $63 \times \frac{6}{7} = 54$
8. $\frac{1}{10} \times 110 = 11$ $\frac{2}{10} \times 110 = 22$ $\frac{3}{10} \times 110 = 33$
   $\frac{4}{10} \times 110 = 44$ $\frac{5}{10} \times 110 = 55$ $\frac{6}{10} \times 110 = 66$
9. $\frac{1}{15} \times 75 = 5$ $\frac{2}{15} \times 75 = 10$ $\frac{3}{15} \times 75 = 15$
   $\frac{4}{15} \times 75 = 20$ $\frac{5}{15} \times 75 = 25$ $\frac{6}{15} \times 75 = 30$
10. $\frac{1}{12} \times 72 = 6$ $\frac{2}{12} \times 72 = 12$ $\frac{3}{12} \times 72 = 18$
    $\frac{4}{12} \times 72 = 24$ $\frac{5}{12} \times 72 = 30$ $\frac{6}{12} \times 72 = 36$
11. $13 \times \frac{1}{2} = 6{\cdot}5$ $13 \times \frac{2}{2} = 13$ $13 \times \frac{3}{2} = 19{\cdot}5$
    $13 \times \frac{4}{2} = 26$ $13 \times \frac{5}{2} = 32{\cdot}5$ $13 \times \frac{6}{2} = 39$
12. $120 \times \frac{1}{20} = 6$ $120 \times \frac{2}{20} = 12$ $120 \times \frac{3}{20} = 18$
    $120 \times \frac{4}{20} = 24$ $120 \times \frac{5}{20} = 30$ $120 \times \frac{6}{20} = 36$
13. $11 \times \frac{1}{4} = 2{\cdot}75$ $11 \times \frac{2}{4} = 5{\cdot}5$ $11 \times \frac{3}{4} = 8{\cdot}25$
    $11 \times \frac{4}{4} = 11$ $11 \times \frac{5}{4} = 13{\cdot}75$ $11 \times \frac{6}{4} = 16{\cdot}5$
14. $9 \times \frac{1}{5} = 1{\cdot}8$ $9 \times \frac{2}{5} = 3{\cdot}6$ $9 \times \frac{3}{5} = 5{\cdot}4$
    $9 \times \frac{4}{5} = 7{\cdot}2$ $9 \times \frac{5}{5} = 9$ $9 \times \frac{6}{5} = 10{\cdot}8$

page 10
Fractions to decimals
Division **N9**

		numerator									
		1	2	3	4	5	6	7	8	9	10
denominator	1	1	2	3	4	5	6	7	8	9	10
	2	0·5	1	1·5	2	2·5	3	3·5	4	4·5	5
	3	0·333	0·667	1	1·333	1·667	2	2·333	2·667	3	3·333
	4	0·25	0·5	0·75	1	1·25	1.5	1·75	2	2·25	2·5
	5	0·2	0·4	0·6	0·8	1	1·2	1·4	1·6	1·8	2·0
	6	0·167	0·333	0·5	0·667	0·833	1	1·167	1·333	1·5	1·667
	7	0·143	0·286	0·429	0·571	0·714	0·857	1	1·143	1·286	1·429
	8	0·125	0·25	0·375	0·5	0·625	0·75	0·875	1	1·125	1·25
	9	0·111	0·222	0·333	0·444	0·556	0·667	0·778	0·889	1	1·111
	10	0·1	0·2	0·3	0·4	0·5	0·6	0·7	0·8	0·9	1

page 11
Halfway numbers
Decimals **N10**

1. 7·5 2. 4·5 3. 13·5 4. 2·45
5. 13·75 6. 6·715 7. 8·345 8. 9·405
9. 7·395 10. 3·238 11. 6·478 12. 5·08
13. 4·95 14. 6·05 15. 7·405 16. 8·695
17. 2·06 18. 3·47 19. 4·686 20. 5·367
21. 0·5 22. $^{-}1{\cdot}5$

page 13
Place the digits
Subtraction **N12**

1. 6·258 – 1·347 = 4·911 **or** 6·438 – 1·527 = 4·911
2. 8·341 – 5·627 = 2·714
3. 7·561 – 2·834 = 4·727
4. 4·568 – 1·372 = 3·196
5. 6·473 – 5·821 = 0·652
6. 8·735 – 1·264 = 7·471
7. 4·357 – 2·168 = 2·189
8. 3·582 – 1·674 = 1·908
9. 5·143 – 2·678 = 2·465
10. 6·753 – 4·218 = 2·535
11. 6·871 – 4·235 = 2·636
12. 5·321 – 4·768 = 0·553

page 14
Power substitution
Powers **N13**

1. $2^2 = 4$ 2. $3^2 = 9$ 3. $4^2 - 4 = 12$
4. $1^3 = 1$ 5. $3^3 = 27$ 6. $3^2 + 5 = 14$
7. $2^3 = 8$ 8. $1^2 = 1$ 9. $3^4 = 81$
10. $4^3 = 64$ 11. $5^3 = 125$ 12. $2^4 = 16$
13. $1^9 = 1$ 14. $2^6 = 64$ 15. $2^5 = 32$
16. $1^{27} = 1$ 17. $1^2 + 2^2 = 5$ 18. $2^2 + 3^2 = 13$
19. $3^3 - 2^2 = 23$ 20. $3^3 - 4^2 = 11$ 21. $2^7 = 128$
22. $5 \times 4^2 = 80$ 23. $6 \times 1^3 = 6$ 24. $\frac{4^2}{4} = 4$
25. $\frac{3^2}{3} = 3$ 26. $\frac{2^5}{2^3} = 4$

page 15
Missing numbers
Positive and negative numbers **N14**

1. $5 + {}^{-}4 = 1$ 2. ${}^{-}5 + 3 = {}^{-}2$ 3. $5 + {}^{-}6 = {}^{-}1$
4. ${}^{-}3 + 7 = 4$ 5. $2 + {}^{-}9 = {}^{-}7$ 6. ${}^{-}1 + {}^{-}5 = {}^{-}6$
7. ${}^{-}7 + 5 = {}^{-}2$ 8. ${}^{-}3 + 2 = {}^{-}1$
9. $4 + ({}^{-}2) + 1 = 3$ 10. $({}^{-}2) + 14 + ({}^{-}5) = 7$
11. $4 + ({}^{-}2) = 5 + ({}^{-}3)$ 12. $({}^{-}3) + ({}^{-}2) = ({}^{-}7) + 2$
13. $6 - 3 = 3$ 14. $1 - 3 = {}^{-}2$ 15. $({}^{-}3) - ({}^{-}5) = 2$
16. $({}^{-}5) - ({}^{-}6) = 1$ 17. $0 - ({}^{-}1) = 1$ 18. $3 - 7 = {}^{-}4$
19. $8 - 9 = {}^{-}1$ 20. $({}^{-}3) - ({}^{-}5) = 2$ 21. $1 - 4 = {}^{-}3$
22. $3 - ({}^{-}2) = 5$ 23. $7 - 5 = 2$ 24. $4 - 4 = 0$

page 16
Italian decimal multiplication
Multiplication **N15**

1. 2·74 × 3·6 = 9·864
2. 31·5 × 2·7 = 85·05
3. 42·3 × 4·5 = 190·35
4. 63·7 × 1·9 = 121·03
5. 53·4 × 4·8 = 256·32
6. 27·9 × 5·6 = 156·24

The method works because the grid splits into hundredths, tenths, units, tens and hundreds which are summed separately.

page 17
Dividing then checking by multiplying
Division **N16**

1. 68·96 ÷ 16 = 4·31 16 × 4·31 = 68·96
2. 75·14 ÷ 17 = 4·42 17 × 4·42 = 75·14
3. 86·10 ÷ 15 = 5·74 15 × 5·74 = 86·10
4. 54·88 ÷ 14 = 3·92 14 × 3·92 = 54·88
5. 54·15 ÷ 19 = 2·85 19 × 2·85 = 54·15
6. 44·98 ÷ 26 = 1·73 26 × 1·73 = 44·98

7. $63 \cdot 18 \div 27 = 2 \cdot 34$ $27 \times 2 \cdot 34 = 63 \cdot 18$
8. $90 \cdot 75 \div 33 = 2 \cdot 75$ $33 \times 2 \cdot 75 = 90 \cdot 75$
9. $53 \cdot 94 \div 29 = 1 \cdot 86$ $29 \times 1 \cdot 86 = 53 \cdot 94$
10. $93 \cdot 16 \div 34 = 2 \cdot 74$ $34 \times 2 \cdot 74 = 93 \cdot 16$

page 18
Percentage chart   Percentages

	£2800	£3600	£5400	£450	£18 000
21%	£588	£756	£1134	£94·50	£3780
16%	£448	£576	£864	£72	£2880
49%	£1372	£1764	£2646	£220·50	£8820
89%	£2492	£3204	£4806	£400·50	£16 020
131%	£3668	£4716	£7074	£589·50	£23 580
61%	£1708	£2196	£3294	£274·50	£10 980
36%	£1008	£1296	£1944	£162	£6480
109%	£3052	£3924	£5886	£490·50	£19 620
7%	£196	£252	£378	£31·50	£1260

page 19
Dice percentages   Fractions, decimals, percentages

1. $\frac{3}{24} = 12 \cdot 5\%$ 2. $\frac{5}{24} = 20 \cdot 8\%$ 3. $\frac{5}{24} = 20 \cdot 8\%$
4. $\frac{4}{24} = 16 \cdot 7\%$ 5. $\frac{3}{24} = 12 \cdot 5\%$ 6. $\frac{4}{24} = 16 \cdot 7\%$
7. $\frac{12}{24} = 50\%$ 8. $\frac{5}{24} = 50\%$ 9. $\frac{16}{24} = 66 \cdot 7\%$
10. $\frac{16}{24} = 66 \cdot 7\%$ 11. $\frac{4}{24} = 16 \cdot 7\%$ 12. $\frac{2}{24} = 8 \cdot 3\%$
13. $\frac{3}{24} = 12 \cdot 5\%$ 14. $\frac{7}{24} = 29 \cdot 2\%$ 15. $\frac{4}{24} = 16 \cdot 7\%$

page 21
Explaining errors   Checking results

1. Adding the units digits of the pence gives $9 + 4 = 13$, final digit should be 3 not 4
2. Doubling the units digit of 76, $6 \times 2 = 12$ final digit should be 2 not 4
3. Squaring the units digit of 23, $3^2 = 9$ final digit should not be 1
4. Halving the pence, $20 \div 2 = 10$ final digits should be 10 not 40
5. Doubling the pence, $48 \times 2 = 96$ final digits should be 96 not 16
6. Adding the units digit of the pence, $6 + 8 + 9 = 23$ final digit should be 3 not 4
7. Multiplying the units digit by 7 days per week, $6 \times 7 = 42$ final digit should not be 6
8. Using an estimate, $70^2 = 4900$ so the answer should be less than 4900

There are other correct methods that can be used to check.

page 22
Number investigations   Squares, cubes, roots

Triangular numbers
1   3   6   10   15   21   28   36   45   55
$1 + 3 = 4 = 2^2$ $3 + 6 = 9 = 3^2$ $6 + 10 = 16 = 4^2$
$10 + 15 = 25 = 5^2$ $15 + 21 = 36 = 6^2$
$21 + 28 = 49 = 7^2$ $28 + 36 = 64 = 8^2$
$36 + 45 + 81 = 9^2$ $45 + 55 = 100 = 10^2$

Pairs of consecutive triangular numbers add up to square numbers, formally if t is the triangular number and n is the position in the sequence: $t_n + t_{n+1} = (n+1)^2$.

Patterns with odd numbers
1   4   9   16   25   36   49   64   81   100
This generates the square number sequence.
1   8   27   64   125   216   343   512   729   1000
This generates the cube number sequence.

If each number is considered as a unit square, the following patterns show how the sums of consecutive odd numbers form the cube number sequence.

 $1 = 1^3$

 $8 = 2^3$

 $27 = 3^3$

 $64 = 4^3$

page 23
Powers and brackets with algebra   Order of operations

1. $2^2 = 4$ 2. $3 \times 2^2 = 12$
3. $2 \times 3^2 = 18$ 4. $4 \times 4^2 = 64$
5. $6 \times 1^2 = 6$ 6. $5(1 + 2)^2 = 45$
7. $6(2 + 3)^2 = 150$ 8. $2(4 - 1)^3 = 54$
9. $3 \times 3^3 - 1 = 80$ 10. $2 \times 2^3 + 3 = 19$
11. $100 - 2 \times 2^2 = 82$ 12. $50 - 3 \times 4^2 = 2$
13. $(1 + 2)^2 + (2 + 3)^2 = 34$ 14. $(4 - 2)^2 + (3 - 1)^2 = 8$
15. $3(2 + 4)^2 - 7 = 101$ 16. $4(3 + 2)^2 = 100$
17. $3(2 \times 1 + 3)^2 = 75$
18. $\frac{5(1 + 2 + 3)}{6} = 5$ 19. $\frac{4(1 + 3 \times 2)^2}{7} = 28$
20. $\frac{15(2 \times 4 - 3)^3}{4} = 30$

page 24
Combining letters   Algebra   **A1**

1. $2z$ 2. $3b$ 3. q 4. z
5. bc 6. pt 7. $5bc$ 8. $3pq$
9. $6a$ 10. $12b$ 11. ay^2 12. pqr
13. a^2 14. p^3 15. $3a^2b$ 16. $2q^2$
17. $\frac{10}{b}$ 18. $\frac{c}{5}$ 19. $\frac{5c}{b}$ 20. $\frac{4b}{3}$

page 25
Missing terms   Algebra   **A2**

1. $3d + 4d + 6d = 13d$ 2. $5y + 4y - 3y = 6y$
3. $3w - w + 1 + 2 = 2w + 3$ 4. $4z + 3z - 6 = 7z - 6$
5. $5 + 2c + 1 = 2c + 6$ 6. $3 + 4y + 5 + 6y = 10y + 8$
7. $8 + 3y - 2y - 1 = 7 + y$
8. $2a + 3a + 5a + 4 = 10a + 4$

9. $6b - 2b - (-3b) - 1 = 7b - 1$
10. $7g + 3g + 4 - 6g = 4 + 4g$
11. $4z + 5 + (-3z - 6) - 2 = z - 3$
12. $8q - q + 3 - 6q = 3 + q$
13. $6 + 7c - 4c - 5c = 6 - 2c$
14. $3t + 5 - 2t - 4t = 5 - 3t$

page 26
Removing brackets

1. $3(a + 4) + 2a = 3a + 12 + 2a = 5a + 12$
2. $5(b - 2) - 3b = 5b - 10 - 3b = 2b - 10$
3. $6(z + 3) + z = 6z + 18 + 2 = 7z + 18$
4. $7(p + 1) - 6p = 7p + 7 - 6p = p + 7$
5. $4(2 + g) + 3g = 8 + 4g + 3g = 8 + 7g$
6. $3(a + b) + 2a = 3a + 3b + 2a = 5a + 3b$
7. $4(b + c) - 3c = 4b + 4c - 3c = 4b + c$
8. $5(d + 4) - 19 = 5d + 20 - 19 = 5d + 1$
9. $5a + 3(a + 1) = 5a + 3a + 3 = 8a + 3$
10. $4q + 2(3 + q) = 4q + 6 + 2q = 6q + 6$
11. $6g + 7(g - 1) = 6g + 7g - 7 = 13g - 7$
12. $2(f + 4) + 3(f + 1) = 2f + 8 + 3f + 3 = 5f + 11$
13. $3(a + 4) + 2(a - 1) = 3a + 12 + 2a - 2 = 5a + 10$
14. $4(z - 3) + 3(z - 2) = 4z - 12 + 3z - 6 = 7z - 18$
15. $4(3 + n) + 2(5 + n) = 12 + 4n + 10 + 2n = 22 + 6n$

page 27
Addition pyramids

1.

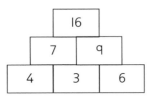

2.

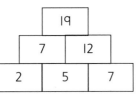

3.

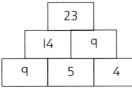

4.

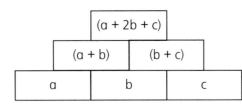

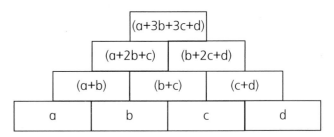

5.

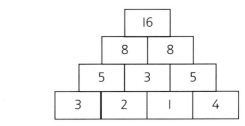

$a + 3b + 3c + d = 3 + (3 \times 2) + (3 \times 1) + 4$
$= 3 + 6 + 3 + 4 = 16$

6.

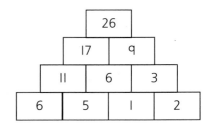

$a + 3b + 3c + d = 6 + (3 \times 5) + (3 \times 1) + 2$
$= 6 + 15 + 3 + 2 = 26$

7.

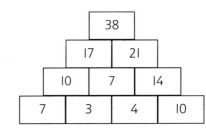

$a + 3b + 3c + d = 7 + (3 \times 3) + (3 \times 4) + 10$
$= 7 + 9 + 12 + 10 = 38$

page 28
Equations practice

1.	$3a + 2 = 17$	$3a = 15$	$a = 5$
2.	$5b - 3 = 12$	$5b = 15$	$b = 34$
3.	$4y + 7 = 19$	$4y = 12$	$y = 3$
4.	$3p - 8 = 25$	$3p = 33$	$p = 11$
5.	$6q + 3 = 27$	$6q = 24$	$q = 4$
6.	$2z - 9 = 43$	$2z = 52$	$z = 26$
7.	$3c + 4 = 19$	$3c = 15$	$c = 5$
8.	$2a - 5 = 13$	$2a = 18$	$a = 9$
9.	$5b + 3 = 18$	$5b = 15$	$b = 3$
10.	$9m - 11 = 25$	$9m = 36$	$m = 4$
11.	$2n + 14 = 30$	$2n = 16$	$n = 8$
12.	$4p - 3 = 25$	$4p = 28$	$p = 7$
13.	$9q + 22 = 40$	$9q = 18$	$q = 2$

14. $3s - 17 = 1$ $3s = 18$ $s = 6$
15. $7t + 13 = 20$ $7t = 7$ $t = 1$
16. $5f - 9 = 6$ $5f = 15$ $f = 3$
17. $2g + 3 = 4$ $2g = 1$ $g = \frac{1}{2}$
18. $4h + 2 = 3$ $4h = 1$ $h = \frac{1}{4}$

---

page 29
Meeting points
Algebra **A6**

Points in tables will vary.
1. $y = x$ and $y = 3$ meet at (3,3)
2. $y = ^-1$ and $y = 2x$ meet at ($^-2,^-1$)
3. $y = x + 1$ and $y = 3 - x$ meet at (1,2)

---

page 30
Electricity charges
Algebra **A7**

1. 1200 units   £110
2. 2000 units   £150
3. 800 units   £80
4. 2400 units   £170
5. £80   800 units
6. £180   2600 units
7. £65   650 units
8. £150   2000 units

---

page 31
What's the rule?
Algebra **A8**

1. $x \rightarrow x + 3$ 9, 12
2. $x \rightarrow 5x$ 5, 40
3. $x \rightarrow x - 5$ 4, $^-3$
4. $x \rightarrow 2x + 1$ 15, 5
5. $x \rightarrow 3x - 2$ 7, 4
6. $x \rightarrow 4x - 1$ 11, 23
7. $x \rightarrow 3x + 1$ 10, 28
8. $x \rightarrow 2x - 1$ 3, 15
9. $x \rightarrow 4x + 5$ 41, 13
10. $x \rightarrow x^2 + 1$ 17, 82
11. $x \rightarrow 10x - 3$ 77, 67
12. $x \rightarrow x^2 - 1$ 15, 63

---

page 32
Fibonacci sequences
Algebra **A9**

a 1 3 4 7 11 18 29 47 76 123 199
b 2 5 7 12 19 31 50 81 131 212 343
c 4 1 5 6 11 17 28 45 73 118 191
digit sequences for above

a 1,3, 4, 7, 1, 8, 9, 7, 6, 3, 9, 2, (repeats from here) 1,3, 4,7,1, 8...
repeat sequence of 12

b 2, 5, 7, 2, 9, 1, 0, 1, 1, 2, 3, 5, 8, 3, 1, 4, 5, 9, 4, 3, 7, 0, 7, 7, 4, 1, 5, 6, 1, 7, 8, 5, 3, 8, 1, 9, 0, 9, 9, 8, 7, 5, 2, 7, 9,6, 5, 1, 6, 7, 3, 0, 3, 3, 6, 9, 5, 4, 9, 3, (repeats from here) 2, 5...
repeat sequence of 60

c 4, 1, 5, 6, 1, 7, 8, 5, 3, 8, 1, 9, 0, 9, 9, 8, 7, 5, 2, 7, 9, 6, 5, 1, 6, 7, 3, 0, 3, 3, 6, 9, 5, 4, 9, 3, 2, 5, 7, 2, 9, 1, 0, 1, 1, 2, 3, 5, 8, 3, 1, 4, 5, 9, 4, 3, 7, 0, 7, 7, (repeats from here) 4, 1, 5
repeat sequence of 60, same pattern as b

pattern starting 2, 2
2, 2, 4, 6, 0, 6, 6, 2, 8, 0, 8, 8, 6, 4, 0, 4, 4, 8, 2, 0,
(repeats from here) 2, 2, 4,
repeat sequence of 20

pattern starting 3, 2
3, 2, 5, 7, 2, 9, 1, 0, 1, 1, 2, 3, 5, 8, 3, 1, 4, 5, 9, 4, 3, 7, 0, 7, 7, 4, 1, 5, 6, 1, 7, 8, 5, 3, 8, 1, 9, 0, 9, 9, 8, 7, 5, 2, 7, 9, 6, 5, 1, 6, 7, 3, 0, 3, 3, 6, 9, 5, 4, 9,(repeats from here) 3, 2, 5, 7, 2, 9, 1, 0, 1, 1, 2, 3, 5...
repeat sequence of 60, same pattern as b, c

pattern starting 4, 2
4, 2, 6, 8, (pattern repeats from here) 4, 2, 6...
repeat sequence of 4

---

page 33
Squares and spots
Algebra **A10**

squares
1. 3   5   7 $2n + 1$
2. 4   8   12 $4n$
3. 1   5   9 $4n - 3$
4. 8   10   12 $2n + 6$

spots
5. 4   6   8 $2n + 2$
6. 6   10   14 $4n + 2$

---

page 34
Units of length
Measures **M1**

1. 2·35 m = 235 cm   2. 0·46 m = 46 cm
3. 19 cm = 0·19 m   4. 340 cm = 3·4 m
5. 8 cm = 0·08 m   6. 35 mm = 3·5 cm
7. 600 mm = 60 cm   8. 450 mm = 0·45 m
9. 10 500 m = 10·5 km   10. 3 ft = 36 inches
11. 7 yards = 21 ft
12. 30 inches = 2 ft 6 ins = $2\frac{1}{2}$ feet
13. 1 ft 8 inches = 20 inches   14. 15·5 cm = 0·155 m
15. 4·3 m = 430 cm   16. 7·35 km = 7350 m
17. 0·0006 km = 0·6 m   18. 0·367 km = 367 m
19. 3·7 cm = 37 mm   20. 15·9 cm = 159 mm
21. 87·5 mm = 8·75 cm   22. 2·5 mm = 0·25 cm
23. 2 km = 200 000 cm
24. 3 450 000 mm = 3·45 km
25. 6550 cm = 0·0655 km
26. 7·325 km = 7 325 000 mm

---

page 35
Cube buildings
Area **M2**

A   26 cm²   B   22 cm²
C   22 cm²   D   24 cm²
E   24 cm²   F   26 cm²
G   24 cm²   H   26 cm²
largest surface area A,F,H = 26 cm²
smallest surface area B,C = 22 cm²

page 36
Missing parts
Surface area **M3**

1. c = 15 cm
2. y = 10 cm
3. h = 8 cm
4. p = 5 cm
5. q = 9 cm
6. z = 6 cm
7. b = 2 cm
8. y = 3 cm
9. z = 7 cm

page 37
Describing angles
Lines and angles **S1**

1. ∠ABC = 60°
2. ∠DEF= 69°
3. ∠GIJ = 147°
4. ∠LMN = 33°
5. ∠QRS = 68°, ∠PRQ = 112°, ∠OSR = 112°
6. ∠XVT = 84°, ∠TXV = 62°, ∠XTW = 34°
7. ∠CBA = 51°, ∠ABC = 66°, ∠ABD = 114°

page 38
Drawing shapes
Coordinates **S2**

There are other correct answers.

1. (⁻5,4)   (2,4)   (2,⁻3)   (⁻5,⁻3)
2. (4,0)   (6,⁻1)   (2,⁻3)   (4,⁻4)
3. (⁻5,⁻3)   (2,⁻3)   (2,4)
4. (⁻4,⁻5)   (4,⁻4)   (4,⁻6)
5. (⁻1,4)   (⁻1,6)   (2,4)   (2,2)
6. (⁻3,6)   (⁻1,4)   (⁻3,0)   (⁻5,4)
7. (5,6)   (2,2)   (⁻1,6)   (2,4)
8. (⁻3,0)   (⁻1,4)   (2,4)   (4,0)
9. (⁻3,0)   (⁻3,6)   (⁻1,6)   (4,0)

page 39
Reflections
Reflections **S3**

1. $(3,2) \rightarrow (3,⁻2)$, $(⁻1,4) \rightarrow (⁻1,⁻4)$, $(5,⁻3) \rightarrow (5,3)$, $(⁻4,⁻2) \rightarrow (⁻4,2)$
2. $(⁻1,4) \rightarrow (1,4)$ $(2,0) \rightarrow (⁻2,0)$ $(3,⁻1) \rightarrow (⁻3,⁻1)$ $(⁻4,⁻5) \rightarrow (4,⁻5)$
3. $(0,4) \rightarrow (0,⁻4)$ $(⁻3,1) \rightarrow (3,⁻1)$ $(⁻1,⁻6) \rightarrow (1,6)$ $(2,\frac{1}{2}) \rightarrow (⁻2,⁻\frac{1}{2})$
4. $(0,3) \rightarrow (4,3)$ $(1,2) \rightarrow (3,2)$ $(⁻4,⁻1) \rightarrow (8,⁻1)$ $(⁻2,3) \rightarrow (6,3)$
5. $(3,⁻1) \rightarrow (3,3)$ $(4,1) \rightarrow (4,1)$ $(1,0) \rightarrow (1,2)$ $(⁻2,⁻5) \rightarrow (⁻2,7)$
6. $(1,⁻4) \rightarrow (⁻4,1)$ $(⁻5,2) \rightarrow (2,⁻5)$ $(3,3) \rightarrow (3,3)$ $(⁻3,⁻3) \rightarrow (⁻3,⁻3)$

page 40
Rotations
Rotations **S4**

1.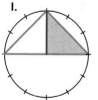
2.
3.
4.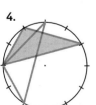
5.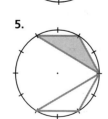
6.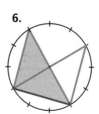

7.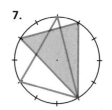
8.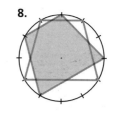
9.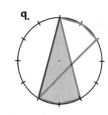
10.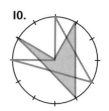
11.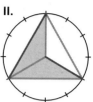
12.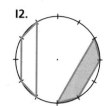

page 42
Name that shape
3-d shape **S6**

1. cone
2. cube
3. cylinder
4. cuboid
5. triangular prism
6. sphere
7. hemisphere
8. tetrahedron
9. pentagonal prism
10. octahedron
11. dodecahedron
12. icosahedron

page 43
Types of triangle
Triangles and quadrilaterals **S7**

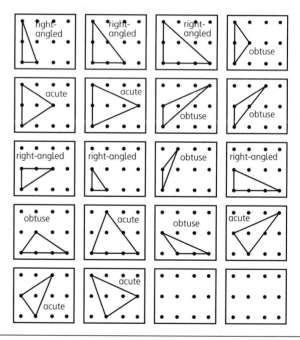

page 46
Sponsored walk
Averages **D2**

distance	frequency	distance × frequency
5 km	III	15
6 km	HHT	30
7 km	HHT III	56
8 km	HHT II	56
9 km	HHT IIII	81
10 km	HHT I	60
11 km	II	22
	40	320

Mean distance = 320 ÷ 40 = 8 km

ANSWERS

	0	I	2	3	4	4
I	I	2	3	4	5	5
2	2	3	4	5	6	6
3	3	4	5	6	7	7
4	4	5	6	7	8	8
5	5	6	7	8	9	9
5	5	6	7	8	9	9

total	chance	probability
0	0 in 36	0
I	I in 36	$\frac{1}{36}$
2	2 in 36	$\frac{2}{36} = \frac{1}{18}$
3	3 in 36	$\frac{3}{36} = \frac{1}{12}$
4	4 in 36	$\frac{4}{36} = \frac{1}{9}$
5	7 in 36	$\frac{7}{36}$
6	6 in 36	$\frac{6}{36} = \frac{1}{6}$
7	5 in 36	$\frac{5}{36}$
8	4 in 36	$\frac{4}{36} = \frac{1}{9}$
9	4 in 36	$\frac{4}{36} = \frac{1}{9}$
10	0 in 36	0

Assessment

Assessment Sheet 1

Positive and negative numbers

1. ‾7   2. 18 °C   3. 9·5   4. ‾5·2
5. check numbers are in the correct positions on the number line
6. fall 14°C   7. rise 1·3°C   8. rise 8·5°C
9. fall 0·7°C   10. fall 15·5°C   11. rise 6·6°C
12. -7   13. -8   14. 10·2
15. -5·2   16. 5·5   17. -7·8
18. 3·7   19. 24·4

Assessment Sheet 2

Fractions, decimals, percentages

1. $\frac{4}{10}$ 2. $\frac{5}{6}$
3. $\frac{9}{20}$ 4. 12·5%
5a $\frac{2}{3}$ b $\frac{2}{5}$ c $\frac{3}{4}$ d $\frac{7}{8}$ e $\frac{5}{7}$ f $\frac{7}{10}$ g $\frac{4}{5}$ h $\frac{7}{12}$
6. $\frac{2}{12}, \frac{7}{12}, \frac{8}{12}, \frac{9}{12}$ 7. $\frac{8}{20}, \frac{10}{20}, \frac{13}{20}, \frac{14}{20}, \frac{15}{20}$
8. 2nd column 0·35, 35%
   3rd column $\frac{42}{100}$ or $\frac{21}{50}$, 42%
   4th column $\frac{3}{8}$, 0·375
   5th column 0·84, 84%
9. $\frac{1}{4}$ 10. 70%

Assessment Sheet 3

Order of operations

1. 4^2 2. 3 x (4 + 7) =33 3. 43
4. 55   5. 4^2 6. 27−17
7. 7 x 4   8. 27 ÷ 3   9. 3^2
10. 4 x 6 **12, 13, 15, 16** should be ticked
17. 12 x (7 + 3) = 120 18. 120 ÷ (47−35) = 10
19. (34 + 7) x 2 = 82 20. (24 − 8) x 15 ÷ 5 = 48
21. (3 x 4) + 48−25 = 35 22. $(6^2 + 4)$ x 7 = 280

Assessment Sheet 4

Mental methods

1. 43·8   2. 66·5   3. $3\frac{1}{5}$
4. £4·20   5. 100·8   6. 55·5
7. 37   8. $20\frac{11}{13}$ 9. 5·41
10. 2·7   11. 1·6   12. 7·51
13. 1·99   14. 7·82   15. 4·46
16. 11·11
17. join a to f, b to e, c to h, d to g

Assessment Sheet 5

Written methods

1. 0·54   2. 14   3. 3·5
4. 9·4   5. 15 962   6. 77·222
7. 280·32   8. 20·5   9. 52·55
10. 3·62   13 and 14 should be ticked

Assessment Sheet 6

Checking results

1. answer between 2800 and 3000
2. Even   3. about 20   4. 24
5. join a to h, b to f, c to e, d to g
6–8 check appropriate explanations
9–12 check the equivalent calculations have been written

Assessment Sheet 7

Appropriate methods

1. multiplication   2. 12·5 cm
3. 75 cm ÷ 6 = 12·5 cm   4. 7 and 13
5. ÷   6. x
7. x, +   8. x, −   9. 918 1
0. 119·12   11. 206   12. 23·1
13. 36 m   14. 13, 15

Assessment Sheet 8

Letters or symbols

1. 12   2. 11   3. 2n
4. $\frac{3a}{2}$
5–6. check answers give given sum and difference
7. 6 + c   8. 3d   9. 7 − 2n
10. 4e   11. 7b − 2   12. $\frac{3}{a} + 2$
13. 10   14. 2   15. 21
16. 9   17. 22   18. 9

ANSWERS

Assessment Sheet 9

Algebraic operations

1. $4a$
2. $2a + 6$
3. $a = b - 3$
4. 3
5. $2b + a$
6. $3a + c$
7. $2p + 4q$
8. $3(a + c)$
9. $4f + 2$
10. $e + 3$
11. Join a to j, b to f, c to i, d to k
12. 7
13. 11
14. 5
15. 4
16. 6
17. 7

Assessment Sheet 10

Sequences

1. subtract 4 from the last number
2. 15
3. 7
4. 10
5. 39, add 4 to the last number
6. 7, add 0.5 to the last number
7. $^-20$, subtract 7 from the last number
8. $8, 13, 18, 23$
9. $9, 5, 1, ^-3$
10. $10, 22, 46, 94$
11. join a to g, b to h, c to f, d to e
12. 65
13. 25
14. $^-4$
15. 36

Assessment Sheet 11

Coordinates

1. $(3,5)$
2. 2
3. Any coordinate on the line
4. $y = 3x$
5. D, E, F
6. B, C, D
7. C
8. E
9. $y = x + 3$
10. $y = x - 2$
11. $y = 3x$
12. $y = 5 - x$
13. $(3,7)\ (5, 11)\ (8, 17)\ (12, 25)$
14. $(^-1, 8)\ (1, 6)\ (3, 4)\ (0, 7)$
15. $(^-2, ^-10)\ (0, ^-4)\ (3, 5)\ (5, 11)$

Assessment Sheet 12

Lines and angles

1. check parallel sides marked
2. $27°$
3. $117°$
4. $153°$
5. **a.** $121°$ **b.** $121°$ **c.** $59°$ 6. **a.** $80°$ **b.** $80°$ **c.** $100°$
7. **a.** $128°$ **b.** $52°$ **c.** $52°$
8. **a.** $61°$ **b.** $61°$ **c.** $119°$ 9. $106°$ 10. $121°$
11. $19°$
12. $120°$

Assessment Sheet 13

Converting metric units

1. 750 ml
2. 150 m
3. 1450 g
4. 65 cl
5. 350 mm, 0.35 m should be circled
6. 0.56 l, 56 cl, 560 cm^3 should be circled
7. 4700 g, 0.0047 tonnes should be circled
8. 3.7 l, 3700 ml, 3700 cm^3
9. 0.015 m, 1.8 cm, 0.2 m, 230 mm, 25 cm
10. 250 cl, 2750 cm^3, 325 cl, 3500 ml, 3.8 l
11. 37 kg, 38.2 kg, 38500 g, 0.039 tonnes, 0.04 tonnes
12. 320 kg
13. 4.7 l

Assessment Sheet 14

Reading and interpreting scales

1. 1.6 kg or 1600 g
2. check scale is marked accurately
3. 85 km/h
4. check scale is marked accurately.
5. $22\,°C$
6. 1200 ml
7. 600 g
8. 45 mph
9. $1{:}21$ a.m.
10. 1350 g or 1.35 kg

11-16 check scales are marked accurately

Assessment Sheet 15

Averages

1. 5
2. 4
3. 9
4. 7
5. 6
6. 8
7. 26
5a. 5
6a. 7
7a. 18
8. $2, 1, 0, 6$
9. $1.4, 1.5, 2, 2$
10. check for reasonable explanation e.g. David would probably use the mean because it is the only measure of average that is higher for United.

Assessment Sheet 16

Probability

1. $\frac{5}{6}$
2. $\frac{3}{6}$ or $\frac{1}{2}$
3. $\frac{3}{10}$ and $\frac{7}{10}$
4. $\frac{2}{9}$
5. check events are placed in the correct place –
   A. $\frac{2}{6}$ or $\frac{1}{3}$, **B.** $\frac{3}{8}$, **C.** $\frac{26}{52} = \frac{1}{2}$, **D.** $\frac{7}{10}$
6. join a to g, b to e, c to f, d to h